MW00607612

CANNED FOODS

Principles of Thermal Process

Control, Acidification and

Container Closure Evaluation

edited by

Austin Gavin

and

Lisa M. Weddig

NATIONAL FOOD PROCESSORS ASSOCIATION

published by

The Food Processors Institute

1401 New York Avenue, N.W.
Washington, D.C. 20005

SIXTH EDITION
© 1995

© 1995 The Food Processors Institute
Washington, D.C.

All rights reserved. No part of this book may be reproduced or altered or utilized in any form or by any means, electronic or mechanical, including photocopying, recording or by any information storage or retrieval system, without permission in writing from the copyright owner. Inquiries should be addressed to

The Food Processors Institute
1401 New York Ave., N.W.
Washington, D.C. 20005

Printed in the United States of America

While the recommendations in this publication are based upon scientific studies and wide industry experience, references to operating procedures and methods or types of instruments and equipment are not to be construed as a guarantee that they are sufficient to prevent damage, spoilage, loss, accidents or injuries resulting from use of this information. Furthermore, the study and use of this publication by any person or company is not an assurance that a person or company is proficient in the operations and procedures discussed in this publication. The use of the statements, recommendations, or suggestions contained herein is not be be considered as creating any responsibility for damage, spoilage, loss, accident or injury resulting from such use.

LIBRARY OF CONGRESS
CATALOG CARD NO.: 95-060296

Canned Foods: Principles of Thermal Process Control, Acidification and Container Closure Evaluation

Washington, D.C.: Food Processors Institute, The

264 p.

ISBN 0-937774-04-9

SPECIAL ACKNOWLEDGMENT

The Food Processors Institute (FPI) gratefully acknowledges the continued support of the Angelus Sanitary Can Machine Company for the development of the sixth edition of *Canned Foods: Principles of Thermal Process Control, Acidification and Container Closure Evaluation*. Publication of the 6th edition will provide students at the Better Process Control Schools and in other learning situation with the latest technical information on production of heat processed foods.

The support of this project by the Angelus Sanitary Can Machine Company continues a tradition which began with a contribution to the development of the first edition in 1973. Angelus has provided generous financial support for each succeeding edition, making a lasting impact upon the quality, safety and wholesomeness of heat processed foods.

ACKNOWLEDGMENTS

Contributions from many people and organizations have made possible the six editions of *Canned Foods: Principles of Thermal Process Control, Acidification and Container Closure Evaluation* which have been published since 1973.

Valuable comments were received from representatives of universities active in the Better Process Control School system. Staff members of the Center for Food Safety and Applied Nutrition of the U.S. Food and Drug Administration and the U.S. Department of Agriculture Food Safety and Inspection Service reviewed the text in its entirety and submitted suggested improvements.

Material on container closure inspection and evaluation was largely supplied by the technical staffs of AOAC International, American–National Can Company, Continental Can Company, Inc., Continental White Cap, Dewey and Almy Chemical Division of W.R. Grace & Company, Heekin Can Inc., Land O' Frost, Ocean Spray, Owens-Illinois, Inc., Reynolds Metals Co., Seneca Foods, and Stegner Food Products Co.

Printed matter and illustrations regarding agitating and hydrostatic thermal processing systems were supplied by FMC Corporation's Canning Machinery Division. Additional illustrations were provided and printed with permission from ATI Orion, Beckman Instruments, Decagon, Cherry-Burrell Corp., and Wilkens-Anderson Co.

Special thanks to staff members of the National Food Processors Association in Washington, D.C. and Dublin, California, including Barbara Blakistone, Dilip Chandarana, Mark Deniston, Regina Hildwine, Lloyd Hontz, Allen Katsuyama, Virginia Scott, Kenneth Stevenson, Denise Trainer, and Jay Unverferth.

May 15, 1995

School Participant:

In plants which pack and thermally process low-acid foods and acidified low-acid foods in hermetically sealed containers, the Good Manufacturing Practice Regulations (21 CFR 113 and 114) prescribe that all operators of retorts, processing systems, aseptic processing and packaging systems and container closure inspectors be under the operating supervision of a person who has satisfactorily completed a school of instruction in these matters. This action of the Food and Drug Administration emphasizes the critical role which operating supervisors play in the canning industry.

This volume, by The Food Processors Institute, represents an effort to emphasize those critical operations and functions over which the line supervisors have control. It has been designed for use by approved schools of instruction, and is its basic text.

I believe that the improvement in the canning operations during the past 23 years is partially attributed to the success of these schools and the follow-up efforts made by industry. Continued effort is needed to maintain this improvement and to achieve additional improvements.

A thorough study of this material is recommended for those who will attend these courses of instruction. We hope you will also use this text on the job, to train retort operators, processors, and container closure inspectors.

Sincerely yours,

Fred R. Shank, Ph.D.
Director
Center for Food Safety and
Applied Nutrition

United States
Department of
Agriculture

Food Safety
and Inspection
Service

Washington, D.C.
20250

JUN 1 2 1995

Ms. Rita M. Fullem
Executive Director
The Food Processors Institute
Suite 400
1401 New York Avenue, NW.
Washington, D.C. 20005

Dear Ms. Fullem:

We welcome the publication of the sixth edition of <u>Canned</u> <u>Foods</u>: <u>Principles</u> <u>of</u> <u>Thermal</u> <u>Process</u> <u>Control</u>, <u>Acidification</u> <u>and</u> <u>Container</u> <u>Closure</u> <u>Evaluation</u> by the Food Processors Institute.

As you know, establishments packing thermally processed, shelf-stable products in hermetically sealed containers must comply with the regulations of the Food Safety and Inspection Service (FSIS) on the canning of meat and poultry products (Title 9 of the Code of Federal Regulations: Part 318, Subpart G, and Part 381, Subpart X). Those regulations require operators of thermal processing systems and container closure technicians to be under the direct supervision of persons who have successfully completed an approved course of study in canning technology.

FSIS has long acknowledged that the Better Process Control Schools sponsored by the Food and Drug Administration provide such an approved course of instruction. Moreover, the Food Processors Institute manual, which has been used for many years as the basic text by the Better Process Control Schools, provides excellent coverage of those areas of instruction that FSIS considers critical to properly train canning plant personnel.

We, along with canning experts in industry and academia, are confident that individuals who successfully complete a course of instruction that uses this Food Processors Institute text will be better equipped to ensure the safety and stability of heat-processed canned product.

Sincerely,

John W. McCutcheon

John W. McCutcheon
Deputy Administrator
Regulatory Programs

FSIS FORM 2630-9 (6/86)   EQUAL OPPORTUNITY IN EMPLOYMENT AND SERVICES

TABLE OF CONTENTS

Chapter 1

INTRODUCTION

The proper beginning point for a text that discusses thermal processing and packaging of canned foods is a working definition of "canning." For purposes of this text, canning is a method of food preservation wherein a food and its container are rendered commercially sterile by the application of heat, alone or in combination with pH and/or water activity or other chemicals. The hermetically sealed container maintains the sterility of the food.

Commercial sterility, which is synonymous with shelf stability, means the destruction of all viable microorganisms of public health significance as well as those capable of reproducing under normal non-refrigerated conditions of storage and distribution. Commercially sterile, aseptically processed and packaged foods are considered "canned" foods even though a wide range of packages other than metal cans might be employed.

The canning process depends on a series of technical operations that must be carefully and accurately performed to ensure the safety of the food. The primary public health concern with low-acid canned foods is formation of botulinal toxin. This toxin or poison is produced by a heat-resistant microorganism called *Clostridium botulinum*. The illness produced by this toxin is known as "botulism." Prevention of the formation of "bot" toxin is the primary purpose of this text and the Better Process Control Schools.

The National Food Processors Association (NFPA) and other industry laboratories have conducted research over many years to establish heating times and temperatures required to destroy organisms of public health significance and other organisms capable of growing in low-acid canned food at normal non-refrigerated temperatures. Acidification and control of water activity in conjunction with pasteurization are also procedures for maintaining commercial sterility. Heat processes suggested for some low-acid foods packed in metal and glass containers are published in NFPA Bulletins 26-L and 30-L,[1] respectively. These heat processes for canned foods must be properly applied in commercial practice, and containers must be properly sealed to prevent spoilage and avoid possible health hazards.

The canning industry, which dates back to the early 1900's, has had sufficient experience with botulism and spoilage to be concerned with commercial application of thermal processes and with container closure operations. For example, in 1963 inadequate supervision of a commercial canning operation led to one botulism incident. In 1971, another incident of botulism was caused by failure to apply a proper heat process to commercially canned product. In 1978 and 1982, single can incidents of botulism were traced to United States-packed product. In the first case the cause was ascertained to be individual container damage. In the second, the incident resulted from an extremely occasional and random malformation of the bottom double seam of the food container.

The 1971 incident led the industry to request heat processing regulations to ensure proper processing of

---

[1]"Processes for Low-Acid Foods in Metal Containers," Bulletin 26-L, 12th edition, 1982, and "Processes for Low-Acid Foods in Glass Containers," Bulletin 30-L, 5th edition, 1984 may be purchased from the National Food Processors Association, 1401 New York Avenue, NW, Washington, DC 20005.

commercially canned food. The result was a recommendation to the U.S. Food and Drug Administration (FDA) for a program known as the National Canners Association (now NFPA)-FDA Better Process Control Plan.

The plan was drawn up as a Good Manufacturing Practice regulation (21 CFR 128b, now recodified as 21 CFR 113) titled "Thermally Processed Low-Acid Foods Packaged in Hermetically Sealed Containers." It became effective in January 1973 and was modified in May 1979. The 1978 and 1982 incidents led to increased observation by FDA and greater awareness of quality control by container manufacturers and food processors to produce as perfect a container as possible under commercial operating conditions.

The Better Process Control Plan (BPC) places the responsibility for production of safe food products on individual food industry employees. In the processing of food, no amount of mechanical devices, regulations, inspections or physical measurements can prevent or offset human error and the resultant potential for tragic consequences to consumers, processors and the industry in general. The BPC Plan includes a provision that addresses the human dimension.

The plan requires that operators of thermal processing and packaging systems work under the supervision of a person who has attended and completed a prescribed course of instruction at a school approved by the FDA Commissioner. The BPC schools represent a cooperative venture of university, FDA and industry personnel. The first schools were conducted in late 1972. To date, more than 25,000 people have been certified in this system.

Since publication of FDA's regulations for low-acid canned foods, concerns were raised regarding the hazard of botulism in heat sensitive low-acid foods that are acidified to permit less severe thermal processing requirements. After several botulism outbreaks from domestic and imported acidified canned foods, the FDA Commissioner added a separate Good Manufacturing Practice Regulation—Part 114 for Acidified Foods—which became effective May 15, 1979. This regulation contains a requirement similar to Part 113 for training of personnel who supervise critical areas in the preparation and thermal processing of acidified foods.

Also in 1979, FDA finalized similar Good Manufacturing Practice regulations for the thermal processing of animal (pet) foods. These regulations also contain a requirement for the training of supervisors of thermal processing and container closure operations. The regulations, found in 21 CFR 507 and 508, are essentially identical to 21 CFR 113 and 108, respectively. Processors of low-acid animal foods are encouraged to obtain copies of the appropriate regulations for reference.

In 1976 and again in 1981, NFPA petitioned the U.S. Department of Agriculture's (USDA's) Food Safety and Inspection Service (FSIS) to promulgate comprehensive regulations for canning meat and poultry food products. These regulations, which follow the general pattern of the FDA regulations, were promulgated on December 19, 1986, and became effective (with certain exceptions) on June 19, 1987. This edition of *Canned Foods: Principles of Thermal Process Control, Acidification and Container Closure Evaluation* reflects points of divergence between the two sets of regulations.

Like the FDA regulations, USDA-FSIS regulations also contain provisions for employee training. Since December 19, 1988, all operators of thermal processing systems and all container closure technicians have been required to be under the direct supervision of a person who has successfully completed a school of instruction that is recognized as adequate for properly training supervisors of canning operations. Those persons who successfully completed an NFPA-FDA Better Process Control School prior to December 19, 1988, were deemed by USDA to have met the requirements for training. Since 1988, when revisions were made to this book specifically to address the USDA-FSIS regulations, NFPA-FDA-USDA Better Process Control Schools have also been deemed satisfactory.

Objectives of This Publication

This publication identifies critical points of responsibility in the canning process, explains their significance, and underlines the importance of meeting critical point requirements without deviation, by:

1. Setting forth critical points in thermal processing of low-acid and acidified foods packaged in hermetically sealed containers.

2. Stressing program organization for effective control of these operations.

3. Emphasizing the critical fact that in certain of these operations there can be no deviation from prescribed procedures.

4. Stressing the importance of proper record forms and recordkeeping both as a control mechanism and a way to document adequacy of operational procedures.

Also important to keep in mind while reading this publication or the regulations is the significant distinction between two common words—should and shall. Their definitions are listed below:

Shall— used to state mandatory requirements.

Should— used to state recommended or advisory procedures or to identify recommended equipment.

This publication, however, does not attempt to teach basic mechanical manipulations required in operating thermal processing systems and performing container double seam teardown inspections. The person supervising these operations is responsible for ensuring that these procedures are conducted properly.

Instead, this publication emphasizes that—after all possible mechanical and physical measures have been taken to ensure production of safe, wholesome foods—prime responsibility for preventing errors rests with individual employees working in the critical areas of food processing establishments. Therefore, it is the supervisor's responsibility to see that employees who actually perform critical functions have the necessary training to do their jobs effectively.

The FDA and USDA-FSIS regulations to which this publication refers are in *Tables 1* and *2*.

The complete regulations—reformatted for easier reading—together with an index for each appear at the end of this book. Highlights of each follow.

FDA Canning Regulations

Highlights of Part 108

Emergency Permit Control—Part 108 is divided into two sections.

Subpart A

Subpart A spells out general procedural regulations to govern both the establishment of requirements and conditions for exemption from or compliance with Section 404 of the Food, Drug and Cosmetic Act for low-acid and acidified canned foods, and pursuant to Section 404 when there is a failure to comply with those requirements and conditions.

The major parts in Subpart A are as follows:

1. Definitions.

2. Procedural requirements for exemptions from and compliance with Section 404 of the Act (Emergency Permit Control). When the Commissioner finds contamination with microorganisms that are injurious to health, the Commissioner shall order the processor to obtain an Emergency Permit.

3. A processor needs a permit when his/her operation does not meet the mandatory conditions in Subpart A.

4. The processor may not then ship product in interstate commerce unless the processor holds a permit.

5. The permit shall be suspended immediately when the permit holder is not in compliance with the mandatory requirements and conditions established by the permit.

Table 1—USDA-Food Safety Inspection Service (FSIS) regulations for thermally processed foods packaged in hermetically sealed containers.

Title 9 Code of Federal Regulations 9 CFR	Title of Regulation	REFERENCE Federal Register (FR)		
		Vol.	Page	Date
Part 318.300 (Meat Products)				
	Canning and Canned Products	51 As Amended	45602	12/19/86
Part 381.300 (Poultry Products)		53	49848	12/12/88
		57	37872	8/21/92
		57	55443	11/25/92

Table 2—Food and Drug Administration (FDA) regulations for thermally processed foods packaged in hermetically sealed containers.

Title 21 Code of Federal Regulations 21 CFR	Title of Regulation	REFERENCE Federal Register (FR)		
		Vol.	Page	Date
Part 108	Emergency Permit Control (Formerly Part 90)	42	14334	3/15/77
	Section 108.25 Acidified Foods	44	16207	3/16/79
	Section 108.35 Low-Acid Foods	42	14335	3/15/77
Part 113	Thermally Processed Low-Acid Foods Packaged in Hermetically Sealed Containers (Formerly 128b)	44	16215	3/16/79
Part 114	Acidified Foods	44	16235	3/16/79

6. The permit is required only during such temporary period as is necessary to protect the public health.

7. A processor may manufacture food without a permit, but such food shall be retained by the processor until written approval is received from FDA.

8. Once the processor is in compliance with Subpart B requirements, and is likely to remain in compliance, the Commissioner shall revoke the determination of a need for permit and the actual permit.

Subpart B

In Subpart B, conditions are established for thermal processing of acidified (108.25) and low-acid (108.35) food packaged in hermetically sealed containers to be exempt from or in compliance with the emergency permit control provisions contained in Section 404 of the Act. These regulations do not apply to meat and poultry products.

The major points covered under Subpart B are:

1. No later than 10 days after first engaging in production, all processors of acidified and/or low-acid foods shall register with FDA the name and location of each establishment in which such processing is carried on, the processing method in terms of acidity and pH control, the thermal processing systems used and a list of the acidified and low-acid foods packed.

2. All processors of acidified and/or low-acid foods shall file with FDA information on their scheduled processes for each food in each container size, including— as applicable—conditions for heat processing and control of pH, salt, sugar, preservative levels, type of processing system, details of the scheduled process, and the source and date of the establishment of the process.

Table 3 lists the required forms needed for registration and process filing. These forms and accompanying instructions are available from the LACF Registration Coordinator (HFS-618), Food and Drug Administration,

3

Table 3—Forms required for food canning establishment registration and process filing with FDA.

Form No.	Required for
FD-2541	Registration for canning establishment.
FD-2541a	Process filing for all processing methods, except aseptic processing of low-acid foods.
FD-2541c	Process filing for aseptic processing of low-acid foods.

200 C Street, SW, Washington, DC 20204, or any FDA District Office. A copy of each form appears in the Appendix for reference.

4. Information filed shall be regarded as trade secrets.

5. The processor shall process each low-acid or acidified food in each container size in conformity with at least the scheduled processes.

6. The processor shall promptly report to FDA any instance of spoilage or process deviation that indicates potential health significance where any lot of such food has entered distribution.

7. The processor shall promptly report to FDA any instance of any lot of such food, which may be injurious to health by reason of contamination with microorganisms, that has entered distribution.

8. The processor shall have a current procedure for product recall.

9. Supervisors of critical operations, such as heat processing, acidification and pH control, and container closure inspections must have satisfactorily completed a prescribed course on these subjects in a school approved by the Commissioner.

10. Processors shall maintain records for three years.

11. If a state regulates processing of low-acid and acidified foods in a manner at least equivalent to 113 and 114, compliance with such state regulations constitutes compliance with 108.35(j) and 108.25(i).

12. Imports are covered like domestic products except that, in lieu of providing for the issuance of an emergency permit, the Commissioner will request that the Secretary of the Treasury refuse their admission into the United States pursuant to Section 801 of the Act. Although foreign processors are not specifically exempted from training in FDA-approved courses of instruction, as a practical matter FDA will accept a statement from a foreign government that the processors are properly trained.

Highlights of Part 113

1. Part 113 defines low-acid foods as any foods, other than alcoholic beverages, with a finished equilibrium pH greater than 4.6 and a water activity (a_w) greater than 0.85. Tomatoes and tomato products having a finished equilibrium pH less than 4.7 are not classified as low-acid foods.

2. The regulation requires that products be prepared and packed in containers in such a way that they can be adequately processed.

3. It requires that the heating process (scheduled process) be designed by qualified persons having expert knowledge of thermal processing requirements.

4. It defines a scheduled process as one that achieves commercially sterility. Commercial sterility of thermally processed food means the condition achieved:
   A. By the application of heat that renders the food free of:
      (i) Microorganisms capable of reproducing in the food under normal non-refrigerated conditions of storage and distribution.
      (ii) Viable microorganisms (including spores) of public health significance.
   B. By the control of water activity and the application of heat, which renders the food free of microorganisms capable of reproducing in the food under normal non-refrigerated conditions of storage and distribution.

5. Part 113 specifies the proper design, controls and instrumentation for all the common retorting systems. It describes the practices necessary in the operation of these systems to ensure safety.

6. It requires that records be kept of all coding, processing and container closure inspections so that, before containers are released for shipment, management reviews their records to ensure commercial sterility. These records also are invaluable in case of spoilage or evidence of potential underprocessing in a product already distributed. In such cases, unless records show conclusively that the product could not be hazardous to health, a recall may be necessary.

7. The regulation covers in detail the situation in which the processor finds, from records review or otherwise, that a retort load or some portion of production is underprocessed. The processor then must either reprocess the load or isolate it pending an evaluation to determine that the lot presents no hazard to health. If it does not present a health problem or if it is reprocessed to commercial sterility, it may be shipped; otherwise, the product must be destroyed.

8. It requires container closure inspection to ensure that containers are properly sealed.

9. The regulation also requires that supervisors responsible for the critical heat processing operations and container closure inspections receive instruction in a school approved by FDA.

Highlights of Part 114

1. Part 114 defines acidified foods as any low-acid foods to which acid(s) or acid foods(s) are added. They have a water activity (a_w) greater than 0.85 and a finished equilibrium pH of 4.6 or below.

2. These foods include—but are not limited to—beans, cucumbers, cabbage, artichokes, cauliflower, puddings, peppers, tropical fruits and fish, singly or in any combination. These foods may be called, or may purport to be "pickles" or "pickled (name of product)."

3. Excluded from coverage under this part are carbonated beverages, jams, jellies, preserves, acid foods (including such foods as standardized and non-standardized food dressings and condiment sauces) that contain small amounts of low-acid food(s) and have a resultant finished equilibrium pH that does not significantly differ from that of the predominant acid or acid food. Also excluded under Part 114 are foods that are stored, distributed and retailed under refrigeration.

4. Procedures for acidification include:
   A. Blanching in acidified aqueous solutions.
   B. Immersion in acid solutions.
   C. Direct batch acidification.
   D. Direct addition of acids to individual containers.
   E. Addition of acid foods.

5. Part 114 requires that the scheduled process be established by a qualified person with expert knowledge and experience in acidification and processing of acidified foods.

6. It defines the procedures to be followed in the event of a deviation from the scheduled process and/or when the equilibrium pH is greater than 4.6.

7. It defines a scheduled process as one selected by a processor as adequate under the conditions of manufacture to achieve and maintain a food that will not permit the growth of microorganisms having public health significance. It includes control of pH and other critical factors equivalent to the process established by a competent processing authority.

8. It describes methods that may be used to determine pH or acidity for acidified foods.

9. The regulation requires that records must be maintained to verify compliance to permit a public health evaluation of any lot and to identify initial distribution of finished product to facilitate segregation, if necessary.

10. It requires that supervisors with responsibility for pH control and other critical factors in acidification receive instruction in a school approved by FDA.

USDA-FSIS Canning Regulations

The Federal Meat Inspection Act is the authorizing legislation for meat inspection regulations. The Poultry Products Inspection Act serves the same function for poultry inspection. In general, food products containing more than 3 percent raw meat (2 percent cooked meat) or 3 percent raw poultry (2 percent cooked poultry) fall under the jurisdiction of the U.S. Department of Agriculture's (USDA's) Food Safety and Inspection Service (FSIS). Because USDA-FSIS regulations for meat and poultry are authorized by different legislation, there are two sets of canning regulations. Fortunately, the regulations (318.300 for meat products and 381.300 for poultry products) are essentially identical and need not be discussed separately.

Highlights of Parts 318.300 and 381.300

1. Section .300 contains definitions of terms used in the regulations. Most definitions have similar intent to the FDA definitions of the same terms; however, there are occasional minor differences in wording.

2. Section .301 describes the requirements for handling containers and closures, including periodic visual and teardown examinations of rigid containers (metal), glass containers and semirigid and flexible containers. It also lists the requirements for examination and cleaning of empty containers, container coding and handling sealed containers.

3. Section .302 lists the requirements for thermal process establishment and submission of information.
   A. A thermal process or process schedule shall be available for each canned product prior to processing for distribution in commerce.
   B. Process schedules shall be established by a processing authority.
   C. Potentially adverse changes in product formulation or other factors not covered in the process schedule shall be evaluated by the processing authority.
   D. Records of process schedule establishment shall be made available to USDA-FSIS Program personnel upon request. (Unlike FDA regulations, USDA has no requirement to submit or file process schedules on official forms.)
   E. The establishment shall provide the inspector with a list of process schedules (including alternate schedules), along with any additional applicable information such as retort come-up operating procedures and critical factors.
   F. Letters of process schedule recommendation shall be maintained on file and made available upon request.
   G. If critical factors are identified in the process schedule, the establishment shall provide the inspector with a copy of the procedures for measuring, controlling and recording these factors, along with the frequency of such measurements. Process schedules or critical factor related parameters shall not be changed without prior written submittal of revised procedures to the inspector.

4. Section .303 requires that critical factors shall be measured, controlled and recorded to ensure that they remain within the limits used to establish the process schedule. Examples of critical factors for the various thermal processing systems are provided.

5

5. Section .304 lists certain requirements for operations in the thermal processing area.

    A. Process schedules (or operating process schedules) and operating procedures shall be posted or readily available to the processing system operator.

    B. A system for product traffic control, use of heat indicators, and bypass prevention design of crateless retort container handling systems are required.

    C. Proper product initial temperatures shall be determined and recorded.

    D. Timing devices shall be accurate. When clocks that do not display seconds are used, at least a one-minute safety factor shall be added to specified thermal processing operation times. Temperature/time recording devices shall correspond within 15 minutes to the time of day recorded on required written records.

    E. Potentiometric methods using electronic instruments shall be used for measurements when the maximum pH is specified as a critical factor in the thermal process.

6. Section .305 specifies the proper design, controls and instrumental requirements for various retorting systems.

7. Section .306 lists the processing and production records required for the various thermal processing systems.

8. Section .307 provides the requirements for documentation, review and maintenance of processing and container closure records. It also provides for USDA-FSIS approval of automated process monitoring and recordkeeping systems.

Records shall be maintained by the establishment identifying initial distribution of the finished product. Processing and production records shall be retained for no less than one year at the establishment and for an additional two years at any location from which records can be made available within three working days.

9. Section .308 discusses the specific requirements for handling process deviations. An establishment may elect to prepare and submit to USDA-FSIS a partial or total quality control program for handling deviations. Without such an approved quality control program, the establishment must comply with the provisions specified in this section. An immediate reprocess, application of an alternate process schedule, or evaluation of the deviation by a processing authority are the options provided. Product shall be held pending the process evaluation; product shall not be shipped until USDA-FSIS has reviewed all the information on the process deviation and evaluation and approved the product disposition action.

Specific procedures must be followed for handling deviations for continuous rotary retorts.

The establishment shall maintain full records of the handling of each process deviation in a file or log.

10. Section .309 provides the requirements for finished product inspection, including product incubation and container condition examinations. As with the handling of process deviations, the establishment may elect to prepare and submit a partial or total quality control program. Unless such a program is approved, the establishment shall follow the requirements prescribed in this section. Samples of product shall be held at $95 \pm 5°F$ ($35 \pm 2.8°C$) for 10 days. Provisions may be made for early product shipment provided the establishment can ensure that product will not reach the retail level before the end of the incubation period and provided the establishment receives written approval from the area supervisor. The finding of abnormal containers requires that affected codes shall not be shipped. In response to a petition from NFPA, USDA-FSIS on August 21, 1992, amended this section to allow firms to operate under finished-product inspection requirements different from those specified by USDA provided they are included in a Partial Quality Control (PQC) program reviewed and found acceptable to the Agency. Any finished product inspection parameter can be addressed in the PQC program, including the length of the incubation period.

11. Section .310 requires that all operators of thermal processing systems and container closure technicians shall be under the direct supervision of a person who has successfully completed a school of instruction that is generally recognized as adequate for properly training supervisors of canning operations.

12. Section .311 requires that establishments shall prepare and maintain a current procedure for the recall of all canned products covered by these regulations. Upon request, the recall procedure shall be made available to USDA-FSIS Program employees for review.

Chapter 2

MICROBIOLOGY OF THERMALLY PROCESSED FOODS

Introduction

Microbiology is the knowledge of living forms so small that they can be seen only with the aid of a powerful microscope. The forms observed have been referred to in a number of ways, such as germs, microbes, bacteria and microorganisms. Leeuwenhoek—the inventor of the microscope in the early 1700s and the first to observe these microscopic living forms—called them "wee beasties." The science of microbiology is employed in a number of fields, such as medicine, agriculture, industry and food preservation. They may be referred to as medical, dairy, agricultural, industrial or food microbiology.

The Microbiology of Food Processing

The history of thermal processing or canning of foods began with Nicholas Appert, a French confectioner, who placed foods in glass bottles or jars, sealed them with corks and heated them in boiling water. Most of the foods so treated did not spoil, and Appert announced his discovery in 1810. Although he was a thorough and careful worker, the science of microbiology was unknown at the time, and he was unable to explain why his method was successful. He believed that the combination of heat and the exclusion of air "averted the tendency to decomposition."

Some 50 years later, Louis Pasteur showed that certain microorganisms are responsible for fermentation and decay. He conducted experiments on food preservation, and the term "pasteurization" bears his name. Although Pasteur's findings could have explained why Appert's method was successful, they were not applied immediately in the field of food canning. Thus, in the early days of food processing, the causes of many spoilage incidents remained unknown. Numerous theories were advanced in a vain effort to learn the cause of these mysterious problems. It was firmly believed by many processors that without vacuum, canned foods would not keep. Research in food microbiology, started at the Massachusetts Institute of Technology in 1895, ultimately concluded that the seemingly mysterious spoilage of canned foods resulted from failure to apply sufficient heat to destroy microorganisms.

Characteristics and Behavior of Microorganisms

We now know that all raw foods normally contain microorganisms that will eventually cause spoilage unless they are controlled or destroyed. Food preservation is a competition between the human species and microorganisms—we attempt to preserve the food, the microorganisms to destroy it.

Since food preservation requires that microorganisms be controlled, it is important to know what they are and how they behave. The organisms of concern to the food processor are called molds, yeasts and bacteria. These organisms may be divided into groups on the basis of their microscopic characteristics or visual appearance in mass growths, called colonies (*Figure 1*). The following factors are also of importance in classification: (1) the materials they can use as foods, (2) the products resulting from the breakdown of these foods, and (3) their tolerance to oxygen, their growth temperatures, and their resistance to such destructive agents as heat and chemicals.

Useful Functions of Microorganisms

Many of the thousands of microorganisms that have been discovered and identified perform some useful function. Without microorganisms, we would not have some of the tasty foods we enjoy, such as breads, cheese, wine, beer, sauerkraut and other fermented foods. In addition, these microorganisms are needed to make products useful to industry and medicine, such as enzymes, antibiotics, glycerol and other alcohols. Still other types of microorganisms have the ability to break down organic matter and return it to the earth in the form of stabilized elements. These become food for plants, which in turn provide food for animals. Without such microorganisms, the earth would accumulate dead animals, leaves and other undecayed matter—all of which would have eliminated life on earth long ago.

Some Microorganisms Cause Disease

About 1865, the "Germ Theory of Disease" was accepted. This theory teaches that most diseases of humans, animals or plants are caused by specific microorganisms. The organism, or the substances it produces, must invade the human, animal or plant body to cause the disease.

Fortunately, very few of the known microorganisms are harmful to humans. While many diseases can be transmitted from person to person or from animals to humans, only a few can be transmitted through foods. The majority of outbreaks of foodborne illnesses are caused by just four microorganisms—*Salmonella* spp., *Campylobacter*, *Staphylococcus aureus* and *Clostridium perfringens*.

Significant Microorganisms in Food Processing

As previously indicated, the microorganisms of significance to food preservation are molds, yeasts and bacteria (*Figure 2*). A review of each group follows.

Molds

Molds exhibit some of the characteristics of the higher plants. They are made up of multicellular, tubular filaments. Molds demonstrate branching and reproduce by means of fruiting bodies, called spores, which are borne in or on aerial structures. Their mycelia, or intertwined filaments, may resemble roots. They are many times larger than bacteria and somewhat longer than yeasts.

Molds are widely distributed in nature, both in the soil and in the dust carried by air. Under suitable conditions of moisture, aeration and temperature, molds will grow on almost any food. The black or green discoloration that appears on moldy bread is familiar evidence of such growth. Molds are also able to survive on a wide variety of substances not normally thought suitable for the support of life. These include concentrated solutions of some acids, water containing minute quantities of certain salts, certain pastes used in labeling and so forth. Molds grow readily on the walls and ceilings of buildings with high humidity and considerable moisture condensation. Mold growth can occur even in refrigerators, because molds are much more tolerant to cold than to heat.

Molds are capable of consuming acids. Their growth in foods has occasionally removed the acid conditions that inhibit growth of *Clostridium botulinum,* a food poisoning organism discussed later in this chapter.

Mold spoilage of food in closed and processed containers is rare but not impossible. Most molds have little heat resistance and cannot survive the thermal processes for low-acid canned foods. Therefore, they can be present only as a result of gross underprocessing or as a post-processing contaminant. Since the organism must have oxygen to grow, only slight growth can occur unless the food container has an opening to the outside environment.

Molds such as *Byssochlamys fulva, Talaromyces flavus, Neosartorya fischeri* and others have been implicated in the spoilage of some canned fruit drinks, fruit and fruit-based products. These molds are reportedly capable of withstanding the heat treatment used to preserve these products because of their ability to form spores, which enable them to survive adverse conditions. The heat-resistant sporeforms of these molds may survive more than one minute at 198°F (92°C) in acid or acidified foods. However, to achieve this degree of resistance, the organisms need days to mature and produce the heat-resistant spores. Therefore, daily sanitation of equipment and tote boxes for raw product is extremely important in controlling the growth of these organisms and preventing the development of the resistant spore.

Mold growth in thermally processed foods does not present a significant public health problem.

Yeasts

Another microorganism of importance to food preservation is yeast. Yeasts are unicellular microscopic living bodies, usually egg-shaped. They are smaller than molds but larger than bacteria. Their greatest thickness is about

Figure 1—Visual appearance of molds, yeasts and bacteria in mass culture (center) and microscopically as individual units.

Mold

Yeast

Bacteria

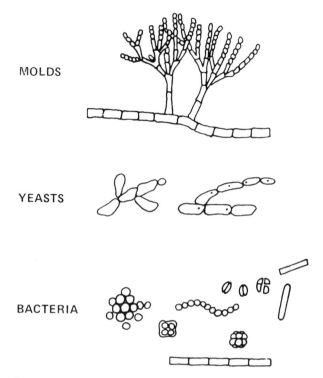

MOLDS

YEASTS

BACTERIA

Figure 2—The microorganisms of concern in food preservation are molds, yeasts, and bacteria.

1/2,000 of an inch. Yeasts reproduce principally by budding. A small bud forms on the parent yeast cell and gradually enlarges into another yeast cell. A few varieties may form spores within a special cell; later these spores may grow into new yeast cells.

Yeasts are widely found in nature and are particularly associated with liquid foods containing sugars and acids. They are quite adaptive to adverse conditions such as acidity and dehydration. Like molds, yeasts are more tolerant to cold than to heat. Compared to bacterial spores, yeasts possess little resistance to heat. Most yeast forms are destroyed on heating to 170°F (77°C). Spoilage may result from the presence of yeast in canned food, but if this happens, gross underprocessing or leakage must be suspected. Usually, growth by yeasts is accompanied by the production of alcohol and large amounts of carbon dioxide gas, which swells the container.

Yeast growth in processed foods does not present a significant public health problem.

Bacteria

Bacteria are the most important and troublesome of all the microorganisms for the food processor.

Most bacteria in themselves are comparatively harmless, but they excrete enzymes that can produce undesirable changes in food, and, in some cases, microorganisms can produce poisonous substances.

Bacteria are single-celled living bodies so small that individually they can be seen only with the aid of a powerful microscope. They are among the smallest living creatures known. The cells of bacteria vary in length from 1/25,000 to 1/1,000 of an inch. The number of these tiny organisms that could be placed on the head of a pin would equal the population of New York City.

Viewed with a microscope, bacteria appear in several shapes or forms. Those most important in processed food spoilage are either round in shape (called cocci) or rod-shaped (called, simply, rods).

Reproduction of bacterial cells

Bacteria reproduce by division, which microbiologists call fission. When a bacterial cell is ready to divide, the cell material gradually increases until its volume is practically doubled. The round forms become oval while rod forms stretch to nearly twice their length. The cell than constricts in the middle. This constriction deepens until the cell contents are held in two distinct compartments separated by a wall. These two compartments finally separate to form two new cells, which are exact counterparts to the former cell and to each other (*Figure 3*). The reproduction of bacteria, or increase in numbers, is often referred to as "growth."

Experiments have been conducted to determine the growth rate of bacteria under conditions purposely made favorable for the organism under study, and each cell divides, on the average, about every 20 or 30 minutes (*Figure 4*).

At this rate of cell division, each single cell will produce four cells at the end of the first hour. At the end of two hours, each cell will have produced 16 new cells. After 15 hours, each parent cell will have produced 1,000,000,000 (one billion) cells identical to the original. For example, if there were 75,000 bacteria per square inch on a conveyor belt, by the end of one hour there could be 300,000 bacteria per square inch of that belt. At the end of a three-hour shift, the bacteria count per square inch of belt surface could be 4,800,000.

Fortunately, conditions for bacterial growth never remain favorable long enough for continuous unrestricted multiplication of the organism. Without a constant supply

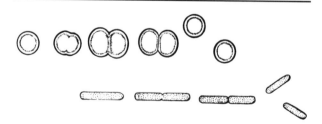

Figure 3—Bacteria reproduce only by division of individual cells. When a cell is ready to divide it enlarges in size and finally a wall separates the cell into two new cells exactly alike.

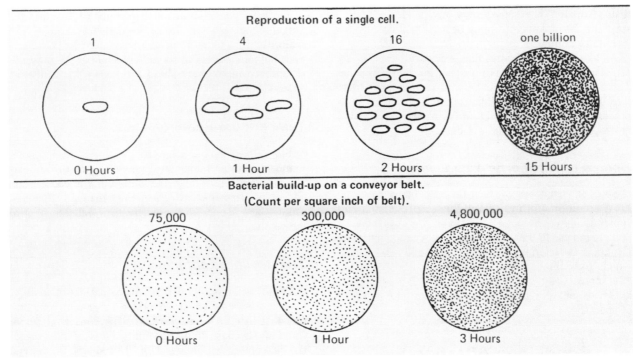

Reproduction of a single cell.

1	4	16	one billion
0 Hours	1 Hour	2 Hours	15 Hours

Bacterial build-up on a conveyor belt.
(Count per square inch of belt).

75,000	300,000	4,800,000
0 Hours	1 Hour	3 Hours

Figure 4—Potential bacterial growth under favorable conditions.

of available fresh food, growth becomes limited or prohibited.

Also, large numbers of bacteria result in an accumulation of substances that are byproducts of bacterial growth and that also act to inhibit growth. With cessation of growth due to pollution of their environment, the cells may die. However, if the organism is a type that forms spores—resistant but dormant forms—these cells can remain alive under conditions that kill other cells.

Sporeforming and non-sporeforming bacteria

Bacteria can be divided into two groups based on their ability to form or not to form spores. Practically, all of the round-shaped bacteria, or cocci, and many of the rod-shaped bacteria cannot form spores and are classed as non-sporeformers. However, a number of the rod-shaped bacteria have the ability to produce spores (*Figure 5*). Spores are a dormant stage in the normal growth cycle of these organisms. They have the ability to survive a wide range of unfavorable conditions. Spores have been compared to plant seeds in that they will germinate and grow when conditions are suitable.

When formed in yeasts and molds, spores represent reproductive bodies, but bacterial spores are a resting stage in the growth cycle of an organism. When a spore germinates, it is simply the same organism continuing its growth.

Resistance of spores to the environment

In general, bacterial spores are extremely resistant to heat, cold and chemical agents. Some bacterial spores can survive in boiling water at 212°F (100°C) for more

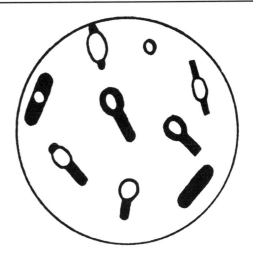

Figure 5—Among the different spore-forming bacteria, the spore body in the parent cell may vary in shape, size, and location in the cell but its appearance and location are always specific for each type of spore-forming organism.

11

than 16 hours. The same organisms in the vegetative state and the non-sporeforming bacteria will not survive heating to boiling.

As a general rule, spores that successfully resist heat are also highly resistant to destruction by chemicals. There are bacterial spores that can survive more than three hours in sanitizing solutions normally used in a food processing plant. Non-sporeforming bacteria are readily destroyed by these sanitizing agents.

Source of foodborne organisms

Soils or waters from which food is obtained are the most common sources of foodborne organisms and spores. Leafy vegetables, such as spinach and other greens that grow close to the soil, usually have high numbers of bacteria and bacterial spores. Asparagus and mushrooms, which grow through the soil, are always contaminated with spores. Crops grown in soils from river bottomlands, lake beds and alluvial plains also contain high numbers of spores.

Conditions Affecting the Growth of Bacteria

A knowledge of the growth requirements for each bacterial group provides the means for their control or elimination.

Food Requirements

The presence of a suitable food supply is the most important condition affecting growth of bacteria. Every plant or animal cell requires certain nutrients to multiply. These include solutions of sugars or other carbohydrates, proteins and small amounts of other materials such as phosphates, chlorides and calcium.

Moisture Requirements

The concentration of moisture and its availability in a food are important factors in prevention of bacterial growth. The bacterial cell has no mouth, and its food must be in a soluble form to enter the cell through the cell wall. It is easy to see how important moisture is for bacterial growth. Without sufficient available moisture, the inflow of food and the outflow of food residues and cell body fluids would be impossible. Later in this chapter we will learn how bacterial growth can be prevented by controlling the amount of moisture available to the bacteria.

Oxygen Requirements

Some bacteria require free oxygen in order to survive and are called aerobes. For others, precisely the reverse is the case, and the smallest quantity of free oxygen prevents their growth. These are called anaerobes. The majority of bacteria are neither strict aerobes nor anaerobes but can tolerate to some degree either the presence or absence of oxygen. These are known as facultative anaerobes.

Temperature Requirements

For each of the bacterial groups there is an optimum, or most favorable, temperature range for growth. Temperatures below and above the optimum for each group adversely affect the growth of the organism. Bacterial groups bear names that indicate their relationships to temperature.

The psychrotrophic group

These bacteria grow best at 58° to 68°F (14°C to 20°C) but can grow slowly in or on food at refrigerator temperature 40°F (4°C). Thus they are called psychro (cold) trophs (growing) because of this capability. None of these bacteria—except C. botulinum Type E and non-proteolytic strains of type B and F—is of concern to food that is canned.

The mesophilic group

This group grows best at temperatures of 86°F to 98°F (30°C to 37°C). This is the normal range of warehouse temperatures. All of the microorganisms that affect food safety grow within this mesophilic temperature range. The sporeforming organism, C. botulinum, is a member of this group.

The thermophilic group

Thermophiles are bacteria that grow at high temperatures. Thermophilic bacteria are found in soils, in manure and compost piles, and even in hot springs. Many are sporeforming bacteria and are divided into two groups based on the temperature at which the spores will germinate and grow. If the spores will not germinate and grow below 122°F (50°C), the bacteria are called obligate thermophiles, i.e., the high growth temperature is an absolute requirement. If growth occurs at thermophilic temperatures of 122° to 150°F (50°C to 66°C) and at lower temperatures—e.g., about 100°F (38°C)—the bacteria are called facultative, meaning they have the ability to grow at both temperature ranges.

Some of the obligate thermophiles can grow at temperatures up to 170°F (77°C). Laboratory tests have indicated that the spores of these bacteria are so heat-resistant that they can survive for more than 60 minutes at temperatures of 250°F (121°C). Thermophilic bacteria do not produce poisons during spoilage of the foods and do not affect food safety.

Bacterial Spoilage

Indications of Bacterial Spoilage

Most bacteria produce gas when allowed to grow in a canned food. Exceptions are the flat-sour sporeforming organisms, which produce acid and sour the food without producing gas, so the container ends remain flat. These organisms are an economic but not a public health problem.

The most obvious indicator of spoilage in processed food is bulging at one or both ends of the container. This implies that the food has possibly undergone spoilage by the action of gas-forming bacteria. Processors caution consumers not to use any container with a bulged end or ends, even though the swelling may be of non-microbial origin.

The appearance and odor of the container contents may also indicate spoilage. If the product is broken down and mushy, or if a normally clear brine or syrup is cloudy, spoilage may be suspected. In jars, a white deposit may sometimes be seen on the bottom or on pieces of food. This is not always a sign of spoilage as starch is sometimes precipitated from certain foods.

Bacterial decomposition of thermally processed product may result from one of four causes:

1. Incipient spoilage—growth of bacteria before processing.

2. Contamination after processing—leakage.

3. Inadequate heat processing.

4. Growth of thermophilic bacteria in the processed food.

Incipient Spoilage Before Processing

Processed food is sometimes held too long between closing and retorting. Such processing delays may result in growth of bacteria normally present in the food and the initiation of spoilage before retorting. This type of spoilage is referred to as "incipient spoilage" and may result in an adulterated product. The degree of spoilage depends on the time and temperature conditions during the delay.

The resulting loss of vacuum may lead to extensive internal pressures in the containers during retorting, which strain the seams and increase the potential of leaker spoilage. Some containers may actually buckle or rupture, rendering them unusable. Steps should be taken to avoid such a delay before retorting the containers.

Contamination After Processing (Leakage)

Leaker spoilage—or post-processing contamination with microorganisms—usually shows up rapidly as swollen containers. It may sometimes take several weeks until all spoilage has ceased. If many swells are present, a small percentage of flat, spoiled containers (flat-sours)

may be expected, and normal appearing cans should be examined with this potential in mind. Leakage is generally due to inadequately formed seams, container damage or cooling water contaminated with large numbers of microorganisms.

It is obvious that measures to prevent leaker spoilage are of paramount importance to the canner, and they are discussed in Chapter 4.

Inadequate Heat Processing

The term inadequate heat processing is practically self-explanatory. Heat processes for thermally processed food are designed to destroy any microorganisms of public health as well as non-health significance. If the heat process is inadequate to destroy *C. botulinum*, the situation is most hazardous, since the health of the consumer may be affected.

A heat process may be inadequate for a variety of reasons, including but not limited to the following: (1) if the time and/or temperature specified in the scheduled heat process for the particular product in the particular size of container or its equivalent is not used or was not established properly, and (2) if the scheduled heat process is not properly applied because of some mechanical or personnel failure.

Thermophilic Spoilage

Generally, the higher the temperature at which a spore-forming organism can grow, the greater will be the heat resistance of its spores. Thus, the spores of a thermophilic organism usually have a heat resistance greater than a mesophilic type.

The spores of thermophilic bacteria are so resistant to heat that heat processes designed to kill the mesophilic type may not be adequate to prevent thermophilic spoilage, unless the product is properly cooled and held below thermophilic temperatures. For products such as peas, corn, certain baby foods and meat where thermophilic spoilage may be a problem, processors should exercise great care in preventing product contamination by thermophilic bacteria. Processors should use ingredients—such as sugar, starch and spices—that are guaranteed free of thermophilic bacteria by the supplier.

Also, thermophiles may grow in equipment that contacts food, if the temperature is within their growth range. Consequently, product should always be held at 170°F (77°C) or above or at room temperature to prevent the growth of thermophiles. Extreme care should be taken to cool the product promptly below 105°F (41°C) after thermal processing and to store these products below 95°F (35°C).

Botulism

Clostridium botulinum (*C. botulinum*) is of great concern to home and commercial canners because (1) when it grows it can produce a deadly toxin or poison, and (2) it can be isolated from soil or water practically everywhere in the world. The term "*Clostridium*" indicates, in the language of the microbiologist, that the organism is able to grow in the absence of air or oxygen and is a sporeformer. The ability to form spores enables it to survive a wide range of unfavorable conditions, such as heat and chemicals. Spores are like plant seeds, being a dormant stage in the normal growth cycle of the organism. The term "*botulinum*" comes from the Latin word "*botulus*," a sausage, because the organism was first isolated from a sausage that had produced the illness now called "botulism."

Certain strains of *C. botulinum* use proteins and are called putrefactive, which describes the odor produced during their growth. They grow best at temperatures between 86°F (30°C) and 98°F (37°C), although growth can occur at any temperature between 50°F (10°C) and 100°F (38°C). Other strains use carbohydrates, such as sugars and starch, and do not produce similar odors. Some of these strains are associated with marine environments; they tolerate lower temperatures of 40°F (4°C) and more oxygen than other types. Their spores will not withstand heating to 212°F (100°C).

Since *C. botulinum* spores are found everywhere, any raw food may be contaminated with them. However, it is only when the vegetative form of the organism grows in a food that the toxin or poison is produced. Certain types of *C. botulinum* spores are very heat resistant and are able to survive five to 10 hours in boiling water, but the toxin is not heat resistant. The toxin can be inactivated by boiling temperatures—212°F (100°C).

Effect of pH on Growth

The term pH will be explained in Chapter 3. In general it refers to the degree of acidity or alkalinity. The pH of a food influences the types of bacteria that will grow in it. This is extremely important, since the pH may determine whether or not *C. botulinum* has the ability to grow and produce its toxin. In *Figure 6*, a number of foods have been arranged according to their pH.

Scientific investigation has determined that the spores of *C. botulinum* will not germinate and grow in food below pH 4.8. A pH 4.6 has been selected as the dividing line between acid and low-acid foods. Spores of *C. botulinum* and other spoilage types can be found in both acid and low-acid foods.

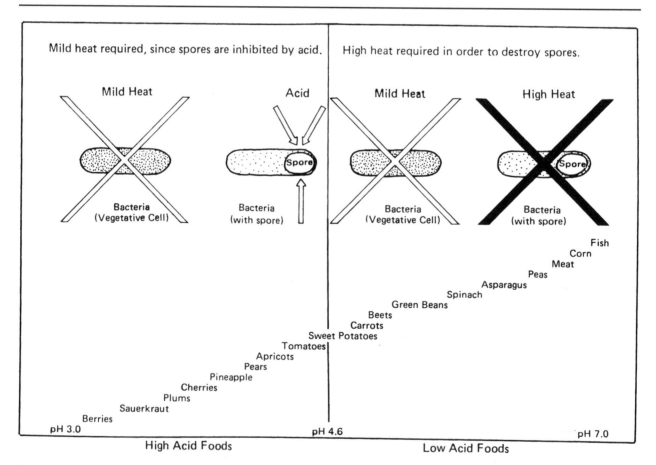

Figure 6—Influence of product pH on degree of thermal processing.

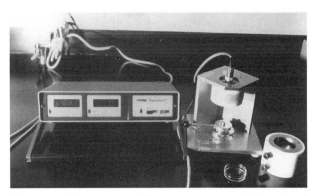

Figure 7—Hygrometer with sensor removed from jar of food. Used for measuring equilibrium relative humidity in headspace or water available to the bacteria in the food.

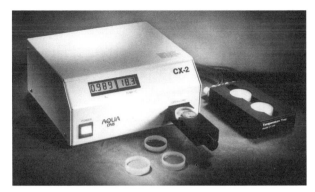

Figure 8—The dew point instrument determines a_w of food by measuring the amount of condensation or dew formation on a mirror.

The application of mild heat destroys all bacteria that are non-sporeformers or all vegetative cells in either low-acid or acid foods. In low-acid foods, high heat must be applied to kill the spores of *C. botulinum* or the spores of other food spoilage organisms. Thus, these foods must be heat processed under pressure. In acid foods, there is no concern with the spores of *C. botulinum*. These spores are prevented from germinating and growing because the pH is 4.6 or below. Since only the vegetative cells must be destroyed in acid foods, boiling water cooks or hot-fill and hold procedures may be used.

Control of Bacteria by Water Activity (a_W)

For thousands of years people have dried fruits, meats and vegetables as a method of preservation. It was also discovered that the addition of sugar would allow preservation of foods such as candies and jellies. Salt preservation of meat and fish has been practiced over the ages.

As late as 1940, food microbiologists thought that the percentage of water in a food product controlled microbial growth, but gradually they learned that it is the availability of the water that is the most important factor influencing growth. A measure of the availability of water in a food can be made by determining the water activity, which is designated a_w.

When substances are dissolved, there is substantial reaction between the substance and the water. A number of the molecules of the water are bound by the molecules of the substances dissolved. All of the substances dissolved in the water reduce the number of unattached water molecules and, in this way, reduce the amount of water available for microbial growth. The extent to which the water activity is lowered depends primarily on the total concentration of all dissolved substances. Thus, if some ingredient—such as sugar, salt, raisins, dried fruits, etc.—is added to food, it competes with the bacteria for available water. The water-binding capacity of a particu-

lar ingredient influences the amount of water left for the growth of bacteria.

Methods for Determining a_w

Several methods exist for determining the water activity of a given food. One commonly used is an electric hygrometer with a sensor to measure equilibrium relative humidity (ERH). The instrument was actually devised by weathermen, and the sensors are the same as those used to measure relative humidity in air. (See *Figure 7*.) A dew point instrument is also commonly used to measure ERH or a_w (*Figure 8*).

The equilibrium humidity above the food in a closed container is a measure of the moisture available or the water activity. A single measurement of ERH on a food provides information as to which types of microorganisms are most likely to cause spoilage and how close the ERH is to the safety limits.

Most foods have a water activity above 0.95, and most bacteria, yeasts and molds will grow above this point. (See *Table 1*.) Spores of *C. botulinum* are generally inhibited at an a_w of about 0.93 or less. Thus, if we decrease the amount of water available to spores to a point where they are inhibited and apply mild heat to destroy the vegetative cells, we have a method of preservation for products whose quality is sensitive to high heat. Examples of such foods are some cheese spreads, peanut butter, honey, syrups, jams and jellies, canned breads and confectionery preparations such as toppings (*Table 2*).

Under the FDA regulation 21 CFR Part 113, canned food with a water activity greater than 0.85 and a pH greater than 4.6 is considered a low-acid food and its minimum heat process will have to be filed by the individual packer. If reduced water activity is used as an adjunct to the process, the maximum water activity must be specified.

If the water activity of any non-meat containing food is adjusted to 0.85 or less, it requires no thermal process and is not covered, regardless of pH, by the acidified

Table 1—Minimum a_w requirements for microorganism growth

Microorganism	Minimum a_w for Growth
Most molds (e.g., *Aspergillus*)	0.75[1]
Most yeasts	0.88[2]
C. botulinum	0.93
Staphylococcus aureus[3]	0.85
Salmonella[3]	0.93

[1]some strains—0.61
[2]some strains—0.62
[3]Non-sporeforming food-poisoning bacteria readily destroyed by heat. Symptoms severe but death is rare.

Table 2—Water activity of some common foods

Food	a_w
Cheese Spread	0.95
Soy Sauce	0.80
Fudge Sauce	0.83
Semi-moist Pet Food	0.83
Peanut Butter—15% total moisture	0.70
Dry Milk—8% total moisture	0.70
Liverwurst	0.96
Salami	0.82

food (Part 114) or low-acid food (Part 113) regulations. If the pH has been adjusted to 4.6 or less and the a_w is > 0.85, it is covered by the acidified food regulation (Part 114) and requires only enough heat to destroy vegetative bacterial cells. Foods with a natural pH of 4.6 or less are not covered by part 113 or 114. (See Chapter 1 and the appendices.)

Meat or poultry containing products with a water activity of 0.85 or less are not covered by the USDA canning regulations. Both low acid and acidified low-acid products are subject to the USDA canning regulations if the water activity is greater than 0.85.

It is apparent that as far as *C. botulinum* is concerned, a water activity of 0.85 provides a large margin of safety. Studies with this organism show that an accurate water activity of 0.93 plus pasteurization will give commercial sterility. However, some questions exist about the precision or accuracy of the instruments and methods used to determine water activity and about some factors that control water activity. Therefore, if water activity plus pasteurization is used to control commercial sterility, data must be obtained and records kept to show that the process yields commercial sterility.

The critical factors in the control of water activity as an adjuvant in preservation are the ingredients in the final product and their effect on water binding capacity that is measured by the ERH (water activity, a_w).

In determining the ERH (a_w) using an electronic hydrometer, one to two hours may be required for the water vapor (relative humidity) to reach equilibrium in the headspace above the food in the closed container.

Therefore, the formulation of the product to give the required a_w must be predetermined and very accurately compounded at the time of packing. The critical points for supervision are the product preparation and the achievement of the required center temperature in the final product.

Samples of the final product should be checked as frequently as necessary to ensure that the appropriate water activity is being achieved.

Salt and Water Activity (a_w)

Another method of preservation is the use of salt. This is particularly applicable to salt-cured meats and fish. In meat, salt is usually supplemented with ingredients that aid in spoilage prevention. In all cases the salt is relied on to inhibit the growth of sporeforming bacteria, such as *C. botulinum*, and only enough heat is applied to kill the non-heat resistant types. Strains of *C. botulinum* that grow in a suitable food containing 7 percent salt are known. Their growth, however, is inhibited at a concentration of 10 percent, which is equivalent to a water activity of approximately 0.93. Although growth can occur at 7 percent, no toxin has yet been demonstrated in this concentration of salt.

Non-Microbial Food Spoilage

Bacterial spoilage is recognized as the most frequent cause of abnormal conditions in canned foods. However, non-bacterial causes of spoilage are also important, including:

1. Chemical reaction of food components with the metal inner surfaces of the container may produce hydrogen gas. The accumulation of gas, usually hydrogen, can dissipate the vacuum in the container and cause the container to swell. These hydrogen swells do not cause concern from a public health standpoint. However, consumers are advised to reject containers with bulged ends, since they cannot distinguish between a "hydrogen swell" and swelling caused by microbial growth.

2. The chemical reaction of food acids on the surface of metal cans may progress to the point of causing "pin-hole" perforations. Bacteria could enter the can through these pin-holes, causing secondary spoilage.

3. An additional cause of bulged ends or apparent spoilage is overfilling of containers, particularly in smaller can sizes and in those with large lid area in proportion to height.

4. Apparent spoilage may be caused by closing cans with a zero or low vacuum. Transported to a high altitude, such cans often become slightly swollen and are referred to as flippers.

Summary

1. Useful microorganisms perform many valuable functions necessary to human life. Only a few are harmful and may cause illness, death and/or food spoilage. Significant microbes in food canning are molds, yeasts and bacteria.
   A. Bacteria are of most concern in spoilage of raw and canned foods.
   B. Bacteria, among the smallest living creatures, reproduce by direct cell division every 20 to 30 minutes under favorable conditions.
   C. Some bacteria can form spores that are a nonreproductive resting stage permitting survival in unfavorable conditions.
   D. *Clostridium botulinum* is a sporeforming bacterium that during growth may produce a deadly poison.
   E. Soil is the most common source of spores, and it must be assumed they are present in all raw foods.
   F. Some spores are highly resistant to killing by heat and chemicals. C *botulinum* is one of them.

2. Bacteria differ in food requirements and growth characteristics in relation to oxygen, temperature, acid and chemical tolerance.
   A. Some bacteria (aerobes) require oxygen while some (anaerobes) grow in the absence of oxygen. Others (facultative anaerobes) grow in either the presence or absence of oxygen. *C. botulinum* is an anaerobe.
   B. The spores of thermophiles are so heat resistant they may survive a heat process designed to kill *C. botulinum* and may spoil the canned foods if they are not cooled and stored according to recommended procedures. Fortunately, none of the thermophiles produce poisons during spoilage of the foods.
   C. Some bacteria are acid-tolerant while acid foods prevent or slow the growth of others.
   D. Foods with pH greater than 4.6 are classified as low-acid foods, and those at or below 4.6 are high-acid foods.
   E. The lower the pH (more acid), the less severe is the required heat process.
   F. Naturally low-acid foods acidified to a maximum pH of 4.6 or lower may not require a pressure process, but the pH must be controlled as required by FDA (21 CFR 114) or USDA regulations.

3. Microbial spoilage is the most frequent, sometimes serious, cause of abnormal conditions in canned foods. Microbial spoilage may result from any of the following:
   A. Incipient spoilage before processing—holding closed containers too long before retorting.
   B. Contamination after processing—leakage contamination by bacteria during water cooling or post-retort handling of the containers.
   C. Inadequate heat processing of the containers—failure to apply adequate heat at the coldest point in the container for sufficient time to kill bacteria.
   D. Thermophilic spoilage—inadequate cooling of containers and/or storage at temperatures above normal.

4. Indications of microbial spoilage in canned foods are:
   A. Abnormal appearance of the container—bulged ends, wet or otherwise stained labels.
   B. Unusual appearance and abnormal odor of the product.
   C. Product mushiness or off-color.
   D. Cloudiness or other signs of abnormal conditions in the liquid portion.

5. Conditions that allow or inhibit growth of *C. botulinum* have been given special attention. This spore-forming, rod-shaped organism has been described as follows:
   A. It is an anaerobe and its growth may be associated with sealed containers.
   B. It grows best at temperatures between 80°F (27°C) and 100°F (38°C). *Clostridium botulinum* Type E found in the marine environment can grow at 40°F (4°C).
   C. Certain types produce spores having moderate heat resistance and whose destruction is the intent of the processes developed for each low-acid canned food.

6. These conditions inhibit the growth of *C. botulinum*:
   A. *Clostridium botulinum* will not grow in foods having a pH value of 4.8 or below. For purposes of categorizing foods, pH 4.6 separates low-acid from high-acid foods. Because *C. botulinum* can grow in low-acid foods, each food in this class must receive a heat process designed to kill spores of *C. botulinum*.
   B. Controlling the moisture content of foods provides a means of inhibiting the growth of *C. botulinum*. Low-acid foods that meet the requirements for low-water activity of 0.85 or below do not require a thermal process sufficient to kill *C. botulinum* spores.

7. Non-microbial spoilage resulting from such conditions as internal corrosion, overfilling and low vacuum must be recognized and distinguished from microbial spoilage.

17

Chapter 3

ACIDIFIED FOODS

Introduction

The preservation of foods using acid is older than recorded history. It is likely that the first foods preserved in this way were fermented foods such as yogurt and sauerkraut. These foods are preserved by lactic acid produced by certain bacteria which are encouraged to grow in the food. The lactic acid retards the growth of undesirable organisms that would spoil the food. It also inhibits or destroys disease-causing microorganisms. Thus, the acid serves as a preservative for the food and extends its shelf-life, but the nutritional quality of the food is relatively unchanged.

Of course, it is not necessary to allow foods to ferment in order to preserve them. Acids, such as vinegar, can be added to low-acid ingredients like vegetables, and the same preservative effect can be achieved. Only those foods preserved by the addition of acid to low-acid ingredients are covered by the FDA regulations for acidified foods, and, as such, only that class of foods will be dealt with in this chapter. Since the proper preservation of acidified foods is directly dependent on correct acidification procedures, this chapter will deal with practices necessary to ensure proper production of acidified foods. We shall discuss the definition of an acidified food, the meaning of the term pH and its importance as a measure of the degree of acidity, as well as actual acidification procedures.

Definition of Acidified Foods

An "acidified food" is defined by FDA as a low-acid food to which acid(s) or acid food(s) is added to produce a product that has a finished equilibrium pH of 4.6 or less and a water activity greater than 0.85. These may be called "pickles" or "pickled foods." Foods such as acidified artichoke hearts, bean salads, and peppers or pimentos, plus marinated vegetables like beets or mushrooms, and fresh-pack pickles are among those considered to be acidified foods. By this definition, certain foods have been excluded from coverage in the FDA regulation on acidified products: Examples include carbonated beverages, jams, jellies and preserves; acid foods such as food dressing and condiment sauces containing small amounts of low-acid foods that have a resultant pH that does not significantly differ from that of the predominant acid or acid food; naturally acid foods like peaches; and foods stored, distributed and retailed under refrigeration. Foods that are preserved by microbial fermentation are also excluded. However, it may be appropriate for the manufacturers to use the principles discussed in this chapter for the manufacture of foods not covered by these regulations.

The USDA defines "acidified foods" in a manner similar to FDA's definition provided at the beginning of this section. However, USDA's definition also includes a stipulation that every component of the product must have a pH that is 4.6 or lower within 24 hours after processing, and covers all meat or poultry canned products that receive a thermal process either before or after being packed in a hermetically sealed container. Fermented products are not excluded, but the USDA canning regulations are not intended to cover refrigerated foods.

Proper acidification is necessary to prevent the growth of *C. botulinum.* Unlike processes for low-acid foods that destroy *C. botulinum* spores, processes for acidified foods depend upon the pH of the food to prevent this organism from growing. The final equilibrium pH of an acidified food must be 4.6 or lower to prevent growth of *C. botulinum.* The steps packers must take when they fail to properly acidify their products will be discussed later. A more detailed discussion on *C. botulinum* and the effect of pH on spores may be found in Chapter 2.

The most important factor in the production of acidified foods is the timely attainment and maintenance of a pH level that will inhibit the growth of *C. botulinum* spores. It also is necessary to ensure that microbial deterioration of the product or ingredients does not take place prior to reaching a pH level of 4.6 or less. To achieve this goal, it is necessary to know the meaning of the term pH and how it can be measured.

Meaning of pH

The term pH is a symbol used to designate the degree of acidity or alkalinity (basicity) of a water solution. Just as a temperature scale is used to measure heat and cold, the pH scale measures how acid or alkaline a solution is. In scientific language, pH is the negative logarithm of the hydrogen ion concentration. The pH is directly related to the ratio of hydrogen (H+) to hydroxyl (OH-) ions present in a solution. All solutions contain both hydrogen and hydroxyl ions. The more hydrogen ions that are present, the more acidic the solution. If hydroxyl ions exceed hydrogen ions, the solution is basic, and if the two ions are present in equal amounts, the solution is neutral.

The actual number of hydrogen ions in a water solution is extremely small. For example, in pure water—which is neutral—the hydrogen ion concentration is 0.0000001 grams per liter. Since using such numbers is difficult, a scale based on the logarithm of the reciprocal of the hydrogen ion concentration was adopted. This scale ranges from 0 to 14, with the pH of pure water equaling 7.0. Numbers smaller than 7.0 indicate an increase in hydrogen ion concentration (more acid); numbers larger than 7.0 indicate a decrease in hydrogen ion concentration and an increase in the hydroxyl ion concentration (more basic). Because the numbers are on a logarithmic scale, a pH of 6.0 represents 10 times more hydrogen ions than are present at pH 7.0, while a pH of 5.0 represents 10 times more hydrogen ions than are present at pH 6.0 and 100 times more than are present at pH 7.0. (See *Table 1.*)

All acids and bases do not act in the same way in solution. When a "strong" acid such as hydrochloric acid is mixed with water, essentially all the hydrogen ions are free in solution. The same is true for the hydroxyl ions of a strong base such as sodium hydroxide (lye). Acids such as acetic and citric acids do not release all hydrogen ions into solution and are known as weak acids.

Most foods have an ability to resist changes in pH. This is known as buffering capacity and varies from food to food. The buffering capacity will affect the amount of acid required to lower the pH of a given food by a given amount. As an example, foods high in protein, such as meat, have a greater buffering capacity than vegetables in brine. Consequently, meat will require more acid than vegetables to lower the pH an equivalent amount. The size, variety and maturity of vegetables will also have an effect on the pH and buffering capacity. Pure water has no buffering capacity. Therefore, it takes very little acid to lower its pH.

Determination of pH

Equipment

The pH of a food may be measured using colorimetric or electrometric methods or by titratable acidity. The use of titratable acidity is less common and requires testing to determine a correlation between pH and titratable acidity. The colorimetric method depends upon the use of certain sensitive dyes to change colors over a limited range of pH values. No one dye is capable of producing characteristic color changes over the entire pH range. The dye selected should be one that has the greatest color change at the pH of the solution being tested. When an indicator solution is used, this color change is compared to a standard in order to determine the pH. Paper strips treated with an indicator dye or multiple dyes are called indicator or pH papers. A drop of the test solution or food product is applied to the indicator paper strip, which changes color depending upon the pH of the solution or product. The paper is then compared to a standard to determine the pH. These methods *only* give approximate pH values and should not be used for routine measurement of the pH of foods unless the pH is 4.0 or less. FDA allows this method to be used for those products with pH's of 4.0 or less.

Table 1—The comparison of acidity of pure water with representative foods at each pH value.

pH Value	Degree of Acidity Compared With Water	Example of Foods
0	10,000,000	None
1	1,000,000	None
2	100,000	Limes
3	10,000	Grapefruit
4	1,000	Peaches
5	100	Carrots
6	10	Beans, Meats
7	1	Black Olives

The recommended method for determining pH—the electrometric method using a pH meter—is also the method most widely used. The pH meter measures the electrical potential developed between a glass and a reference electrode when they are immersed in a solution. The meter converts this potential to a pH value, which is read from the meter. New, inexpensive digital pH meters have all but replaced pH papers. The USDA requires the electrometric method to be used any time pH is specified as a critical factor for a scheduled process.

Meters for measuring pH are basically of two types—digital or analog. These two types of meters, as shown in *Figures 1* and *2*, can be compared with electronic digital watches vs. analog or conventional watches. Since pH values are read directly on digital meters, less likelihood exists for making a mistake in reading the pH values. The analog meter contains a scale of numbers and a needle which will point to the corresponding pH value on the scale (*Figure 1*). For an accurate reading, a reflection of the needle should not be seen in the strip of mirror backing below the scale. For best results, these meters should be operated in accordance with manufacturer's instructions.

The sensing elements used with pH meters are called electrodes. Two electrodes—a glass electrode and a reference electrode—are immersed in the sample to measure pH (*Figures 3* and *4*). These may be joined in a single unit to form a ''combination'' electrode.

Combination electrodes contain both a glass and reference electrode in a single probe (*Figure 5*). They come in a number of different sizes and conformations, which increases the applications of this type of electrode. For example, flat-surface electrodes are useful for measuring the surface pH of a solid sample; long, thin electrodes may be inserted in tubes for measuring pH of small sample volumes or inserted into the process stream for continuous monitoring of pH. Unbreakable electrodes should be used in food processing plants to minimize the chances of contaminating food in process areas. *Figure 6* shows

some of the commercially available combination electrodes.

Some glass electrodes are made with full pH range. Others are made for specific applications. The pH meter manufacturer should be consulted for the appropriate electrodes for your applications. When not in use, the glass electrode should be stored in a pH 4.0 buffer or according to the manufacturer's instructions.

The reference electrode may use calomel as an internal element or a silver/silver chloride internal element. The

Figure 2—Photograph of a digital pH meter.

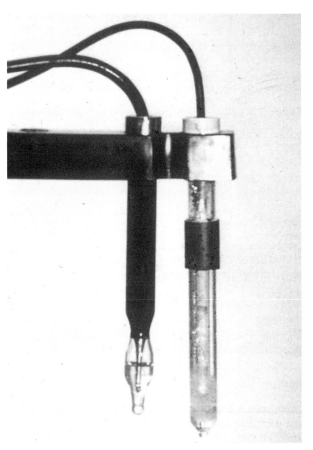

Figure 3—Photograph of glass and calomel reference electrodes for measuring pH.

Figure 1—Photograph showing dial of an analog pH meter with a reading of 4.6.

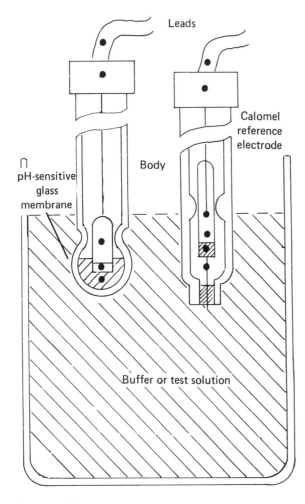

Figure 4—Diagram of glass and calomel reference electrodes for measuring pH.

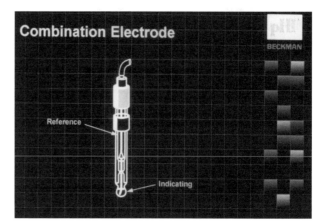

Figure 5—Diagram of the internal components of a combination electrode.

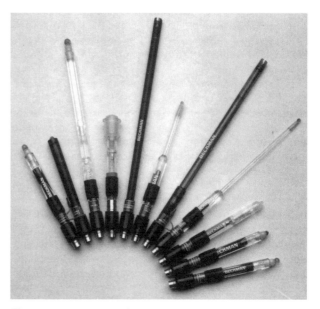

Figure 6—A variety of combination electrodes.

reference electrode should have the filling solution above the storage or sample solution level in order to force filling solution out through the junction. The junction is the critical part of a reference electrode. Difficulties in pH measurement can often be traced to a clogged or high resistance junction. Keeping the junction wet is important to keeping it unclogged. Follow the manufacturer's recommendations to rejuvenate the junction should it become clogged. The reference electrode, if stored for long periods, should be kept in 0.1 M KCl solution, unless otherwise specified by the manufacturer.

Precautions

Electrodes should be rinsed between samples and after use. The purpose of rinsing is to prevent cross-contamination between solutions. Rinsing with distilled water is recommended. However, if enough sample is available, rinsing with the next solution to be measured and throw-

ing away the rinse solution is the best way to prevent cross-contamination. If distilled water is used, the water should be blotted—not wiped—off the electrodes. If the electrode is rinsed with the next solution, this step is not necessary. Electrodes should not be wiped, because wiping could implant a charge on the electrode causing it to drift. Oil and grease from samples may coat or clog elements; therefore, electrodes should be cleaned with ethyl ether or acetone in accordance with the manufacturer's instructions, and the instrument should be re-standardized frequently.

The length of time required for the meter to stabilize depends on the type of sample tested. Generally, about one minute is required to obtain a stable reading. Values should be reported to two decimal places—the nearest hundredth of a pH unit. The pH varies with changes in temperatures. Weakly buffered solutions are affected the most. For greater accuracy, the temperature of the sample and the standard buffer should be about the same.

Standardization

Once the unit has been turned on and allowed to warm up, the meter should be properly standardized using two buffers to cover the pH range of interest, such as, one at pH 4.0 and the other at pH 7.0. The meter should be standardized (1) before any food pH measurements are taken and (2) at least once an hour following that. More frequent standardization and possibly cleaning may be necessary with some products that contain oil.

Sample Preparation

The sample to be tested must be properly prepared, and this preparation is dependent on the type of product to be evaluated. Homogeneous products, such as sauces or puddings, require little preparation. Products that consist of solid and liquid components should have the solid components tested separately to determine if they have been properly acidified. One means of sample preparation is to transfer a portion of the solid component to a screen, rinse it with a small volume of distilled water (10-20ml), and thoroughly blend before taking a pH. Detailed explanation of the methods used to determine the pH of food samples—especially marinated products—is presented in the FDA regulation on acidified foods (21 CFR 114.90).[1] Sufficient tests must be made to ensure that the finished equilibrium pH of the product is not higher than 4.6. These tests indicate whether the acidification process is sufficient to bring the product to the appropriate pH.

Acidification Procedures

To produce products with a pH of 4.6 or less, acidification must be properly carried out. It should be remembered that perishable ingredients must be properly protected from microbial spoilage *before* acidification and *until* an equilibrium pH of 4.6 or less is reached. Here are some methods to obtain properly acidified foods:

1. **Blanch the food ingredients in an acidified aqueous solution.** To acidify large food particulates, the particulate could be blanched in a hot acid bath. The ability to obtain a properly acidified product is dependent upon blanch time and temperature, as well as the type of and concentration of acid.

2. **Immerse the blanched foods in an acid solution.** That is, blanch the product in the normal steam or water blancher. Then, dip it into an acid solution, remove it

---

[1]For additional information, see section 981.12, in *Official Methods of Analysis*, 16th edition, 1995, published by Association of Official Analytical Chemists.

from the acid solution and place into containers. Proper acidification depends upon how well the product is blanched, the concentration of the acid and the contact time.

3. **Direct batch acidification.** This is normally the best way to acidify fluid material. Ingredients are mixed in a kettle, and acid is added directly to the batch. (An elevated temperature may improve the rate of acid penetration into solid particles.) The pH of the batch is checked before the material is sent from the batch kettle to the filler.

4. **Add acid foods to low-acid foods in controlled portions**. Essentially, this is how a formulated product such as zucchini with tomato sauce is made. Zucchini is a low-acid food, while the tomato sauce is an acid food. The acid food is mixed with the low-acid food to get an acidified food product. The proportion of tomato sauce to zucchini at the filler is critical to obtain uniform and accurate control of pH of the finished product.

5. **Directly add a predetermined amount of acid to individual containers during production.** This involves addition of acid pellets, known volumes of acid solution, or some other means of direct acidification to each container. This is probably the least dependable and most inaccurate method of acidification, because acid addition to a given container may be overlooked. It may be difficult to obtain solid-to-liquid ratio controls, adequate mixing of the acid throughout the product or proper penetration of the acid into the solid materials. Although this is a permissible way to acidify, it is not recommended.

The five methods discussed above are used by the industry. All are acceptable ways of acidification. However, each requires a certain amount of control in order to acidify a particular product properly. No single means is appropriate for all situations. A company may utilize more than one procedure depending on the kind of products and the scheduled process that the processing authority has designed from supporting data.

Critical Control Points

For proper production of an acidified product, several critical control points must be checked to ensure that the acidification procedure is under control:

1. Every container of food must be acidified in the same proportions.
   A. When producing a solid-liquid mixture that will be acidified in the container by direct acidification, it is necessary to know and control the amount of solid material in each container. This permits the addition of the appropriate amount of acid to obtain a finished product pH of less than 4.6.
   B. Know the buffering capacity of the food.
   C. It is necessary to control the unit operations of peeling, blanching, exhausting, brining and clo-

sure. For example, some products are lye peeled, and if the lye carry-over is not controlled, the product will have a higher initial pH than accounted for in the formulation. The end result will be a product that is not in control and which has a higher pH value than required. The operations that, according to the scheduled process, will affect the pH of the final finished product must be controlled and recorded.

2. Monitor acidification by pH measurement before and after equilibrium. The key is that the finished product pH must be 4.6 or less. Finished product pH means the pH of the product (components included) in the final container after thermal processing—not the raw product pH. The pH measurements must be recorded and the records reviewed at the appropriate time intervals.

3. Monitor the scheduled thermal process. The objective of the thermal process is to destroy vegetative cells of microorganisms of public health significance and those of non-health significance that are capable of reproducing in the food under normal conditions of storage and distribution.

  A. *Figure 7* shows the influence of product pH on processing. Those products that are high acid or acidified to a pH of 4.6 or less do not require a high temperature process. The foods may be processed at the temperature of boiling water— 212°F (100°C)—or lower. The thermal process is designed to pasteurize the product—to destroy vegetative cells and some heat labile spores. The product's low pH (4.6 or less) will prevent the remaining spores from growing out. On the other hand, low-acid foods—those with a pH greater than 4.6—require a high temperature process (greater than that of boiling water) in order to destroy spores as well as vegetative cells that could grow in the product under normal (non-refrigerated) conditions of storage and distribution.

  B. Acidified foods may be processed using hot-fill-hold techniques. In this procedure, hot product is filled and sealed into a container, held for a given time period at a given temperature, and the container is cooled. Temperatures less than boiling water are always used. Some acidified foods are processed using an atmospheric process. In this procedure, product—either cold or hot—is filled into the container and the container

Figure 7—Influence of product pH on degree of thermal processing.

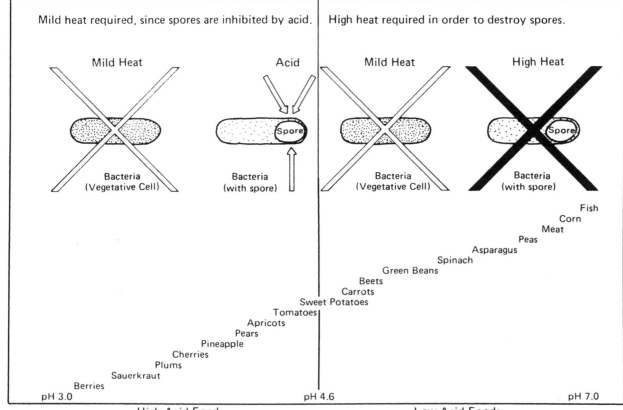

24

is closed. Then, the container is sent through a pasteurizer using flowing steam or hot water. The product is held for a given time period to ensure destruction of yeast and vegetative cells of bacteria. Appropriate records *must* be kept to verify delivery of the scheduled process to the product.

4. Control container handling. Processed containers should be handled in such a manner as to minimize damage to the seals and to prevent product recontamination. Further information is provided in Chapter 4.

Regulations Governing Acidified Foods

Requirements for USDA-regulated acidified foods are included in the USDA canning regulations. FDA regulations governing acidified foods are found in three parts of 21 CFR. Part 114 contains the acidified foods regulations; Part 110 contains current good manufacturing practices; and Part 108.25 deals with emergency permit control for acidified foods.

The regulations of both agencies are reprinted in the Appendix. They include requirements for plants engaged in the manufacturing, processing or packaging of acidified foods. The FDA regulations stipulate that a company shall register and file a process—including conditions for heat processing and control of pH, salt, sugar and preservative levels along with the source and date of the establishment of the process—for each acidified food in each container size. The USDA does not have a separate regulation for acidified foods. Therefore, acidified products containing meat or poultry products are subject to the general provisions of the USDA canning regulations. Both agencies require manufacturers to process in accordance with the filed or scheduled process. If requested by the regulators, a processor shall provide them with process and pH information to determine the adequacy of the process.

FDA also requires that any spoilage, process deviation or contamination of public health significance shall be reported to the agency if any part of the defective lot has reached the channels of interstate commerce. A company shall have a recall procedure prepared. All personnel shall operate only under the supervision of persons who have been certified to supervise acidified food processing operations.

Failure to Properly Acidify Products

Proper acidification of the low-acid components of acidified foods is necessary to prevent the growth of *C.*

botulinum. Product that is found to have an equilibrium pH greater than 4.6 shall be:

1. Fully reprocessed using a reprocess established by a competent processing authority to ensure safe product.

2. Thermally processed as a low-acid food.

3. Set aside for further evaluation by a processing authority as to public health significance.

4. Destroyed.

Unless this product can be proven to be safe, it shall be reprocessed to render it safe or destroyed. (More information on handling deviations may be found in Chapter 8.)

Record Requirements

In addition to the record requirements outlined in Chapter 6, there are certain specific requirements for acidified foods. The following records shall be kept:

1. Processing and production records showing adherence to scheduled processes including pH measurements and other critical factors.

2. Records of all deviations from the scheduled process.

Records shall be retained in an accessible location for three years.

Summary

1. The term pH is a symbol used to designate the degree or intensity of acidity.

2. The pH is determined by either of two methods: (1) electrometrically with a pH meter, or less desirably, (2) colorimetrically with dyes when product pH is 4.0 or less.

3. Care should be exercised in the operation and maintenance of pH meters to ensure that accurate readings are obtained.

4. The following methods are used to acidify foods properly:
   A. Blanching of foods in acid solution.
   B. Immersion of blanched foods in acid solution.
   C. Direct batch acidification.
   D. Addition of acid foods to low-acid foods in controlled proportions.
   E. Direct addition of a predetermined amount of acid to individual containers.

5. Proper acidification is possible only by strict observance of the critical control points indicated in the scheduled process.

6. Thermal processes for acidified foods are designed to destroy vegetative cells. Spore outgrowth is prevented by maintaining the pH of the product below 4.6.

FOOD CONTAINER HANDLING

Introduction

The sturdiness of most present day food containers makes it easy to take container integrity for granted. Recognition of the possible causes and consequences of loss of container integrity and steps to prevent these problems are the basis of discussion in this chapter.

Food Containers

Food preservation by the process known as canning could not have attained the widespread acceptance and commercial application that it enjoys today without the continuing development of improved containers. Containers for canning must be sturdy and durable and, most importantly, must be capable of remaining hermetically sealed under commercial operating conditions.

The invention of the metal can provided the first answers to questions of container durability and seal integrity. Methods of manufacturing and sealing metal cans have steadily improved from the original cans with soldered body and end seams, to the development of crimped double seams for attaching the top and bottom ends, to today's cans with a one-piece body and a single double seamed end.

As better cans were being developed, the glass container was being refined and improved. Advancements in glass manufacturing technology have resulted in containers that are sturdier and better able to withstand thermal shock and automated handling. Glass container closures have also undergone many improvements. Present day closures allow automated, high-speed closing with a high degree of seal integrity.

Some of the newer innovations in food containers include semirigid and rigid plastic containers with double seamed metal ends or heat sealed lids. These containers—along with the flexible retort pouch and paperboard package—offer the processor a wide variety of container sizes and shapes (*Figure 1*). In some cases, a flexible or semirigid container may be designed for a specific aseptic packaging system with the size and shape to suit the type of product. Consumer convenience and microwave use are in part responsible for the growth of these new containers. Although these containers are obviously different from the traditional rigid metal and glass containers, the protection of seals and container integrity by avoiding container abuse is just as important.

Figure 1—Examples of innovative containers.

Requirements for Safe Preservation of Canned Foods

Safe preservation of foods by thermal processing—both retorting and aseptic processing—depends on the accomplishment of three conditions:

1. The use of proper filling and sealing procedures that result in hermetically sealed containers capable of preventing the re-entry of microorganisms into the product after achieving commercial sterility.

2. The application of heat or other sterilization method to the degree necessary to ensure commercial sterility of the product and container.

3. The use of post-process handling procedures that protect the integrity of the sealed and processed containers.

The details of proper heat processing are covered in other chapters of this text; however, it is important that container abuse be avoided in this step. The remaining conditions are both concerned with producing a hermetic seal and maintaining the integrity of the sealed container. These two conditions depend not only on proper filling, closing, processing and cooling but also on the handling that the containers receive during these operations and during post-processing operations. The possibility always exists for the re-entry of spoilage bacteria into the container by way of some defect in the container, such as a poorly-made seam or seal, a seam or seal opened by rough handling, or gross mishandling of the container by the processor, the distributor, the retailer or the consumer. Spoilage from container abuse may result in commercial loss and consumer dissatisfaction.

Production Operations

In commercial canning procedures, certain basic operations may influence the integrity and length of the shelf-life of the food container.

Pre-Process Container Handling

USDA regulations require and good manufacturing practice dictates that empty containers be examined for damage and cleaned prior to filling.

All container-handling equipment from empty container storage through warehousing must be operated in such a manner that container damage is avoided. Empty containers must be protected from damage. Dents on can bodies or flanges or damage to container ends may result in closure defects and leaker spoilage. Rough handling or improperly adjusted or maintained runways or cable conveyers may damage containers, resulting in leaking containers with punctures, cable burns or seam defects. Flexible and semirigid packages are susceptible to damage. The container handling systems should be inspected regularly for sharp edges, burrs or other protrusions that could puncture the container.

Blanching

Blanching is an operation in which raw food material—mainly vegetable products—is immersed in hot water or exposed to live steam or hot gases. The blanch serves a number of purposes and may directly affect not only container integrity but also the adequacy of the heat process and the quality of the finished product.

During the blanch, the product shrinks and the respiratory gases contained in the plant cells are expelled. The release of gas prior to filling the container is desirable, since this reduces strain on the container during heat processing by contributing to the development of a higher vacuum in the product. Other methods of deaeration are available, such as vacuum mixing, which may be used to remove entrapped air prior to processing. Shrinking of the product facilitates proper fill of the container.

The blanching operation also inhibits further enzymatic action that might cause oxidative reactions and detrimental quality changes in the product. Blanching in hot water or steam is used on some products to facilitate peeling, cutting, dicing or other preparatory steps. The blanch may serve as an added cleaning measure and also may remove raw flavors from foods. A final function of the blanching operation is to fix or set the natural color of certain products.

Filling

In addition to providing adequate headspace in the container (*Figure 2*), it is essential that precautionary measures prevent product from contacting the seal area or from coming between the lip of the container and the lid placed over the container. Food trapped in the seam

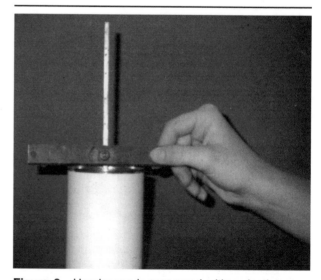

Figure 2—Headspace is measured with a depth gauge with a horizontal bar and a vertical rule calibrated in 32nd and 64th inches. Other types of depth gauges may be used.

or seal could cause seam or seal deformation or could act as a wick to draw contamination into the container.

Container Closure

In order to avoid container leaks, seaming or sealing equipment must be properly maintained and operated. Overfilling, using cans or other containers with defective flanges, jars with damaged lugs or threads, and letting product overhang the flange or seal area are all causes of container failure and should be avoided. Periodic inspections must be conducted and records kept to ensure that containers with defective seals are not produced. Closures for metal and glass containers and semirigid and flexible packages are covered in detail in Chapters 16, 17 and 18.

Thermal Processing Operations

Cars, crates or gondolas, racks and divider plates used for holding containers in the retort should be examined frequently to ensure they are not broken or damaged. Sharp projections, possibly resulting from improperly maintained equipment, could puncture or damage containers. Racks that do not allow containers to rest properly in the racking system may inflict damage. This is especially true for semirigid or flexible containers. Container loading and unloading systems should be designed in such a manner that container damage is minimized.

Proper operation of the retort system is necessary to maintain container integrity and to minimize container distortion. This is especially important during the cooling period.

Post-Processing Container Handling

USDA regulations require and good manufacturing practice dictates that, after retorting, containers be protected from damage that could affect their integrity. Careful handling of filled, processed containers must continue through labeling, palletizing or casing, and warehousing. In these areas, container damage and leaker spoilage may result from improper equipment operation, careless forklift maneuvers or improper stacking procedures.

Prevention of Bacterial Contamination of Containers

The use of proper production procedures, such as heat processing and adequate container sealing or closure, should result in a hermetically sealed, commercially sterile product. However, care must be taken to ensure that further practices and conditions do not result in loss of container integrity and bacterial contamination.

Container Vacuum

There are several reasons for obtaining vacuum in canned foods. For rigid containers these include: maintenance of container ends in a concave position during normal storage, reduction of the oxygen level inside the container and prevention of permanent distortion of container ends during thermal processing (*Figure 3*). For a few products, such as vacuum-packed corn, the adequacy of the thermal process is based on a rather high initial vacuum in the container. For certain flexible and semirigid containers, the reasons for obtaining vacuum are similar to rigid containers: reduction of the oxygen level and protection from distortion during thermal processing—which in many cases could affect the adequacy of the thermal process. Container vacuum is formed in the container by use of high-fill temperatures, steam-flushed closures or mechanical evacuation of air.

Since the inception of commercial canning, a vacuum has been produced in the container. Bacterial spoilage usually results in gas formation that causes bulging of the container. Consequently, any distortion of the container from the normal shape is taken as an indication of spoilage by the industry and by the consumer. The presence of vacuum in a processed container of food normally indicates that the container seal is intact. However, the presence of vacuum in the container does not assure that flat-sour spoilage has not occurred.

A low oxygen content in canned foods is desirable to minimize adverse chemical changes in the product such as oxidation of fats or vitamins, to prevent discoloration in some products, and also to reduce internal corrosion of the cans.

For a few products packed in only a small amount of brine, the thermal process is dependent on the heating

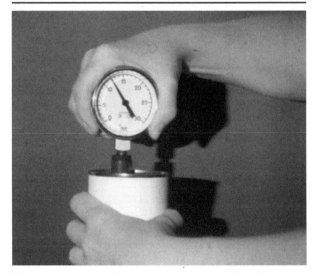

Figure 3—Vacuum is usually measured with a Bourdon-type gauge calibrated to read vacuum from 0 to 30 inches.

rate that results from the maintenance of a high vacuum. For some products packed in flexible pouches and some meat products packed in cans having large flat areas, adequate vacuum is necessary to maintain contact between these flat surfaces and the product for satisfactory heat transfer during thermal processing.

Regarding container integrity, the primary purpose for the maintenance of adequate container vacuum is to reduce stress to the container and its seams or seals caused by pressure building-up inside the container during thermal processing and subsequent handling.

Leaker Spoilage in Canned Foods

Despite the engineering skill that has gone into designing and manufacturing the hermetically sealed containers and despite the precautions the industry takes in protecting the seals, leakage spoilage may occur in canned foods as it does in other types of preserved foods. Many canners have quality control procedures for incoming container inspection to protect against defective containers.

Most containers of processed food are closed in a manner that produces a vacuum. This creates a condition where anything less than a secure seal could permit air, water or other particles to be drawn into the closed container as the vacuum is being formed. The probable result would be spoilage of the product due to entrance of microorganisms present in the air or water.

This spoilage is called "leaker-type" and is due to bacterial contamination after processing. Microscopic and/or cultural examination of canned foods that spoil in this manner often show the spoilage organisms to be a mixed flora of non-spore-forming bacteria, both rods and cocci, having a varied heat resistance (*Figure 4*). It is obvious that the organisms entered the containers after the product had begun to cool because the bacteria would not have survived the thermal process. In other words, contaminated air, water or other material must have leaked into the container. Hence, the term leaker-type spoilage.

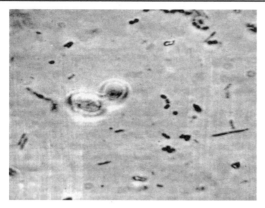

Figure 4—Photograph of typical mixed flora of non-heat resistant bacteria found in foods that have spoiled because of container leakage.

The point of leakage may be a defect occurring during manufacture or closing of the container. It may be a momentary failure in the seal caused by a disturbance of the seal after a partial vacuum has been formed. Leaking seals or seams may or may not result in loss of vacuum depending on the severity and duration of the leak. Some leaking seals or seams may reseal themselves with product or sealant.

Leaker-type contamination may occur during water cooling of the containers. It may also occur in warehouses or retail stores if seams are damaged to the point of leaking or the container is punctured by a knife or hook when the case is being opened. Flexible and semirigid packages are particularly susceptible to damage of this nature.

Influence of the Cooling Operation

Heat-processed containers of food are usually water cooled. This is done either by cooling in retorts, cooling canals, agitating spin coolers, rotary pressure coolers or a combination of the above. Before cooling, can ends are distended due to the pressure that builds up during processing. This built-up pressure causes the components of the newly made double seam to change slightly in their relationship to each other. Seals on glass or flexible containers are similarly stressed. During cooling the ends are pulled in by the vacuum forming in the package. Because the seam compound is still semi-fluid and the seam is stressed, this action—as well as a blow to the seam—may allow entry of minute amounts of cooling water. If the droplet of water contains a bacterium capable of growing in the product and if conditions are favorable for growth, leaker spoilage will occur.

Seams and seals must be protected from recontamination until they are cool and dry. The bacterial condition of the cooling water is important. The higher the number of bacteria, the greater the chances of leaker spoilage. Even low numbers may cause spoilage when the ability of even the best closed containers to keep out bacterial contamination is taxed. Water of good sanitary quality must be used. Chlorination or other sanitizers are employed to keep contamination at a minimum. A measurable free chlorine residual at the discharge end of the cooler is required for cooling canals and recirculated water cooling systems, and it is recommended for single-use water systems. Other suitable sanitizers may also be used.

Under some cooling conditions, the pressure inside the container will exceed the pressure in the cooling system. If the cooling pressure is reduced too rapidly, metal containers can be subjected to a differential pressure that may exceed the strength of the ends or seal, and a condition known as buckling may occur (*Figure 5*). Adequate container vacuum is very important in preventing buckling, but cooling under pressure may be necessary. Buckles may represent a very serious problem. When a metal container is buckled, the double seam may be pulled apart

Figure 5—Cans that are buckled during retorting may leak during the cooling operation because the double seam has been strained.

Figure 6—Paneling of cans is not serious as a cause of spoilage.

enough to leak and the contents may spoil due to bacterial contamination. Glass, flexible and semirigid packages and some larger metal containers almost always require cooling under pressure to prevent the seal from being damaged.

Paneling may occur when the pressure, during pressure-cooling in the retort, is too high or maintained for too long a time while the cans cool and a vacuum forms. Paneling is not serious except that the deformation of the can detracts from its appearance and may make labeling difficult (*Figure 6*).

Post-Cooling Container Handling

The problem of maintaining container integrity also extends to the post-cooling container-handling systems. Studies have indicated that excessive bacterial contamination may develop on wet and soiled post-cooling can handling equipment, even though the cooling water is chlorinated or is naturally of good sanitary quality. Bacterial contamination is transferred in varying degrees to the seam or seal areas of containers as they pass through the handling systems. Under such conditions, post-cooling container handling systems have been the cause of spoilage due to recontamination.

When filled cans are handled at high speeds in automatic equipment elevators and runways, small dents may occur under the seams. These could momentarily break the seal at the point. Larger cans are more susceptible to under-seam denting because of the momentum imparted by the weight of their contents. Even well designed, properly adjusted equipment may cause imperceptible dents on and under the seams. Controlled laboratory tests have shown that even these imperceptible dents may cause momentary leakage. If spoilage bacteria are present, some may be drawn through the seam at the time (*Table 1*).

Rolling cans on the body rather than on the double seams will prevent the double seams from contacting

runway surfaces which may be contaminated. Runways may be adapted as shown in *Figure 7*.

Unsanitary condition of the container handling lines and resultant contamination transferred to the containers are directly related to the amount of moisture present in which the spoilage organisms are suspended and can grow. Moisture is needed for transfer of bacteria to the container closure. Moisture is also needed for the bacteria to move through the closure into the container. The effects of rough handling in emptying baskets, unscrambling, labeling, casing, etc., are considerably minimized when the containers are perfectly dry. In continuously operating lines, high velocity air jets efficiently dry containers as they emerge from the cooler by blowing excess water from the containers. Tunnel dryers in which the containers are carried upright through a current of warm air are not very efficient. In non-continuous lines, allowing containers to dry in the retort crates before they are discharged into automatic container handling systems is advantageous.

Studies show that a significant build-up of spoilage organisms collects on conveyor belts and runways wet with cooling water, despite the fact that water of good

Table 1—Relation of can abuse and microbial count on double seam areas to rate of spoilage—(cans taken at caser).

Severe Can Abuse		Minimum Can Abuse	
Microorganisms Per Can	Spoilage Rate (Cans/1,000)	Microorganisms Per Can	Spoilage Rate (Cans/1,000)
23,000	18	1,000	0
32,000	30	1,600	0
35,000	23	25,000	<1
69,000	22	52,000	<1
73,000	24	209,000	<1
130,000	25	900,000*	<1
327,000	25	1,790,000*	<1

*Seams inoculated with *Aerobacter aerogenes* (Data from Continental Can Co.).

31

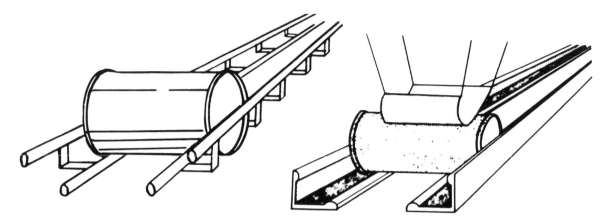

Figure 7—Can runways, slow downs and other handling equipment may be constructed to prevent double seam areas from contacting runway surfaces where moisture and bacteria may accumulate.

sanitary condition is employed in the cooler. Consequently, it appears more attention should be given to cleaning and sanitizing these portions of the lines regularly in order to hold contamination to a minimum (*Table 2*). All tracks, belts and bars that come in contact with containers should be scrubbed thoroughly to remove extraneous materials. Substances often are gummy, become caked in the equipment and are not removed by simple flushing. The entire line, therefore, should be scrubbed with a stiff brush or cleaned by other suitable means, using a detergent prepared in the concentration recommended by the manufacturer. After cleaning and subsequent rinsing, a germicidal solution should be applied freely to all container elevators and conveyors at the time of each plant cleanup.

Table 2—Microbial counts of filled can handling system before and after cleanup.

	Microorganisms/Sq. In.	
Sampling Point	Before Cleanup	After Cleanup
Can track leaving rotary cooker-cooler	< 10,000	< 1,000
Runway to bar flight elevator	> 500,000	< 1,000
Bar flight elevator	315,000	< 1,000
Runway following bar flight elevator	> 500,000	120,000
Pulley at end of hold cable	30,000	5,000
Lowerator to labeler	230,000	11,000
Canvas covering on bar flight elevator leaving labeler	200,000	2,000
Star wheel lowerator feeding caser	525,000	3,000
Gravity track to caser	900,000	1,000
Caser	> 1,000,000	12,000
Brushes on hold cable between cooler and labeler	> 1 Billion*	Removed
Double seam areas on cans at caser (Organisms/can)	—**	< 1,000
Spoilage rate—cans/1,000	5	0

*Organisms/gram
**Data not available: line was shut down when survey was made. (Data from Continental Can Co.)

Post-Retort Handling Precautions

In addition to handling empty containers carefully before use and during filling to ensure they are not damaged before closing, the following are steps a processor may take to avoid post-processing recontamination:

1. Inspect all closures periodically to ensure they are properly formed and of the highest quality. A slight abnormality in the seal may be magnified by rough handling and, in the presence of contaminated cooling water or contaminated handling equipment, recontamination may result. Containers should also be examined for the presence of other defects such as dents or seal damage.

2. Control the entire retort operation. Use a system for transferring containers to the retort that does not dent or damage the containers. Also, avoid overfilling retort crates to prevent crushing. Check retort operations to be sure that the preliminary cooling is carried out properly (pressure cooling where necessary) to avoid straining the seal and/or buckling double seamed metal containers. Unload retorts and handle filled containers subsequent to retorting as gently as possible to avoid abuse. Use of belt elevators, belt retarders and seamless conveyor belts are suggested.

3. Chlorinate or otherwise sanitize cooling water.

4. Evaporate the water by holding the containers, where space permits, or use a suitable container dryer.

5. Replace all worn and frayed belting and porous materials with new, nonporous ones. Improve the installation and adjustment of high-speed automatic container handling equipment to minimize container abuse.

6. Clean and sanitize the filled-container handling system on a regular basis.

7. Examine containers taken periodically during the day's operation from significant points in the filled container handling system for evidence of damage. Where

damage is apparent, smooth out the operation to minimize container abuse.

8. A final container examination should be made before lots leave the cannery to ensure that containers with defects are not being produced. For cans, automatic dud detection equipment is available that can be adjusted to sort out containers that have lost their vacuum.

9. Design equipment to allow an even, continuous flow of flexible or semirigid containers through the line. These packages should not be dropped onto conveyors or other pieces of equipment. Synchronize line speeds to avoid excessively fast movement or piling up of packages.

Summary

1. Safe preservation of canned foods depends on: the application of heat or other methods to the degree necessary to ensure commercial sterility, the use of container closures that prevent entry of microorganisms and the use of container handling procedures that protect the integrity of processed containers.

2. Leaker spoilage may occur when an insecure seal allows air, water or other material to be drawn into the container.

3. Line operations, such as blanching and filling, may influence the integrity and shelf-life of the product and the container.

4. Procedures to prevent product overhang or use of damaged or defective containers are important to minimize post-process leakage. When defective containers of any type are found, it is important to remove them. It is equally important to determine the cause of the defects and correct those conditions.

5. Containers must be handled carefully prior to their use and during filling, retorting and storage. Rough container handling may be a major cause of leaker spoilage.

6. Container cooling water should be chlorinated to maintain a measurable residual of chlorine at the discharge end of the cooler. The sanitary condition of container cooling water is directly related to leaker spoilage.

7. The filled container handling system should be cleaned and sanitized regularly to avoid spoilage due to recontamination.

8. During the day's operation, containers should be taken from significant points in the line to check for any evidence of rough handling. Problem areas should be smoothed to minimize container abuse. A final container examination prior to labeling and casing should be made to remove any defects.

Chapter 5

FOOD PLANT SANITATION

Introduction

The term "sanitation" is frequently applied in a food plant only to the cleaning of equipment and production areas of a plant. In reality, however, sanitation includes activities that are designed to prevent product adulteration during the processing of foods. Although protecting the health of the consumer is of primary importance, sanitation programs also include activities designed to minimize economic loss from spoilage and to prevent contamination of foods with materials that may offend the consumer's aesthetic sense.

To establish criteria for acceptable food plant sanitation, the FDA published *Current Good Manufacturing Practice* regulations (CGMPs, also known as the "umbrella" GMPs) for the manufacturing, packaging or holding of human foods. The CGMP regulations appear under Title 21, Code of Federal Regulations, Part 110 (21 CFR 110). Additionally, the FDA promulgated regulations for thermally processed low-acid foods packaged in hermetically sealed containers (21 CFR 113) and for acidified foods (21 CFR 114). USDA requirements for sanitation in meat and poultry establishments are covered in 9 CFR 308 and 9 CFR 381, Subpart H (.45 to .61), respectively.

The purpose of all of these regulations is to ensure that food products are not manufactured under conditions that render the foods unfit for human consumption or that the foods have not been prepared, packed or held under insanitary conditions whereby the foods may have become contaminated or whereby the foods may have been rendered injurious to health.

Canned foods are the safest commercially processed foods, because they are given a final heat treatment that is designed to destroy or inactivate microorganisms capable of causing human illness and causing foods to spoil. Furthermore, the hermetically sealed containers protect the foods against recontamination. The thermal processes, however, are designed to destroy and inactivate only a limited number of microorganisms. Therefore, even canning operations must include appropriate steps to minimize the number of microorganisms—especially those that are heat resistant—that are present on the foods before those foods are placed into the containers.

A comprehensive sanitation program is essential for controlling microorganisms in a food processing plant. Chlorine and other sanitizing agents are necessary chemicals for this purpose. However, sanitizers alone cannot ensure food safety nor prevent product spoilage. Effective cleaning of equipment and raw product, proper operating procedures and practices, and the appropriate controls over all factors that can lead to food contamination are all important elements of a successful sanitation program. Nevertheless, sanitizers do play a major role in ensuring product safety. This chapter provides information on various sanitizing agents and their use in controlling microbial contamination of foods.

Sources of Microbial Contamination

The thermal process for each canned food product must destroy or inactivate all microorganisms capable of growing and reproducing in that product. Thermal processes are established to accomplish this task effectively, resulting in the production of commercially sterile foods. However, a thermal process may be rendered ineffective if there are excessive numbers of microorganisms present on or in the food. The numbers and types of microorganisms present in a canned food as it enters the thermal processing system depends on the following:

1. The microorganisms brought into the processing plant on the raw products.

2. The microorganisms picked up by the food as it passes through or over food handling equipment or from employee contact.

3. The microorganisms contributed by process waters during washing, conveying or preparing the product.

4. The microorganisms contained in ingredients that may be added to the product.

5. The microorganisms that may be present in the water used to cool thermally processed containers.

Control of Microbial Contamination

Since spore-forming and non-spore-forming microorganisms are present on raw agricultural products, all raw products must be cleaned and washed as thoroughly as possible when they enter the processing plant. An effective initial cleaning and washing step is also essential to maintaining a clean plant.

All food handling equipment must be cleaned frequently to minimize the growth of microorganisms on food-contact surfaces and thereby minimize the transfer of microorganisms to the food. This cleaning is especially important for heated equipment where a potential exists for a build-up of bacterial spores, particularly those of the thermophilic (high heat resistant) variety. If it is possible to do so, product that has passed through heated equipment should be immediately washed, preferably with cold water. Heated equipment should be kept at temperatures above 170°F (77°C) during operation and should be promptly cleaned and cooled when production is completed.

Water used for washing, conveying or preparing food products must be of good sanitary quality or rendered so by suitable means. The use of appropriate sanitizing agents is an effective method to control microorganisms in water and on raw products, as well as those that grow on equipment surfaces.

Ingredients such as starch, sugars, powdered milk and spices are frequently used in the formulation of food products. These materials are potential sources of microbial contamination. The most important microorganisms in these ingredients are the thermophilic types that become incorporated into the ingredients during their manufacture or preparation. Contamination of products susceptible to thermophilic spoilage may be controlled by using ingredients that are guaranteed by the supplier to be free of thermophilic microorganisms.

Sanitizers

Sanitization—using germicidal or sanitizing agents—is important in preventing spoilage of prepared foods and in maintaining a sanitary food processing environment. Sanitizing is defined as adequately treating food-contact surfaces by a process that is effective in destroying vegetative cells of microorganisms of public health significance and in reducing the numbers of other microorganisms substantially. Such treatment must not adversely affect food products or their safety for consumers.

The sanitizing agents most widely used in food processing plants are chlorine compounds, iodine compounds and quaternary ammonium compounds (quats or QACs). Since chlorine and chlorine compounds are by far the most common germicides or sanitizers used in food processing plants, they are discussed here in detail and compared with the other applicable sanitizers.

Chlorine and Chlorine Compounds

Chlorine gas compressed in convenient-sized cylinders or containers is widely used in food processing plants in the United States. When injected into water, it forms hypochlorous acid—the form of chlorine responsible for germicidal properties. The addition of chlorine gas to processing water is easily controlled; various mechanical devices are commercially available for this purpose. Gaseous chlorine is relatively inexpensive based on the quantity of available chlorine per weight of chlorine gas.

Chlorine may be combined with calcium hydroxide or sodium hydroxide to provide calcium hypochlorite or sodium hypochlorite, respectively. The degree to which the hydroxide is chlorinated determines the percentage of total available chlorine in the compound. The trade or common names and the chlorine contents of several commercially available chlorine compounds are listed in *Table 1*. Included in the table are chloramines, which are formed by the reaction of chlorine with ammonium nitrogen in aqueous solution.

Chlorine dioxide gas, a combination of chlorine and oxygen, is now used in a number of plants. It is less affected by organic matter and variable pH than other chlorine compounds. Currently FDA has no objection to the use of water containing up to 5 ppm chlorine dioxide for rinsing uncut, unpeeled fruits and vegetables or up to 1 ppm chlorine dioxide for rinsing cut and peeled potatoes, provided that such treatment is followed by a potable water rinse. Note that these concentrations are measured directly in the rinse water and should not be confused with feed rates. When using chlorine dioxide, the processor should verify that the concentration used

Table 1—Names and chlorine content of various chlorine compounds

Type of Compound	Common or Trade Name	Percent Total Available Chlorine
Low-test calcium hypochlorite	Chloride of lime Bleaching powder Chlorinated lime	30 to 35[1]
High-test[1] calcium hypochlorite	Perchloron HTH B-K	70 15 to 65[2]
Sodium hypochlorite	Purex, Clorox or equivalent	Household = 2 to 6 Industrial = 10 to 18
Chloramines	Sterichlor[3] Chloramine-T Dichloramine-T Azochloramide Antibac	4 Varies from 30 to 70 16

1. Pure lime chlorinated to a very high degree.
2. High test 70% hypochlorites are often diluted with $NaCO_3$ to yield 65, 50, 15 or other percentage available chlorine. The higher the percentage of sodium carbonate they contain, the less rapidly they deteriorate.
3. A trade name material containing 16% chloramine-T and a mild alkali.

is appropriate for the product and the method of use. There are no restrictions on the use of chlorine dioxide for sanitizing container cooling water. There should be a measurable residual of the sanitizer at the discharge of the container cooler.

Chlorine dioxide gas is generated at the point of use in special reaction chambers either (1) by mixing an acid with a sodium chlorite solution or (2) by injecting gaseous chlorine into water and mixing the hypochlorous acid that is formed with sodium chlorite. The gas is solubilized in water to form the sanitizing solution.

Chlorine dioxide gas and chlorine gas are toxic. Therefore, both chlorine dioxide generating equipment and chlorinators for handling gaseous chlorine must be appropriately designed, well maintained and leak-proof.

Selection of Chlorine Compounds

An appropriate chlorine compound must be selected for each particular purpose. In addition to applicable regulatory restrictions for using a chlorine compound, the primary criterion for selecting a suitable chemical is the time required for various concentrations of the sanitizer to kill 99 percent of the exposed microorganisms under laboratory conditions. Other factors—such as the pH of the water and the amount of inorganic and organic impurities present in the water—must also be evaluated. The effect of concentration, pH, impurities and temperature on the germicidal effectiveness of chlorine compounds are discussed in greater detail later in this chapter.

In laboratory studies neither gaseous chlorine nor either of the hypochlorites exhibited any advantage over the others in the time required to kill bacterial spores. However, chloramines under the same test conditions required 12 to 15 times longer at all pH levels to achieve a 99 percent reduction in the number of bacterial spores. (See *Figure 1.*)

The action of chloramines is slower but longer-lasting than that of hypochlorites. Thus, they are useful in situa-

tions where a long contact time is possible, such as in soak tanks. However, their germicidal action is too slow for use in chlorination of process waters, cooling waters or waters used for sanitizing rinses.

In addition to its germicidal action, the selection of a chlorine compound should include consideration of cost and ease of application, the initial pH of the water to be treated, plus the water's buffering resistance to pH change. In the case of the hypochlorites, one must also consider the fact that calcium or sodium salts are being added. In the case of both hypochlorites and chloramines, one also must consider the desirability of adding compounds other than chlorine to the water.

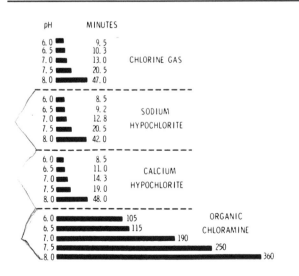

Figure 1—Comparison of time required to kill the spores of one food spoilage organism exposed to different germicides at varied pH levels.

Chlorination Terms

Chlorine and chlorine compounds have been used for years for cleaning and sanitizing purposes and for controlling the number of microorganisms in water. However, it was not until 1946 that in-plant chlorination was put into practice. Before chlorination procedures and practices can be understood, it is necessary to become familiar with some of the terms used in the chlorination of water.

Chlorine dosage

The total amount of chlorine added to water is often called the ''chlorine dosage''. This value is reported in either parts per million (ppm) or in pounds per 24 hours—the number of pounds of chlorine added to the water in a 24-hour period.

Chlorine demand

When chlorine is added to pure water, the resulting chlorine solution will possess germicidal properties. However, most waters contain some inorganic impurities that will react with the initial amount of added chlorine, reducing that amount of chlorine to a form that no longer provides germicidal action. These impurities, in turn, are oxidized during the reaction and are converted to forms that do not react further with chlorine. Chlorine added to water will continue to react and be reduced by these impurities until the impurities have been completely oxidized. The amount of chlorine required for this purpose is known as the ''chlorine demand'' of the water.

The amount of chlorine reacting with inorganic impurities depends on the quantity and type of impurities, the duration of contact and the pH and temperature of the water. The impurities responsible for the chlorine demand of water include compounds containing iron, manganese, nitrites and sulfides. Since the chlorine used for these chemical reactions no longer has germicidal properties, it is not measured by the chlorine test methods described in this chapter.

Residual chlorine

The amount of chlorine added after the chlorine demand of the water has been satisfied exists as either ''combined residual chlorine'' or ''free residual chlorine.''

Naturally-occurring waters also contain organic impurities, in addition to the inorganic impurities responsible for the chlorine demand, with which chlorine will combine. Chlorine will combine loosely with nitrogenous matter to form chloramines or other chloro-nitrogen compounds. These forms are collectively referred to as combined residual chlorine and possess relatively weaker germicidal properties.

After chlorine has combined with organic matter, further additions of chlorine will exist as free residual chlorine. The rate at which bacteria are killed is proportional to the concentration of free residual chlorine.

The sum of the combined residual chlorine and the free residual chlorine is the ''total residual chlorine.'' Total residual chlorine may be measured by the starch-iodide and other titrametric methods or by using various commercially available test kits. Free residual chlorine may be determined with commercially available color comparators that use the DPD (N,N-diethyl-p-phenylene-diamine) reagent.

Break point chlorination

When small amounts of chlorine are added to water under controlled conditions, the first chlorine is used to satisfy the chlorine demand of the water as just described. Chlorine added after the chlorine demand has been satisfied will initially combine with nitrogen-containing organic matter to form combined residual chlorine. Some of these chloro-nitrogen compounds greatly intensify the unpleasant chlorine odor and taste associated with many municipal water supplies.

Once the chlorine demand has been satisfied and the formation of combined residual chlorine has reached its maximum, further additions of chlorine result in the formation of free residual chlorine at a rate that increases almost in direct proportion to the rate of chlorine addition. The point at which this occurs is called the ''break point.'' The chlorine odor and flavor caused by chloro-nitrogen compounds are practically eliminated beyond the break point.

Break point chlorination—as well as chlorine dosage, chlorine demand and the residual chlorines—can be compared to the volume of water required to fill an empty thimble and saturate a sponge (See *Figure 2*). The first amount of water will be retained by the thimble until it is completely full. The overflow from the thimble will be retained by the sponge until the absorptive capacity of the sponge is satisfied, after which the same amount of water that is added to the sponge will run off. The total amount of water applied represents the chlorine dosage. The volume retained in the thimble represents the chlorine demand. The water retained by the sponge represents the combined residual chlorine, while that which freely runs off the sponge after capacity has been exceeded represents the free residual chlorine. The sum of both the combined residual chlorine and the free residual chlorine is the total residual chlorine. The point at which the absorptive capacity of the sponge is exceeded represents the break point.

In-plant chlorination

In-plant chlorination takes advantage of the break point phenomenon to control free residual chlorine in plant waters at desirable concentrations throughout the plant water system. By ensuring that plant waters are chlorinated beyond the break point, free residual chlorine concentrations of significant bactericidal power (usually 2–7 ppm) can be controlled and applied to equipment continually

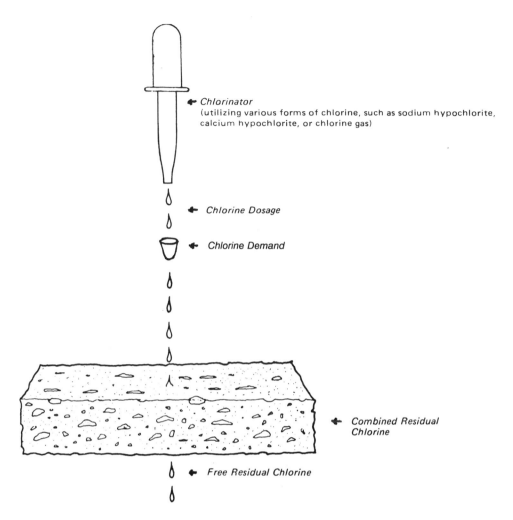

Chlorinator
(utilizing various forms of chlorine, such as sodium hypochlorite, calcium hypochlorite, or chlorine gas)

◄ *Chlorine Dosage*

◄ *Chlorine Demand*

◄ *Combined Residual Chlorine*

◄ *Free Residual Chlorine*

Combined Residual Chlorine + Free Residual Chlorine = Total Residual Chlorine

Figure 2—Break point chlorination analogous to adding water to a sponge.

during operation and cleanup by means of continuous or intermittent sprays and by flooding. The free residual chlorine concentration can be readily increased during cleanup if desired (e.g., 20–50 ppm). In-plant chlorination systems provide several advantages, including the following:

1. Use of chlorine prevents or reduces microbial buildup on equipment surfaces.

2. Chlorination permits longer hours of operation and/or reduces U.S. labor costs by shortening the time required for plant cleanup.

3. Bacterial counts on raw and prepared products are reduced if the products are washed in chlorinated water and conveyed over equipment washed with chlorinated water.

4. Use of normal-strength chlorine solutions reduces corrosion of metal surfaces by preventing growth of microorganisms that produce acids.

Chlorine should not be used indiscriminately in food plant sanitation. The following precautions should be observed:

1. It must be determined that the flavor of the product is not adversely affected by chlorine.

2. Strict measures must be taken to prevent contamination of chlorinated water with phenols or related compounds. The combination compound—chlorophenol—is detectable as an off-flavor at extremely low concentrations and is independent of the type of food being canned.

3. Brines and syrups going into the product should not be chlorinated. However, very low concentrations of chlorine will not cause problems, especially if the brine or syrup is heated before being added to the container.

4. The chlorine concentration in the water should be measured frequently.

5. Standard industrial safety measures must be employed when handling chlorine containers and working

with the systems used for injecting chlorine into food processing waters.

Factors in Chlorination

The four primary conditions affecting the germicidal properties of chlorine solutions are:

- The concentration of added chlorine.
- The pH of the chlorinated water.
- The organic and inorganic matter in the water.
- The temperature of the water.

Chlorine Concentration

The rate at which microorganisms are killed is usually proportional to the level of free residual chlorine and, hence, to the amount of the chlorine compound that is added to water beyond the break point. This is true in the case of chlorine gas or acidified chloramines. In the case of hypochlorites, however, it has been shown experimentally that the addition of hypochlorite to water to give 1,000 ppm of chlorine requires approximately three times as long to kill the same number of bacteria as a solution containing 25 ppm.

Since hypochlorites are produced by combining chlorine with hydroxides, the addition of hypochlorites results in the addition of a proportional amount of alkali, thereby raising the pH of the solution. The solution containing 1,000 ppm of chlorine would have a pH of 11.0 to 12.0, while a solution with 25 ppm would have a pH of 8.0 to 9.0.

Effect of pH

The pH of the water after the addition of chlorine determines how fast the microorganisms will be killed.

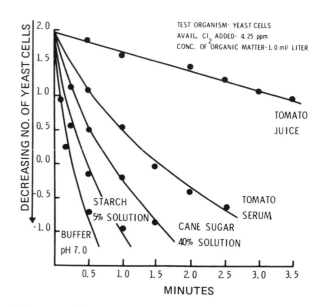

Figure 4—Effect of organic matter on the germicidal activity of chlorine.

Generally, the lower the pH, the faster the microorganisms are killed. It has been shown in laboratory experiments that at pH 8.0, about 25 minutes will be required for 15 ppm of chlorine to kill the same number of bacterial spores that are killed in five minutes at pH 6.0 (*Figure 3*). The reason for increased effectiveness when the pH is below 7.0 (neutrality) is that the chlorine exists almost exclusively as hypochlorous acid, the germicidal form of chlorine. Hypochlorous acid begins to dissociate—or break down—as the pH rises above neutrality; at pH 10, almost no hypochlorous acid is present. In-plant studies have shown that the pH of chlorinated processing waters normally falls between 6.5 and 8.5.

Effect of Organic Matter

The presence of organic matter in chlorinated water has a marked effect on the killing power of the solution. The extent of loss in germicidal activity due to the presence of organic matter depends on the type of organic matter and on the pH and strength of the chlorine solution. (See *Figure 4*.)

It is significant to note that apparently no appreciable chemical reaction takes place between chlorine and starches or sugars. The chlorine is adsorbed onto the surface of the molecules and retains most of its germicidal activity. For this reason, chlorine should be excluded from the water used for making syrups. Chlorine present in a syrup remains as active chlorine, retaining its chlorine taste and chlorine odor. However, if the syrup is brought to a temperature near boiling (212°F or 100°C) before it is used in canning, the chlorine will be driven off and product off-flavors will not result.

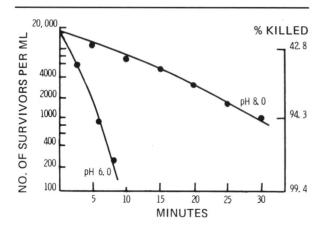

Figure 3—Laboratory experiments have shown that bacterial spores are killed more slowly when the pH of the water is above pH 7.0.

Suspended matter in chlorinated water solutions will reduce the germicidal effectiveness of chlorine. Both organic and inorganic suspended matter will protect the microorganisms. Oil also has this effect. For example, bacteria will live longer in chlorinated water containing sand or silt than in clean water, while bacteria suspended in oil may not be affected at all by chlorine.

Effect of Temperature

Laboratory studies demonstrate that the germicidal activity of chlorine solutions increases with temperature. But as discussed in the following section, temperature also will have a negative effect on the solubility of chlorine gas in water. A rise in temperature will increase the effectiveness of chlorine but also decrease the amount of chlorine present in solution. Therefore within the range of temperatures normally used in processing, temperature is usually not a significant factor in food plant chlorination.

In food plant sanitation, the feasibility of elevating temperatures of chlorine solutions in order to take advantage of increased germicidal activity depends on the type of chlorine compound from which the solution is prepared, the purpose for which the solution is to be used, and the manner in which the solution is to be applied. Because chlorine gas in solution will be rapidly reduced to an ineffective level as the temperature approaches the boiling point, hot water used for plant cleanup should not be chlorinated with chlorine gas. Chloramine solutions, however, are more stable at increased temperatures than solutions of dissolved gaseous chlorine, but chloramines are less effective for killing bacteria spores.

Solubility of Chlorine Gas

When sanitizing solutions are prepared by dissolving gaseous chlorine in water, the solubility of chlorine gas in relation to temperature should be considered. (See *Table 2*.) Increasing the temperature of the chlorinated water solution causes considerable depletion of the chlorine content, unless the solution contains organic nitrogen to allow chloramines to form. Chlorinated water prepared with gaseous chlorine is widely used in large-scale operations—such as product washing or container cooling—where the contact time between the microbial cells and the chlorine is sufficiently long to provide adequate germicidal action at ambient water temperatures.

Bacterial Spore Resistance to Chlorine

The high resistance of certain bacterial forms to the germicidal activity of chlorine must be taken into consideration when implementing food plant chlorination. This factor is important when the bacterial cells are in the spore stage. Bacterial spores have been found to be 10 to 1,100 times more resistant to chlorine than are vegetative forms.

Since it is impractical to achieve and maintain a concentration of chlorine in processing water that would kill all types of spores, the usual chlorination procedures in food plant operations are designed to destroy only the vegetative forms of bacteria. The objective in the chlorination of food processing water is to apply chlorine continuously in a concentration sufficiently high to kill all vegetative forms within the contact time allowed, thereby interrupting the bacterial life cycle and preventing the development of the spore forms.

Chlorination of Container Cooling Waters

A tendency exists in most canneries to speed up both empty and filled container handling operations. Another tendency is to produce higher final vacuums in the containers. Since small deformities in the container closure cannot be completely avoided, these practices may be significant factors in the incidence of product spoilage due to post-process recontamination.

Significance of Bacteria in Cooling Waters

The bacteriological condition of the water in which containers are cooled is extremely important. Since there are approximately 20 drops of water in a milliliter, cooling water containing 100 bacteria per milliliter would have five bacteria per drop. Under this condition, the container seals must protect against the entrance of 1/5 drop of cooling water to prevent bacterial contamination of the thermally processed product. Most unchlorinated cooling waters contain at least 100 bacteria per milliliter.

However, if the cooling water were to contain one million bacteria per milliliter, one drop of water would contain 50,000 bacteria and the container seals would have to protect the product against the entrance of as little as 1/50,000 of a drop. Even the best closure would not guarantee protection against leaker spoilage at this level.

The sanitary quality of cooling water must, therefore, be maintained. Chlorination of the water—properly carried out—is a dependable means of ensuring that the bacterial count in cooling water is minimized.

Table 2—Solubility of chlorine gas in water at various temperatures.

Temperature		Chlorine Dissolved
°F	°C	ppm
50	10	9800
68	20	7600
86	30	5600
122	50	3900
140	60	3200
176	80	2200
194	90	1200
212	100	00

Regulations for Container Cooling Waters

The FDA regulations for thermally processed low-acid foods packaged in hermetically sealed containers (21 CFR 113) state that container cooling water in cooling canals or in recirculated cooling water systems must be chlorinated or otherwise sanitized. Furthermore, there should be a measurable residual of the sanitizer at the point where the water is discharged from the cooling system.

USDA canning regulations similarly require the use of sanitizers in cooling canals. However, cooling systems using recirculated waters have additional requirements, including maintaining information on the design of the system, its construction, operation and maintenance, and on the quality of the water in the system. These requirements are covered in 9 CFR 318.305(h) and 381.305(h). In most cases, water from a municipal system is inadequately chlorinated to meet the regulatory requirements.

Recirculation of Container Cooling Waters

As a water conservation procedure, container cooling water can be recirculated over a cooling tower to reduce the temperature so that the water can be reused for container cooling. The microbial count in such systems can increase to very high levels in a relatively short time. Therefore, the water must be chlorinated or otherwise sanitized before being returned to the container cooler. It is also desirable to chlorinate the water being pumped to the cooling tower to prevent or minimize the growth of microorganisms within the cooling tower. When the water is chlorinated prior to the cooling tower, some of the chlorine may remain at the end of the cooling cycle, thereby requiring only minimal rechlorination to achieve the recommended measurable free residual chlorine level at the water discharge end of the container cooler. A schematic diagram of a cooling tower recycling system for container cooling water is provided in *Figure 5*.

One advantage to treating recycled cooling water with a sanitizer is that bacterial spores in the water are exposed for a prolonged period to the germicidal action of the sanitizer. However, chlorine is quickly neutralized by some types of rust inhibitors and anti-spotting compounds. For example, sodium nitrite exerts a high chlorine demand and, therefore, is incompatible with chlorination. Although the addition of chromate to prevent rusting does not neutralize chlorine, it does produce a color that may interfere with chlorine test procedures. Some wetting agents also may neutralize chlorine; therefore, such chemicals must be selected with care.

Reclaimed Water

The consumption of fresh water and, thereby, the volume of wastewater produced by a food processing plant may be reduced substantially through water conservation practices. Significant reductions are achieved by recovering the water discharged from one operation and reusing it in another. However, chlorination of reclaimed water is often essential to ensure that the microbiological quality of the water is acceptable. Chlorination or use of other sanitizers is especially important when reclaimed water is used for cooling thermally processed containers or for washing or conveying raw products.

Water Reuse Systems (Other Than Container Cooling)

The volume of fresh water used in a single system—such as a spray washer—can often be reduced by using fresh water only in the second half of the system,

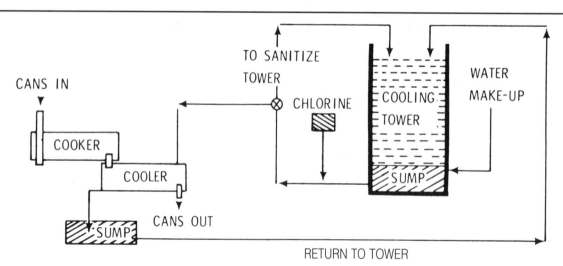

Figure 5—Schematic of cooling tower recycling system for container cooling water. Chlorine is added in an amount required to maintain a measurable residual of chlorine at the water discharge of the container cooler. Periodically, highly chlorinated water may be recycled through the cooling tower only to "burn off" microbial slime growth from the tower surfaces.

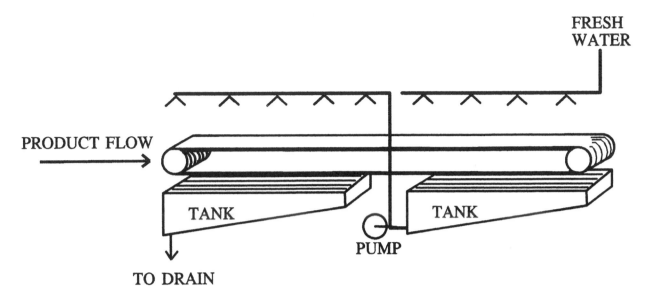

FRESH WATER

PRODUCT FLOW

TANK

TANK

PUMP

TO DRAIN

Figure 6—Water consumption in a spray washer can be reduced by recovering water from the final half of the unit and reusing the water in the initial section.

recovering the used water, and reusing that water in the first half. (See *Figure 6*.) The reused water in such systems usually does not require chlorination, because the product receives a final rinse with fresh water. Such systems must be carefully designed to ensure that all the material is thoroughly washed or rinsed and that the system is not overloaded with raw product, thereby hindering washing efficiency.

The collection of used water and its reuse can be extended to include other preceding operations. For example, the water used in the spray washer in the previous example can be collected and reused in an earlier operation, such as initial raw product washing and conveying. This practice is referred to as ''counterflow reuse,'' since the movement of water is opposite to the movement of raw product through the preparation lines. In many plants, water may be reused several times in this manner. Well planned counterflow reuse systems have reduced water consumption by as much as 50 percent in several processing plants. The quantity of dissolved organic matter and the numbers of microorganisms in such systems, however, increase with each use. Therefore, the water should be rechlorinated before each successive use to prevent product spoilage due to excessive numbers of bacteria, as well as to maintain good plant sanitation.

Chlorination of Reused Water

The most economical and effective chlorine concentration in reused water is a chlorine dosage that completely satisfies the chlorine demand of the water. This condition (break point chlorination) is considered accomplished when tests show a trace of free residual chlorine in the treated water.

The sanitary condition of reused water depends on the number of bacteria growing in the water. Two major factors that influence the number of bacteria are the chlorine concentration and the rate of product flow during production. Of these two, the former in the reused water has the greater influence on microbial population.

If chlorination is stopped in a counterflow water reuse system, bacterial numbers in the water will rapidly increase. Foul odors and slime buildup may become quickly evident. When chlorination is resumed, bacterial counts will rapidly decline and sanitary conditions of the plant will improve.

Simultaneous sampling at corresponding points in counterflow systems at three canneries gave a striking comparative picture of the effect on bacterial numbers due to the difference in the extent of chlorination. (See *Figure 7*.) Water was used four times at each plant. At Plant A, where the incoming water was chlorinated and the reused water rechlorinated at three successive points, the bacterial counts averaged 16,000 cells per ml. At Plant B, where the water was chlorinated only initially, the bacterial counts averaged 37,000 cells per ml. No water chlorination was provided at Plant C, resulting in an average cell count of 8,000,000 per ml!

Influence of Production Rates

Since the volume of water in a reuse system is fairly constant, any increase in the production rate is usually accompanied by a corresponding decrease in the number of gallons of water used per case or per ton of product. As a result, more product is washed in each gallon of water, resulting in a higher concentration of organic matter in each unit volume of water. Since the organic matter

43

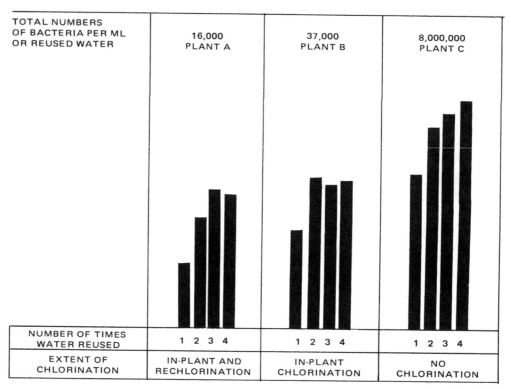

TOTAL NUMBERS OF BACTERIA PER ML OR REUSED WATER	16,000 PLANT A	37,000 PLANT B	8,000,000 PLANT C
NUMBER OF TIMES WATER REUSED	1 2 3 4	1 2 3 4	1 2 3 4
EXTENT OF CHLORINATION	IN-PLANT AND RECHLORINATION	IN-PLANT CHLORINATION	NO CHLORINATION

Figure 7—Effect of chlorination on numbers of bacteria in flume waters reused in the four-stage counterflow systems of three canneries.

will decrease the free residual chlorine concentration in the water, bacterial numbers will increase. Thus, it is important to monitor the chlorine concentration frequently and to adjust the chlorine injection rate so that appropriate free residual chlorine levels are maintained.

Control of In-Plant Chlorination

Continuous monitoring and control are essential for the safe and effective application of in-plant chlorination. The following minimum schedule is recommended:

1. Initially, check the free residual chlorine level every two hours to help establish what variations are likely to be encountered in chlorine demand.

2. Once the appropriate dosage is determined, check the free residual chlorine level at several points in the plant at least twice a day. Always sample at the same places each day.

3. Keep a record of all results.

4. Record the chlorinator setting each time the free residual chlorine is measured. After a few days, it may be possible to correlate the free residual chlorine levels with chlorinator settings; large discrepancies would indicate that the concentration of impurities in the system varies widely or that something is wrong with the chlorinator. Also, the total chlorine demand of the water (i.e., the amount of chlorine required to reach the break point)

may be estimated by determining the chlorine dosage in parts per million and subtracting from this the measured free residual chlorine concentration.

5. Weigh the chlorine cylinder each day at the same time and record the loss in weight. This procedure checks the accuracy of the chlorinator feed setting, and the results indicate when a new cylinder is needed.

6. Check the chlorinator operation. At least once a day inspect for leaks using an ammonia bottle as described in the operating manual for the chlorinator.

7. For hypochlorinators, check and record the volume and strength of the chlorine solution in the supply tank, and each day calculate the gallons of solution that have been fed into the water system.

Test Methods and Kits

Since orthotolidine has been classified as a carcinogen, this former standard reagent for measuring chlorine concentrations has been abandoned. The current official procedures—as published in the *Standard Methods for the Examination of Water and Wastewater*— prescribe the use of DPD (N,N-diethyl-p-phenylene-diamine). A number of commercial test kits are available, and other official procedures exist for quickly and easily measuring free and total residual chlorine at both high and low concentrations. When using test kits, follow the accompanying instructions.

Other Sanitizers

In addition to chlorine and chlorine compounds, several other sanitizing agents may be useful in a food plant sanitation program. Among these are iodine-based compounds (iodophors) and quaternary ammonium compounds (quats or QACs). The characteristics of these sanitizers, as well as of chlorine dioxide, are compared to chlorine in *Table 3*. Ozone and ultraviolet irradiation also may be useful in special situations. Some of the alternatives to chlorine are briefly discussed below.

Iodophors

Sanitizers that are chemical combinations of nonionic wetting agents and iodine are called iodophors. Unlike chlorine sanitizers in which the active molecule is HOCl (hypochlorous acid), the iodine molecule, I_2, has the antibacterial activity in iodophor sanitizers. The iodophors are most active in acid pH ($\pm$ pH 3) where this molecule predominates; the activity is minimal at pH 7. Therefore, most iodophor sanitizers contain acid—usually phosphoric acid—to maintain acidity. Against vegetative cells the activity of 25 ppm of iodine at low pH is roughly equivalent to that of 200 ppm of chlorine at neutral pH. However, chlorine is much more effective against spores than are the iodophors.

Iodophors are more useful than chlorine compounds for certain uses because they:

1. Do not irritate skin at recommended levels of use.

2. Contribute an amber color to solutions while they remain active (no tests for concentration are necessary).

3. React less readily with organic soils.

In comparison with chlorine, iodophors have some disadvantages because they:

1. Stain epoxy, polyvinylchloride (PVC), and other surfaces.

2. Discolor starchy food.

3. Are only minimally effective at neutral pH.

4. Are generally more expensive (prices vary by location and vendor).

5. Are usually not stable above 120-140°F (49-60°C) because the iodine vaporizes.

6. Are not effective against spores.

Chlorine and iodine preparations are alike in that they both:

1. Are non-selective in antimicrobial activity.

2. Are non-corrosive at low levels, but corrosive at excessive levels.

3. At high concentrations will adversely affect some food flavors but not others.

4. Are relatively unaffected by water hardness.

5. Are acceptable as final treatment on food equipment without a final rinse.

In addition to their use for sanitizing food-contact surfaces, iodophors are widely used in hand dips and foot baths. The distinct amber color of iodophor solutions makes it easy to monitor these stations to ensure that the sanitizing solutions have appropriate germicidal activity.

Quaternary Ammonium Compounds (Quats)

The quats are effective sanitizers, but are frequently selective for certain types of bacteria. For example, they destroy lactic organisms but not bacteriophage or gram-negative organisms such as *E. coli* or *Pseudomonas aeruginosa*. The latter organism may actually grow in quat hand-dip solutions. Because of their selectivity, an occasional chlorine treatment is a useful supplement to maintain the effectiveness of the sanitizing system.

Nevertheless, quats have special attributes not shared by other sanitizers, because they:

1. Leave a non-volatile residue that inhibits growth of molds and other microorganisms.

2. Are stable to heat.

3. Are effective over a wide pH range (although most effective in slightly alkaline solutions).

4. Are non-corrosive and non-irritating.

5. Have no taste or odor (although they can impart off-flavors to some foods).

6. Are less affected by organic matter than is chlorine.

The quats, as cationic compounds, are compatible with nonionic wetting agents, but they are not compatible with soap or anionic wetting agents or with some of the inor-

---

Table 3—Characteristics of sanitizers other than chlorine.

Sanitizer	Cost(U.S.)	Skin Irritation	Heat	Spores	Action in Slightly Alkaline Solutions	Disadvantages
Iodophors	More Expensive	Less	Less Stable	Less Effective	Less	Stain some surfaces, discolor starchy foods.
Quats	More Expensive	Less	More Stable	Less Effective	Same	Inactivated by wood, cotton, nylon, some inorganic phosphates.
Chlorine Dioxide	More Expensive	—	Less Stable	Comparable	More Active	Unstable. Must be generated on site.

ganic phosphates. An unfortunate limitation is their inactivation by wood, cotton, nylon, cellulose sponges and some plastics. This means that equipment for applying the sanitizer—if made of such materials—may inactivate the quat. Because quats leave a non-volatile residue that extends their effectiveness, they are commonly used in food processing plants to sanitize the floors, walls, ceilings, racks and other devices of refrigerated compartments.

Ultraviolet (UV) Irradiation

Microorganisms die rapidly when exposed to direct rays of ultraviolet (UV) light at wavelengths near 2537 Å. UV has minimal effect against microorganisms on the food itself, but it kills airborne bacteria, especially mold spores. Practical difficulties in using UV are:

1. Maintaining direct contact between the microorganisms and the irradiation.

2. Maintaining the UV output of the lamps.

3. Protecting employees from eye damage, skin burns and ozone.

Window glass, a surface convolution that casts a shadow, or even a thin film of cloudy liquid will block UV rays and protect microorganisms. For this reason, UV light has limited practical value, such as to treat air above packaging systems, over vats of food, over bread slicers, in chill rooms, in the headspace of liquid sugar storage tanks, or in air recirculation systems. UV also has been used to sanitize drinking water. Because the effectiveness of UV is drastically affected by turbidity, UV has very limited application for treating food processing waters.

The output intensity from UV lamps drops continuously during use and becomes negligible long before the visible light fails. Lamps should be tested for UV production every six months. When the UV level reaches 50 percent of that of a fresh lamp, the lamp should be replaced. All UV sources must be adequately shielded to avoid damage to eyes and skin.

Ozone

Produced by high voltage sparks or by an ozone generator, ozone (O_3) has some value as a sanitizer. It will kill microorganisms in air and in water, but food materials interfere with its efficacy. Ozone oxidizes foods, producing rancidity. Inhibitory concentrations of the gas are higher than human beings can tolerate. Storage room air might be treated to remove odors by recirculating it through a separate chamber containing ozone, and then through charcoal or metal oxides to remove the ozone before it is reintroduced into the storage area.

Ozone is effective against microorganisms in cold water, such as in drinking water, and in a recirculated water system. It kills spores at temperatures up to 95°F (35°C), but its solubility is limited and becomes negligible at higher temperatures. Ozone breaks down rapidly in water and has little residual efficacy.

Other Sanitizing Agents

Phenol and its derivatives are highly microbicidal but are not acceptable in food plants because they impart strong odors to equipment and off-flavors to foods. Furthermore, phenol—even at levels as low as parts per billion—may combine with chlorine to form odorous, off-flavored chlorophenolic compounds. Hexachlorophene, once the active ingredient in antibacterial soaps, is now prohibited by FDA for safety reasons.

Compounds containing heavy metals have no place in food plants for food safety reasons.

Choosing a Sanitizer

The ideal sanitizer has the following characteristics:

1. Kills microorganisms quickly.

2. Is safe and non-irritating to employees.

3. Is safe for consumers and acceptable to regulatory agencies.

4. Is rinseable.

5. Has no adverse effect on food being processed.

6. Is economical.

7. Tests easily for solution concentration.

8. Is stable in concentrated form and in solution.

9. Is compatible with other chemicals and equipment.

10. Is readily soluble in water.

Since no single sanitizing agent possesses all of the above characteristics, each sanitizer must be carefully considered. The most important consideration is efficacy under practical conditions. A sanitizer that will not destroy a specific organism of concern is useless. On the other hand, efficacious sanitizers that destroy a treated surface or are inactivated under conditions of intended use are likewise inappropriate.

Since sanitizing agents are classified as pesticide chemicals, the EPA requires that labels of all sanitizers list the name(s) of the active ingredient(s). FDA and USDA also have established strict rules for the choice and use of sanitizers. USDA regulatory programs and the fish inspection program of the U.S. Department of Commerce permit only those commercial preparations named in *List of Proprietary Substances and Nonfood Compounds Authorized for Use Under USDA Inspection and Grading Programs*. This publication is available from the U.S. Government Printing Office. Specific sanitizer formulations approved by FDA for use on food processing equipment and utensils are listed in Title 21, *Code of Federal Regulations*, Part 178.1010. Only sanitizers approved either by USDA or by FDA should be used in a food processing plant. Those sanitizers must be used strictly according to the restrictions (such as permitted uses) and limitations (such as maximum concentrations) that may be imposed by the regulatory agencies.

Summary

1. Good sanitation practices protect the health of the consumer, minimize economic loss from food spoilage and minimize consumer complaints.

2. The numbers and kinds of microorganisms present in a canned food as it enters the thermal processing system depend on those contributed by (a) the raw product, (b) the food handling equipment, (c) the plant waters contacting the foods and (d) the ingredients.

3. Organisms are controlled by cleaning and washing the food and equipment, using water with low bacterial count, and using ingredients that are free of thermophilic organisms.

4. The practice of sanitizing (using germicidal chemicals) can be a valuable aid in the prevention of spoilage in canned foods and in the maintenance of a clean plant. The more common sanitizing agents are chemicals such as chlorine, iodine compounds and quaternary ammonium compounds or moist heat.

5. Chlorine and chlorine compounds are by far the most common germicides or sanitizers used in food processing plants. Although this section deals principally with chlorine compounds and chlorination procedures, the basic information is applicable to any sanitizer of comparable usefulness.

6. The development of break point chlorination led to in-plant chlorination, which allowed the continuous addition of germicidal concentrations of chlorine to processing water. This extensive use of chlorine has inhibited microbial growth on equipment, reduced bacterial counts in finished products, and permitted longer periods of plant operation by reducing the time required for plant cleaning.

7. The concentration of chlorine required to kill all types of spores would not be practical for use in the canning plant. However, the continuous application of chlorine, in concentrations sufficient to kill vegetative forms of microorganisms, could prevent the development of spores that, if present in the product, might survive the thermal sterilization process and cause spoilage of the food.

8. The successful chlorination of food processing waters requires an understanding of the chemical and physical conditions that influence the germicidal activity of chlorine solutions. Included among these conditions are the pH of the solution, the concentration of free residual chlorine, the concentration of inorganic and organic impurities, and the temperature of the solution.

9. The continuous addition of chlorine to recirculated processing and container cooling waters has made possible considerable reductions in water consumption without undesirable effects on food quality, plant sanitation or leaker spoilage.

10. When used as recommended, chlorination has not been detrimental to food quality; corrosion of metal equipment due to chlorine has not be appreciable.

11. Chlorination cannot substitute for good plant operation. It cannot replace cleaning in the plant sanitation program, and it cannot correct a poor container seaming or capping operation.

12. Other sanitizing agents—such as iodophors and quaternary ammonium compounds—are effective sanitizers that can be used beneficially in the plant sanitation program to minimize or eliminate microbial contamination of foods.

13. Sanitizing agents, as well as all other chemicals used in a food processing plant, must be approved by the regulatory agencies and used strictly in accordance to all restrictions and limitations imposed by the agencies.

Chapter 6

RECORDS FOR PRODUCT PROTECTION

Records Essential to Canning

The records discussed in this chapter relate to product protection for acidified and thermally processed low-acid foods. They include charts of process times and temperatures, production records, pH control and records of other factors critical to the thermal process and container closure evaluation (*Figures 1* and *2*).

Reasons for Keeping Records

Canning records are kept for the following reasons:

1. Records indicate to management whether foods are produced in compliance with applicable federal regulations. Management of firms producing FDA-regulated food products is responsible for compliance with the Federal Food, Drug and Cosmetic Act and related regulations, including 21 CFR 113 and 114 "Thermally Processed Low-Acid Foods Packaged in Hermetically Sealed Containers and Acidified Foods" and 21 CFR 108 "Emergency Permit Control." (See Chapter 1 and Appendix.) Under the Act, criminal penalties can be assessed against the responsible parties, and civil actions—including seizure of product or injunction to prohibit sale of product—may be taken as a result of violations of the Act. This action may be taken even though the responsible parties

were unaware of the violations and had no intent to violate the Act.

Similarly, management of firms producing products regulated by the Food Safety Inspection Service (FSIS) of the U.S. Department of Agriculture (USDA) is responsible for compliance with the Federal Meat Inspection Act and/or the Poultry Products Inspection Act and related canning regulations: 9 CFR 318.300-311 and 9 CFR 381.300-311, respectively. (See Chapter 1 and Appendix.) Civil and criminal actions similar to those described above can be taken for violations of these Acts.

These regulations state that certain records must be maintained and kept on file. The records required by FDA are listed in 113.100 for low-acid canned foods and in 114.100 for acidified foods. USDA-regulated operations must comply with the recordkeeping requirements noted in the various sections of 318.306 and 381.306. The procedures for producing, reviewing and maintaining records are covered in sections 318.307 and 381.307.

2. Records provide written evidence of proper and safe application of thermal processes. Processing records can offer assurance that a particular lot of product received a safe process, or they can clearly show that an improper process was applied.

Records are the only references available to trace the history of a lot of product. If questions arise concerning any canned foods, it may be necessary to know—and even to prove—that the product and the container received proper handling by the canner.

3. Careful review of properly maintained records can be valuable in providing early indications of potentially

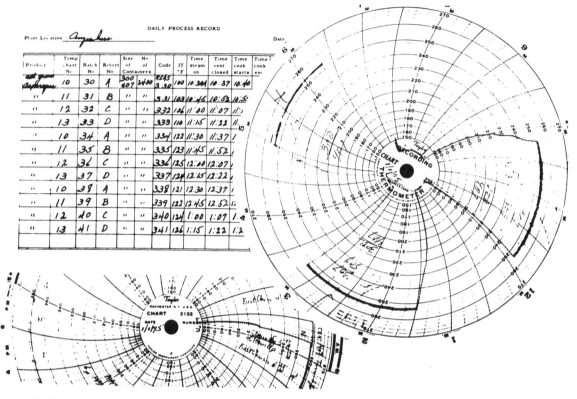

Figure 1—Daily process record and temperature recording charts.

serious difficulties. This review permits responsible individuals to take corrective action before problems occur.

4. Records can help to ensure the quality of canned products. Quality assurance records document raw and canned product quality. Records of product quality are not generally required by the FDA regulations, and, except under unusual circumstances, these records need not be shared with FDA inspectors.

Records and Responsibilities

Management, supervisors and line employees all have responsibilities for the safety of food products and the integrity of containers. To meet these responsibilities, they must be acquainted with both present and past operations. Consequently, records must be kept that accurately document the operating conditions for past production.

Personnel responsible for preparing production records must never prerecord data in anticipation of the actual values. Likewise, personnel should not wait for a convenient time to make entries on record forms in hopes that the values will all be remembered correctly. *Individual memories do not fulfill recordkeeping requirements!*

Each entry on the processing or closure record form shall be made by the processing system operator, container closure inspector or other designated person at the time the specific retort or processing system condition or operation occurs. To be used effectively, processing and closure records should be on forms standardized for a company or plant and shall be reviewed within one working day by a responsible representative of plant management to ensure completeness and that critical factors have been satisfied.

Automated recordkeeping systems (computers) can be used for thermal processing and are usually integrated with thermal processing control systems. (Further information on electronic control systems may be found in Chapter 8.) Both FDA and USDA have encouraged the industry to work cooperatively in the development of automated recordkeeping systems. Both agencies have allowed the use of such systems for thermal process system control, critical factor control and container integrity testing, provided they meet the intent of the regulations.

Record Retention

The regulations specify that copies of all required records of thermal processing, container closure, pH measurements, deviations in processing, and other critical factors shall be retained at the processing plant for one year from the date of manufacture and for an additional two years at a reasonably accessible location. FDA per-

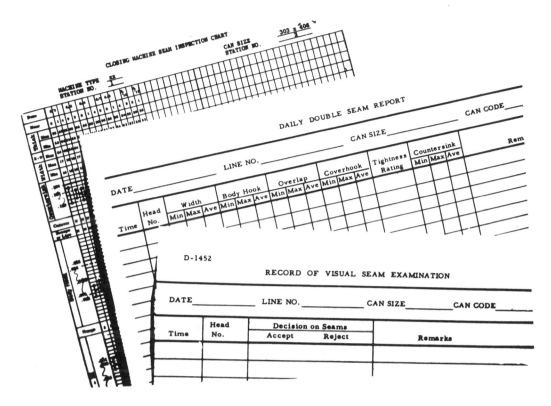

Figure 2—Examples of seam inspection forms.

mits seasonal operations to transfer records away from the plant at the end of the seasonal pack. USDA requires that during the last two years of the record retention period, records be made available to an agency official within three days.

Record Availability and Reporting

Commercial processors of thermally processed low-acid foods packaged in hermetically sealed containers are required to make records available in certain situations upon demand by duly authorized FDA or USDA-FSIS employees. The inspection and copying by FDA employees of records that verify process adequacy, container closure integrity and the container coding system must be permitted.

In addition, the FDA regulations stipulate the following:

1. Upon written demand, the processor shall provide FDA with any information concerning processes and procedures that is deemed necessary by the FDA to determine whether commercial sterility has been achieved.

2. Any instance of spoilage or process deviation that indicates potential health significance of any lot of food that has in whole or in part entered distribution shall be promptly reported to FDA.

3. All process deviations involving failure to satisfy the minimum requirements of the scheduled process shall be documented. These records of the deviations shall be kept in a separate file or log identifying the appropriate processing records, corrective actions taken, evaluation procedures and disposition of the lot in question.

4. Records of examinations of raw materials, packaging materials, finished acidified products, and of suppliers' guarantees or certifications that verify compliance with FDA regulations and guidelines or action levels shall be maintained.

5. FDA requires that a record in the form of a code shall be embossed or printed on every hermetically sealed container of food. The FDA requires that the code identify the establishment where packed, the product contained therein, and the year, day and period packed.

The code shall be changed with sufficient frequency to enable easy identification of lots during their sale or distribution. The container's shipping cases should have the code(s) stamped on the case where they can readily be seen.

6. FDA requires the processor to maintain records that identify the initial distribution of the finished product. Such records facilitate the segregation of specific food

lots that may have become contaminated or otherwise rendered unfit for use.

7. Processors of acidified and/or low-acid foods shall register the processing facility with FDA. Additionally, information on scheduled processes for each food in each container size shall be filed with the agency. Appropriate registration and filing forms are available from FDA. (See Chapter 1 and Appendix for more details.)

The USDA canning regulations require that records of process adequacy and container closure integrity be made available to USDA-FSIS Program employees. The USDA regulations also contain the following stipulations:

1. Upon request, complete records of process establishment, and any associated incubation tests, shall be made available to the USDA-FSIS Program employee.

2. The establishment shall maintain on file and, upon request, make available letters or other communications recommending process schedules. The establishment shall provide a copy of procedures for measuring, controlling and recording critical factors specified in the process schedule, as well as the frequency of monitoring these factors.

3. The manufacturer's specifications for container closure parameters or the processor's acceptance guidelines shall be on file and available for review.

4. A company shall have documentation from the equipment manufacturer or a processing authority for the temperature distribution adequacy of the following items:
   - A. Steam spreaders that run less than the full length of horizontal retorts.
   - B. Bleeder arrangements other than specified in the regulations.
   - C. Container stacking equipment and divider plates with perforations less than the equivalent of one-inch holes on two-inch centers.
   - D. All vent or bleeder mufflers.
   - E. Retort systems other than those still retort installations specified in the regulations.

5. Information on recycled or reused container cooling waters (other than cooling canals) shall be maintained and made available to USDA-FSIS Program employees for review.

6. The establishment shall maintain full records regarding the handling of each deviation in a file or log. These should include appropriate processing and production records, corrective actions taken, evaluation procedures and results, and disposition of the affected lot.

7. The USDA requires that the code identify the product (unless the product name is lithographed or printed directly on the container) and the day and year packed.

8. The establishment shall also maintain records for each incubation test, including product name, container size, container code, number of containers incubated, in and out dates for incubation samples, incubation results, and copies of incubator temperature recorder charts.

Recalls

A current procedure for recalls at the consumer level must be prepared and should include a plan for identifying, collecting, warehousing and controlling recalled product; a plan for determining the effectiveness of the recall; a procedure for notifying the FDA or USDA-FSIS; and details of recall implementation. FSIS Directive 8080.1, Revision 2, dated November 3, 1992, provides procedures and useful information about USDA-FSIS policy regarding the recall of meat and poultry products.

Records are vital to the recall process. A recall removes defective products that present a risk of injury or gross deception. Reliable records can help a firm quickly identify the factors that led to the need to recall product. Furthermore, accurate and detailed records can be used to pinpoint the problem and safely limit the scope of the recall. Incomplete or unreliable records may necessitate recall of a much larger amount of product than is actually necessary. Temperature/time charts, processing system records, required control procedures and production records are most critical to any recall. The recall plan should be tested occasionally to determine its efficiency and to train the personnel who will be involved.

Legal Liability

As a general rule FDA inspectors are not authorized to obtain compulsory access to company records. Under Part 108 of the FDA regulations, however, processors of acidified and low-acid canned foods are required to permit the inspection and copying by FDA of "all records of processing, deviations in processing, container closure inspections, and other records specified in Part 113 or Part 114." Although FDA is authorized to impose an emergency permit requirement on a company that refuses to allow FDA inspectors their right to inspect and copy such records, failure to permit such inspections may not result in criminal prosecution.

The language of the Federal Meat Inspection Act and the Poultry Products Inspection Act is different from that in the Federal Food, Drug and Cosmetics Act. USDA-FSIS has somewhat broader authority than FDA to review plant records. The regulations state that all processing and production records required in the canning regulations shall be made available to USDA-FSIS Program employees for review. USDA does not normally issue written requests to review processing records.

Description of Records

There are normal and acceptable fluctuations in most operations. These will be apparent in the records, but it is necessary to know when the fluctuations are normal and when they indicate something is wrong. The range or amount of acceptable fluctuation varies with different operations. For example, the retort process is an operation in which fluctuations in time or temperature below specified minimums are not acceptable. On the other hand, can seam specifications do allow for fluctuation within certain limits or tolerances.

Most canning operations must be maintained within certain tolerances, but errors can happen in any operation. These errors may be human or mechanical. They may be easily observable or almost impossible to see. Therefore, it is essential that routine procedures be placed in effect that will make errors immediately apparent. It is also important to know when the monitored conditions are within normal ranges and adjustments are unnecessary. Control charts are a means to accomplish these objectives.

A typical quality control program may require records of various product preparation procedures. Fill of container, net weight, drained weight, can headspace and the condition of the double seams may be factors that must be controlled to standards. In order to control them, observations, measurements and/or tests must be made on samples and compared. These results provide the figures for the "record." However, it is often difficult to see the meaning of so many tabulated figures. It takes time to examine and analyze the record.

To assist in the analysis, the recorded figures are frequently converted to points on a chart (*Figure 3*). The chart can also include the standard or target limits and the permitted tolerance, limits or variation from the target. This is known as a statistical quality control (SQC) chart. It gives a picture of the operation at a glance and also is a permanent record for future reference. Such charts permit a quick check when conditions are normal and an easily read signal when an abnormally high or low reading occurs, or when a trend in the data suggests impending trouble. SQC can provide answers to problems of control in many canning procedures, including evaluation of raw product quality, investigation of equipment operation, and decision making regarding product quality. A statistical quality control chart puts data into picture form for the operator on the line.

Figure 3 is a typical statistical quality control chart. The dots on the "average" chart indicate the average of the samples taken at designated intervals. The dots on the "range" chart indicate the range or spread of the samples taken at designated intervals. The broken line is the target. The solid lines indicates upper and lower control limits, and a dot outside the solid lines indicate a problem in need of attention. Dots within the solid lines generally indicate that no action is needed unless they begin to group on one side of the center or form a trend that indicates they may go "out of control."

Limitations of Control Charts

SQC charts may not be effective for all operations that must be kept in control. For example, the consistency of

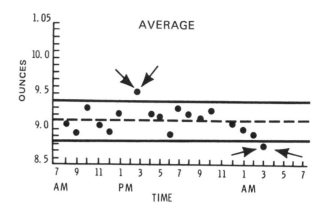

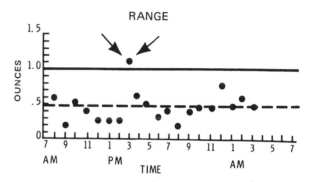

Figure 3—Example of SQC control charts for average and range.

some products affects the rate of heat penetration into the product and must be monitored. These products may be prepared in a batch operation, where the consistency of each batch is determined, adjusted if necessary, and rechecked before filling into containers. Similarly, the pH of brines added to acidified products may be checked batch-by-batch and adjusted as needed before use. In these cases, records of batch testing should be made. If these factors are critical to the process and safety of the product, complete and accurate records are required. Samples of the canned product should be opened for confirmation of the pH or other critical characteristics.

SQC charts are also inappropriate for certain other process or production records. For example, the temperature/time recorder chart is a continuous record made at the time of processing and cannot be averaged for an SQC chart. Operations such as filling are controlled by people, and SQC charts merely help them decide when to exercise controls. Therefore, the limitations of SQC charts should be recognized so that they are used only where appropriate. Also, the SQC charts should be prepared and interpreted by people who are aware of their value and their limitations.

Processing Records

Temperature/time recorder charts and the written records of the thermal processing operations are the heart of the process control program. These records must document the process used for each lot of containers in the day's production. The regulations require that they be complete, accurate and retained on file.

Recorder charts shall be identified in such a manner that they can be correlated with the operator's written record. A system that uses consecutive numbering and/or lettering is recommended.

There must be a recorder chart curve for each cook listed on the operator's written record. No batches are to be released for shipment unless there is a satisfactory temperature curve on the chart.

Recording instruments must be observed for agreement with the mercury-in-glass thermometer and adjusted as required. Accurate readings of the mercury thermometer and the recorder must be entered on the operator's written record. Any chart with an irregular curve is subject to question.

To prevent irregularities in temperature recorder readings, the following procedures should be followed:

1. Check that the recorder is functioning properly and supplied with chart paper and adequate ink at the beginning of each shift and as necessary during operation.

2. Assure that the chart drive is turned on and functioning properly at the start of each shift.

3. Operate the retort so that small fluctuations of the recorder pen do not fall below the prescribed retort temperature. This action will prevent concern about the adequacy of the process when the chart is reviewed by the plant management representative.

The proper chart for the particular recording instrument in use must be employed, otherwise the adjustments and recordings will be erroneous. The chart should be set for the correct time of day to correlate properly with consecutive lots or batches on the operator's written record. USDA requires agreement within 15 minutes between the chart time and the actual time of day.

A sample of an operator's daily processing record form containing the information that must be recorded for still retorts is shown in *Figure 4*. The form can be modified to contain other appropriate processing data and any critical factors specified in the scheduled process. For example, the reel speed of agitating retorts must be recorded. Generally product-related critical factors are kept on separate forms. Many firms find it advantageous to keep the records required by the regulations on separate forms from those used for product quality-related factors.

The processing system operator or other designated persons must:

- Record the required information when observed.
- Sign or initial each record form.

Not later than one working day after the actual process and before the product is released for distribution, a quali-

fied representative of plant management must review, date and sign the records. The review is necessary to ascertain whether:

1. The data are complete.
2. The scheduled process has been properly applied.
3. The critical factors have been correctly controlled.

All records should be neat and made out in ink or other permanent markers. Errors on records should not be erased or marked over. If a recording error is made at the time of entry, it should be lined out and the correct entry inserted and then initialed by the person making the entry.

Container Closure Inspection Records

Since the container must protect its thermally processed contents from recontamination with microorganisms, its integrity is critical for the shelf stability of canned foods. Container closure inspections maintain an almost continuous record of the quality of the container closures. Therefore, these inspections ensure that metal containers, glass containers and other packaging forms are adequately sealed. The records are proof that the required inspection program was carried out. In the event of spoilage, the closure records can be studied to determine if closure seal defects were causative factors of the problem.

The regulations (21 CFR 113.60, 21 CFR 114.80, 9 CFR 318.301 and 9 CFR 381.301) specify that regular observations of container closures shall be made at intervals of sufficient frequency to ensure closure integrity. The regulations (21 CFR 113.100; 9 CFR 318.307 and 9 CFR 381.307) further state that written records of all container closure examinations shall specify the product code, the date and time of container closure inspections, the measurements obtained and all corrective actions taken. In addition, the records shall be signed or initialed by the container closure inspector and reviewed by management with sufficient frequency to ensure that the containers are hermetically sealed. USDA requires that these records be reviewed and signed by the establishment within one working day after actual production and that they be made available to USDA-FSIS Program employees for review.

Can Seam Evaluation Records

Two types of container examinations are required: visual and teardown. The visual examination of the can seam, glass or other package closure is a non-destructive check. At least one container from each closing machine head shall be examined and the interval between observations should not exceed 30 minutes. *Figure 5* shows an example of a form that may be used for recording the

DAILY PROCESS RECORD FORM FOR STILL RETORTS

COMPANY NAME _____   PLANT LOCATION _____   DATE _____

Product (and/or Style of Pack)	Scheduled Process			Retort and Recorder Number	Container		Actual I.T. (°F)	Time Steam On	Vent Closed		Time Temp. Up	Esti-mated Time Steam Off	Actual Time Steam Off	Actual Process Time (min.)	Temperature	
	Code	I.T.	Time	Temp.		Size	Approx. No.			Time &	Temp. (°F)					Mercury	Recorder

Note: Allow headings for critical factors, such as maximum drained weight and minimum net weight etc. where applicable to scheduled process.

Signed (or initialed) by:
Operator or Designated Person: _____
Reviewed by _____   Date _____

Figure 4—Example of operator's written record form.

RECORD OF VISUAL EXTERNAL SEAM EXAMINATION

Product _____

DATE _____ LINE NO. _____ CAN SIZE _____ CAN CODE _____

Time	Spindle No.	Decision on Seams		Remarks
		Accept	Reject	

Can Supplier

Signed by (Container Closure Inspt) _____

Reviewed by (Management Rep) _____

Date _____

Figure 5—Form for recording visual seam examination.

visual seam examination. If a serious defect is observed, the regulations require that the exact nature of the defect and the steps taken for correction be recorded. Any marginal or unusual condition observed should also be recorded in the "Remarks" column.

The teardown examination is a destructive test that permits the internal observation of can seams and closures. The interval between observations should not exceed four hours. (For a detailed discussion of container closure evaluation turn to Chapters 16, 17 and 18.) *Figure 6* is an example of a form used for recording the teardown examination of double seams. Dimensions that are out of tolerance should be circled or highlighted.

When an adjustment is necessary, the description of the adjustment must be recorded, normally in the "Remarks" column as indicated in *Figure 7*.

Figure 8 is an example of a statistical type-chart that combines the previously described SQC Average and Range Chart for recording double seam measurements. In the example, each horizontal line represents 0.001 inches, and the ideal dimension for each item measured is shown at the left of the chart. Instead of plotting a single point representing the average of the measurements, the maximum and minimum dimensions obtained are recorded on the chart for the appropriate time. The closure inspector does not need to record most dimensions by writing numbers on this type of chart, since it is only necessary to record the points in the appropriate position and connect them with a vertical line. The dotted lines on the chart represent the operating limits. Points that

fall outside of the dotted lines are beyond operating limits. If this problem occurs, a repeat sample should be checked at once. If it is also outside the limit, a corrective action is in order.

The exact position of the lines representing upper and/ or lower limits of seam measurement values will depend on the seam specifications for each type of container. Observations such as "wrinkle" can be recorded on the appropriate line. Any seamer adjustments are noted by writing in the "Remarks" space.

This type of chart has several important advantages over the "table chart" (*Figure 6*), where one simply has a series of measurements. The SQC type chart allows the supervisor and seamer operator to note the seam dimension at a glance and be aware of any trends or marginal dimensions that may occur from seamer wear or maladjustments.

Glass Closure Evaluation Records

Forms for glass closure evaluation records may also use the columnar or the statistical control chart (SQC) format. The advantages and disadvantages of these two formats are the same as just described for metal containers. The exact type of form used will be determined by the requirements of the individual canner, but it should provide for both visual non-destructive and destructive examination.

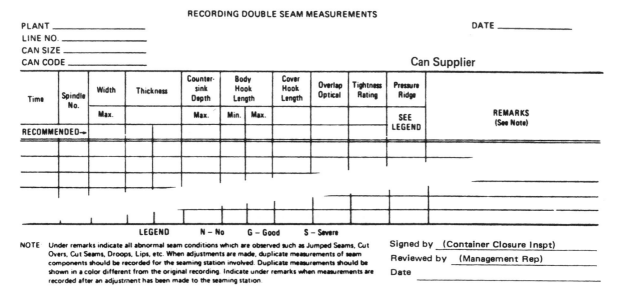

PLANT _____

LINE NO. _____

CAN SIZE _____

CAN CODE _____

DATE _____

Can Supplier

Time	Spindle No.	Width	Thickness	Counter-sink Depth	Body Hook Length	Cover Hook Length	Overlap Optical	Tightness Rating	Pressure Ridge	REMARKS (See Note)
		Max.		Max.	Min.	Max.				SEE LEGEND	
RECOMMENDED→											

LEGEND   N – No   G – Good   S – Severe

NOTE: Under remarks indicate all abnormal seam conditions which are observed such as Jumped Seams, Cut Overs, Cut Seams, Droops, Lips, etc. When adjustments are made, duplicate measurements of seam components should be recorded for the seaming station involved. Duplicate measurements should be shown in a color different from the original recording. Indicate under remarks when measurements are recorded after an adjustment has been made to the seaming station.

Signed by ___(Container Closure Inspt)___

Reviewed by ___(Management Rep)___

Date _____

Figure 6—Columnar form for recording double seam measurements.

Figure 9 is an example of a columnar recording form that could be used for both non-destructive and destructive tests on glass containers. It is self explanatory. The form can be modified to suit the individual packer's needs.

The nature of any defects, corrective steps, and marginal or unusual conditions observed should be noted under the "Remarks" column.

Figure 10 is an example of how the statistical control chart may be used for recording glass closure evaluations. The dotted lines are set at the upper and lower points representing the desired range. The solid lines indicate the upper and lower critical control limits. When readings fall outside the solid lines, immediate remedial action is usually indicated. Occasional readings outside the dotted lines—but within the solid lines—are not a cause for immediate action but should serve to notify the person responsible for the capper settings that minor adjustments may be necessary. Persistent readings outside the dotted lines usually indicate a trend and should be acted on to keep the operation in control.

Any adjustments made or remarks that would be recorded in the "Comments" or "Remarks" column of a columnar form can be checked on the "Comments" line and recorded on a separate log.

Summary

1. Management, supervisors and inspectors all have responsibilities for the safety of food products and containers. Adequate records must be available to provide this assurance.

2. Records that are accurate and reflect operating conditions at the time specified must be kept.

3. Copies of all required processing and production records shall be retained for not less than three years.

4. Inspection and copying of the records that verify the adequacy of thermal processing operations, the integrity of container closure, and the container coding system must be permitted on written request by duly authorized FDA employees and when requested by USDA-FSIS Program employees.

5. All process deviations involving failure to satisfy the minimum requirements of the scheduled process must be identified, and records maintained in a log or file. USDA requires all instances of spoilage or deviation to be reported to the agency. FDA requires that any instances of spoilage or deviation that indicates potential health significance must be reported to the agency if the product has left the control of the packer.

6. FDA requires container codes to identify the establishment where packed, product contained therein, and the year, day and period packed. USDA requires container

Max	Ave	Remarks
127	176	
125	124	(Excessive counter-sink
135	1335	) Short overlap
176	125	(Adjusted pressures
124	1735	Resample head #3

Figure 7—Remarks column of seam inspection report.

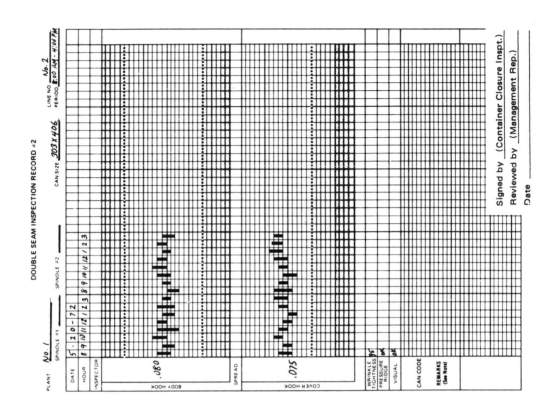

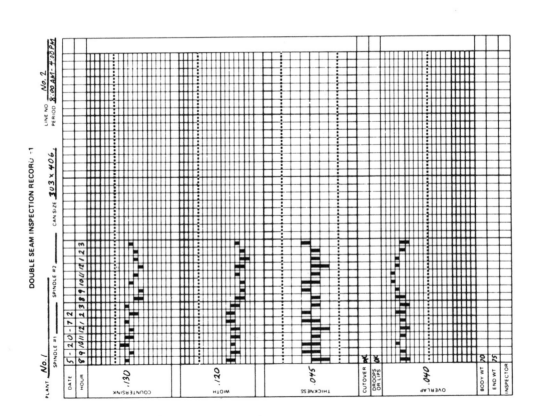

Figure 8—Example of a statistical chart for recording double seam measurements.

PACKAGE EVALUATION RECORD – AT CAPPER

Plant _____ Line No. _____ Product _____

Container Size & Mfg. _____ Closure Size _____

Date _____ Code _____

Time	Type Capper	Product Vac. and IT	Cold Water Vac.	Head Space	Cap Tilt	Pull Up	Sec.	Closure Impressions	Remarks

Signed by ___(Container Closure Inspt.)

Reviewed by ___(Management Rep.)

Figure 9—Columnar form for recording glass closure evaluation.

___

codes to identify the product, day and year the product was packed.

7. Records must identify the initial distribution of the finished product, and a current procedure for recalls to the consumer level must be prepared and its effectiveness tested.

8. Records may be in the form of SQC charts, if fluctuation of data within limits is acceptable. SQC charts put columns of data into picture form.

9. SQC charts are not appropriate for process or production records or other operations that require recordings of specific data, such as pH.

10. SQC charts should be prepared and interpreted by people who are aware of their values and limitations.

11. There must be a temperature/time recorder chart curve for each cook listed on the operator's written record (daily process record log).

12. The process system operator must record the required information when observed and sign or initial each record form. The record must be reviewed and signed or initialed by a qualified representative of management not later than one working day after the actual process.

13. Regulations specify that regular observations of container closure shall be made at intervals of sufficient frequency to ensure closure integrity, and that all corrective actions taken must be indicated.

14. Registration of the canning establishment and filing of thermal processes with FDA must be made on appropriate forms (obtainable from FDA).

15. The process, along with acceptable documentation, shall be made available to USDA-FSIS Program employees.

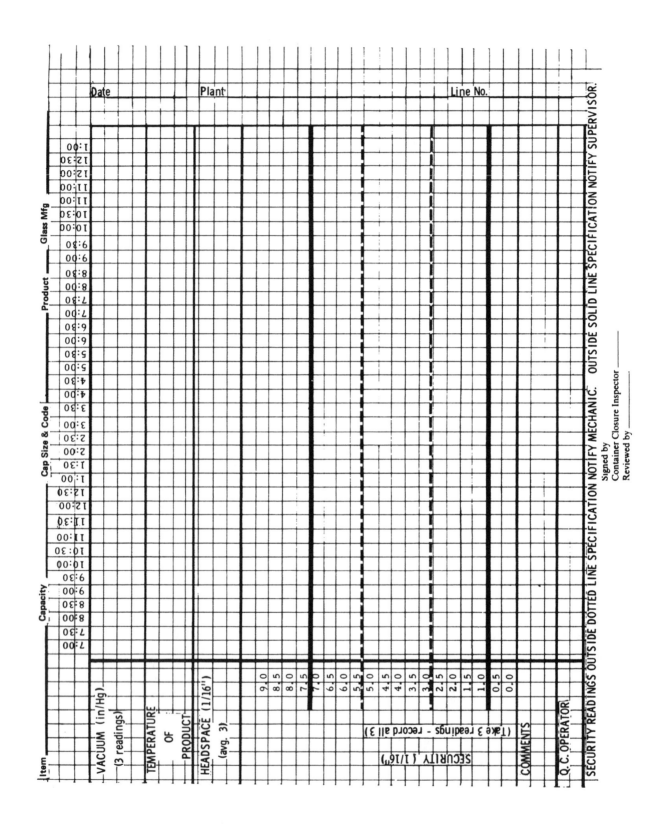

Figure 10—Statistical control chart for recording glass closure evaluation.

60

Chapter 7

PRINCIPLES OF THERMAL PROCESSING

Introduction

In 1874, A.K. Shriver, a Baltimore, Maryland canner, invented the closed-kettle, the first retort system, using steam under pressure for processing foods at high temperatures. This event signaled the beginning of the commercial processing of canned foods.

Before Shriver's invention, boiling water baths were used to apply heat to canned foods. The length of time in the boiling water required to prevent spoilage depended on the food product and on the canner's previous experience with food spoilage. Not only did spoilage frequently occur, but it was dealt with by an arbitrary increase in the time of the boiling water process. The result of this unscientific method of processing canned foods was well expressed by a canner who said, "Sometimes they kept, and sometimes they didn't."

This chapter discusses the theoretical considerations that form the basis for the scientific application of thermal processes to canned foods. The principal purpose of this discussion is to identify and review some of the major factors affecting thermal processing.

Basis of Thermal Processes

The basis for establishment of thermal processes for canned foods is a sound knowledge of food microbiology and of processing methods. Food spoilage microorganisms are present on virtually all raw food ingredients. Since they are living organisms, they cannot grow under adverse environmental conditions, and they die if their surroundings become unfit. The most easily regulated feature of their environment is temperature, although other sterilization agents may be used such as chemicals or high energy radiation. Food contaminated with microorganisms, when placed in a sealed container, can be prevented from spoiling when subjected to high temperature for a sufficient time. The high temperature kills the microorganisms already present and the sealed container prevents recontamination of the food.

Determining the proper temperature and length of time needed to sterilize a container of food has been the subject of earnest study in the canning industry. The procedure for process determination is not simple. It depends upon the knowledge of a number of factors, including the nature of the product, the dimensions of the container in which it is to be packed, and the details of the thermal processing procedures used. Of equal significance is knowledge of the growth and survival characteristics and thermal resistance of the contaminating microorganisms. Once this information has been obtained, the process must be based on the answer to the following question: How long and at what temperature should a particular product in a particular container be processed in order to destroy the spoilage organisms?

The regulatory agencies require that scheduled processes be established by a processing authority having expert knowledge of thermal processing requirements. A processing authority is a person or organization having expert knowledge of thermal processing requirements for foods packed in hermetically sealed containers and having adequate facilities to make process determinations.

Process Schedule

The scheduled process or process schedule is designed by a processing authority to provide a commercially sterile or shelf-stable product. Commercial sterility (FDA) or shelf stability (USDA) means the condition achieved in a product by the application of heat to render the product free of microorganisms capable of reproducing in the food at normal non-refrigerated conditions of storage and distribution.

The scheduled process includes thermal process parameters such as product initial temperature, process temperature and process time, plus critical factors that may affect the attainment of commercial sterility. Critical factors may include any characteristic, condition or aspect of a product, container, preparation procedure or processing system that affect the scheduled process.

Establishment of the Thermal Process

The establishment of a thermal process is based on two factors. First, the heat resistance of microorganisms—the amount of heat required for their destruction—must be known in each specific product. Second, the heating rate of a specific product must be determined. These two factors are used to calculate the scheduled process (*Figure 1*).

Once a process has been established for a particular food, it is specific for that one food—its formulation, its method of preparation, the container size in which it is processed and the kind of thermal processing system used. A process must not be altered unless specific instructions for change are obtained from a processing authority.

Thermal Resistance of Microorganisms

The thermal resistance of microorganisms is dependent upon a number of factors that must be considered. These can be divided into three broad categories—the growth characteristics of the microorganisms, the nature of the food in which the microorganisms are heated, and the kind of food in which the heated microorganisms are allowed to grow. Thermobacteriology is a highly complex science, and variations in any of these factors can affect the heat resistance of microorganisms.

The amount of heat required to destroy microorganisms in a product can be obtained through thermal death time (TDT) tests that involve the TDT tube, TDT can and/or three-neck flask methods. (See *Figures 2, 3,* and *4.*) The TDT tubes are useful with liquid suspensions while TDT cans are most useful with thick purees or solid materials that must be heated to a temperature above that of boiling water. The three-neck flask is useful for product heated at temperatures less than boiling water. The choice of method depends upon a variety of factors, including the type of food and the processing system to be used.

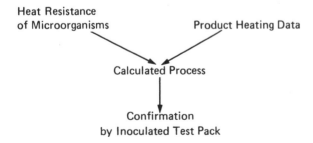

PROCESS DETERMINATION

Heat Resistance
of Microorganisms   Product Heating Data

Calculated Process

Confirmation
by Inoculated Test Pack

Figure 1—Establishing a thermal process.

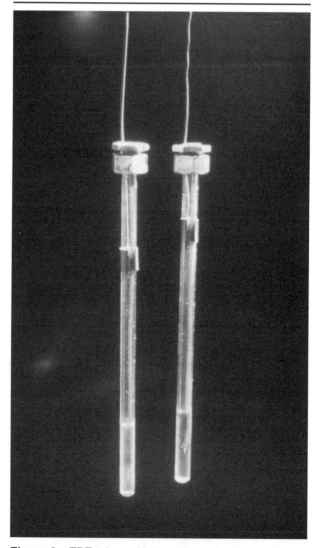

Figure 2—TDT tubes with thermocouples inserted.

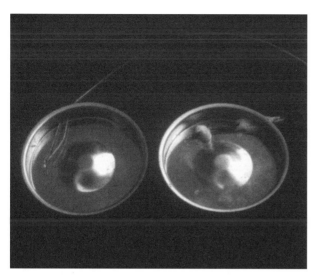

Figure 3—TDT cans with thermocouples inserted.

Product Heating Data Determinations

The rate at which a product heats can be measured using devices that monitor the change of temperature as the food is being heated. The determinations are accomplished with a temperature sensor or thermocouple located in the product at the slowest heating region of the container. The slowest heating region of the container will depend on the type of product, container size and processing method. The time/temperature data are monitored on a temperature recording device. These data are necessary to determine the heating rate of the product and to calculate the scheduled process. This procedure may be used for both low-acid and acidified products.

Calculated Processes

The processing authority will calculate a process using the product heating data and the thermal resistance data for the significant spoilage organisms or organisms of public health consequence expected to be present in the product. A number of ways exist to calculate the process. Since it is not within the scope of this discussion to go into these calculation methods, it need only be indicated that it is mathematically possible to use the product heating data to arrive at a process adequate to commercially sterilize the product.

Acidified Foods

For acidified foods, a hot-fill-hold process may be used. This involves filling the product hot, and holding the product for a period of time before cooling. This type of process is based on a given pH and fill temperature relationship and may be obtained from a processing authority. No specific time/temperature data is necessary to establish hot-fill-hold processes.

Figure 4—Three neck flask for thermal death time determinations. A thermometer is inserted through one of the side necks, a stirrer through the center neck. The sample is withdrawn through the second side neck at selected time intervals. The flask is immersed in the heating medium, usually water.

Acidified products may also be processed in a pasteurizer, atmospheric cooker or retort for a given period of time. In this case, it is necessary to base the process on the heating rate of the product. Pasteurizers or atmospheric cookers are usually continuous, in which case the process may be based on the final product temperature at the end of the heating section. Maximum reading thermometers can be used to establish processes for acid and acidified products.

Inoculated Test Pack

It is possible and sometimes desirable to confirm the calculated process by means of inoculated test packs. In this procedure, the test product is prepared under commercial plant operating conditions. Appropriate test microorganisms of known heat resistance are added to the product. The product is inoculated with a known number of microorganisms and is then subjected to various time periods at one or a number of different processing temperatures. The product is then incubated at an appropriate growth temperature. Product that received a process inadequate to destroy the added microorganisms will show evidence of spoilage. A satisfactory process is demonstrated by the absence of spoilage. Substantial agreement between calculated processes and those determined by inoculated packs furnish the strongest possible assurance of the adequacy and safety of a particular process.

Occasionally, due to peculiarities in the thermal processing systems or in the product, reliable heating data cannot be obtained. Under these circumstances, consideration may be given to using an inoculated pack alone to establish a safe thermal process.

Another method of process establishment that has been used in the past is count reduction. The count reduction procedure is similar to an inoculated pack except that, instead of incubating the inoculated test containers, the organisms that survive the thermal treatment are counted.

Thermal Processing Methods

Many methods exist for processing products packed in hermetically sealed containers. Most products are filled into containers, which are sealed and then processed in some type of retort (pressure vessel). These types of thermal processing systems have become known as conventional thermal processing.

A different and newer thermal processing method is aseptic processing. The number of systems and the variety of products being aseptically processed are rapidly expanding. This method involves the sterilization of the product and package separately and bringing them together in a sterile environment for filling and sealing. Both conventional and aseptic processing methods, which are discussed thoroughly in later chapters, may be used for acidified or low-acid products.

Retorts and other thermal processing systems must be constructed and operated in such a manner that the finished product will be commercially sterile. The operating procedures shall be developed by a processing authority or the equipment manufacturer.

Determination of Retort Operating Procedures

Processing authorities use temperature distribution tests to assist in establishing operating procedures for all retort types. Temperature sensors or thermocouples are located between containers throughout the retort load. The temperatures are monitored during the process to ensure that the temperature indicating device (mercury-in-glass thermometer—MIG) for the retort is representative of the temperatures throughout the retort.

Retort operating procedures shall be designed to provide uniform temperature distribution in the heating medium throughout the retort. Regardless of the heating medium, process timing shall not start until the temperature indicating device reaches processing temperature, and uniform temperature distribution has been attained within the retort. (*Figures 5* and *6*) The specific operating steps depend upon whether steam, water or a steam/air mixture is the heating medium. In all cases, however, proper temperature uniformity should be accomplished during the come-up-time, which is defined as the elapsed time between the start of heating (''steam on'') and the start of process timing. Process timing ordinarily begins when the retort reaches the prescribed processing temperature as indicated by the temperature indicating device (MIG) and when required operating steps (e.g. venting procedures or come-up requirements) have been completed.

For retorts using steam as the processing medium, it is important that air be removed from the retort prior to the beginning of process timing, because it is a much less efficient heating medium than steam. This procedure is referred to as venting. Steam carries considerable heat or ''stored energy'' that results from conversion of water to vapor. When steam condenses, as occurs in the retort, this heat is given up. In other words, the steam has been able to carry an ''extra load'' of heat from the boiler to the retort—a task that hot air would not have accomplished. This fact can be demonstrated by comparing the effect of placing one's hand in a dry heat oven at 250°F (121°C) and live steam at 212°F (100°C).

Summary

1. A process is the application of heat to food for a scientifically determined specified time and temperature.

2. A process that has been scientifically determined is specific to the given product, its formulation, method of preparation, container size and type of retort system.

3. The determination of a process depends upon reliable heating information and the heat resistance of microorganisms in the product.

4. The heat resistance of microorganisms depends upon the microorganism used, the food in which it is heated and the food in which the organism grows.

5. The determination of heating data (time/temperature data) should be conducted on a product which simulates commercial preparation.

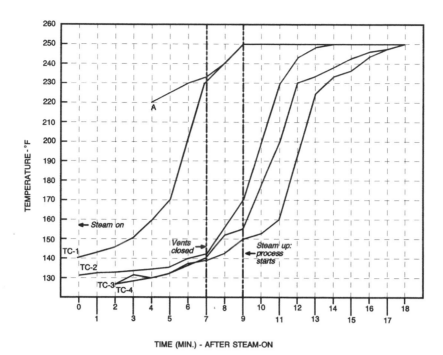

Figure 5—Heat distribution test example demonstrating an inadequately vented retort. TC's 1, 2, 3 and 4 represent time/temperature data from four locations in retort. TC 1 was in a well-vented area, while TC's 2, 3 and 4 were in air pockets. "A" represents the mercury thermometer. Timing of the process was started at 9 minutes when the mercury thermometer indicated 250°F(121°C). Containers in the air pockets (TC's 2, 3 and 4) would not receive the full specified process.

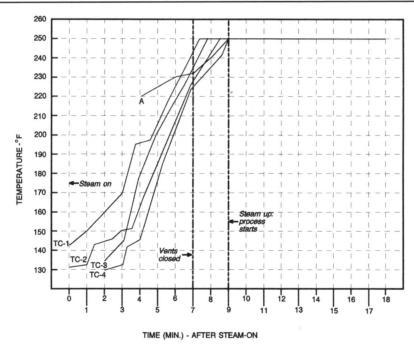

Figure 6—Heat distribution test example demonstrating a properly vented retort. All TC's are up to 250°F(121°C) when process timing began at 9 minutes.

6. The data obtained from thermal resistance and heat penetration tests are used to calculate a process.

7. Hot-fill-hold processes that are based on a pH and fill temperature relationship may be used for acidified foods.

8. It is sometimes desirable to check the calculated process by means of an inoculated test pack.

9. Standard operating procedures for thermal processing systems should be available to authorized plant personnel.

Chapter 8

PROCESS ROOM INSTRUMENTATION, EQUIPMENT AND OPERATION

It is of vital importance that thermal processing systems are properly installed and operated by trained personnel and that adequate records are maintained. The regulations require certain instrumentation on all thermal processing systems. The information in this chapter provides an overview of those regulations and serves as a guide to the selection and maintenance of equipment and proper systems operation. It is important to prevent processing deviations. Through proper equipment and instrument maintenance, as well as proper operating practices, this goal may be achieved.

Instrumentation

Temperature Indicating Device

Low-acid foods

The mercury-in-glass thermometer (MIG) serves as the official temperature indicating device for all thermal processing systems except aseptic systems, where other devices such as thermocouples are used. The MIG thermometer is the most widely used temperature measuring device in the canned food industry. Its relative simplicity makes its use desirable in thermal processing operations. FDA and USDA regulations require that each retort system be equipped with at least one mercury-in-glass thermometer. USDA and FDA also require that a mercury-in-glass thermometer have easily readable divisions to 1°F (0.5°C) and a temperature range that does not exceed 17°F (9.4°F) per inch of graduated scale. USDA regulations allow processors to propose other types of temperature indicating devices.

Thermometers shall be installed where they can be read easily and be protected from mechanical damage. A metal guard should be installed to protect the thermometers. Thermometers should not be installed in the retort doors, lids or anywhere they would be subject to jolts or jars. The bulbs of mercury thermometers shall be installed within the retort shell or in external wells attached to the retort. The external wells shall be connected to the retort through at least a 3/4-inch diameter opening and equipped with a 1/16-inch or larger bleeder opening.

The specific installation locations will vary depending on the specific retort and will be discussed in each of the following chapters. Thermometers shall be tested against a known accurate standard upon installation, at least once a year thereafter, and at any time the accuracy of the thermometer is questionable, such as when the mercury column is divided. A thermometer with a divided mercury column or defect shall be replaced before further use of the retort system. The records of thermometer accuracy checks shall be maintained and shall specify the date, standard used, methodology, results and person(s) performing the tests. Each thermometer should have a tag, seal or other means to identify that thermometer with the standardization records.

Acidified foods

No specific requirements dictate the type of temperature indicating device to use when processing acidified foods in atmospheric cookers or pasteurizers. Dial thermometers are used to monitor fill temperatures, and mercury-in-glass or dial thermometers are used in pasteurizers as temperature indicating devices. Regardless of the type of thermometer used, it should be calibrated as described for low-acid foods.

Checking the Accuracy of Thermal Processing Thermometers

The mercury-in-glass thermometer is not a foolproof instrument. It must be calibrated and maintained in good operating condition.

One system for checking the accuracy of mercury-in-glass thermometers is illustrated in *Figure 1*.

This system employs the following equipment:

1. A mercury-in-glass thermometer of known accuracy that has been standardized against a certified thermometer at the appropriate thermal process temperatures.

2. A cross of 3/4-inch pipe fittings for holding thermometers, with 1/16-inch holes for bleeders drilled in the couplings holding the thermometers.

Install the testing equipment in any convenient 3/4-inch hole in a retort or in the steam manifold. Remove the cover glasses from the thermometers to be tested and check for loose stems by gently attempting to move the stem up and down. Thermometers with loose stems should not be used; they should be repaired or replaced. Place the thermometers in the test equipment with the known accurate standard thermometer between them.

Bring the retort or steam manifold to the appropriate thermal processing temperature, making certain that it is vented sufficiently to eliminate all air.

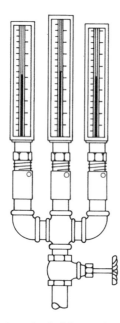

Figure 1—Pipe fittings for holding 3 thermometers.

Open the steam valve on the test equipment and allow the thermometers to come to equilibrium, which will require 10 to 15 minutes. If adjustment is required, loosen the screws on the temperature scale and adjust it up or down so that it reads the same as the standard thermometer.

Tighten the scale adjustment screws and take another reading to make certain the thermometers are properly standardized. For identification purposes, mark each thermometer and keep a record of the date on which each thermometer was standardized. Mark broken thermometers in such a way that they will not be used. Clean the cover glasses and replace them on the thermometers.

Temperature/Time Recording Device

Low-acid foods

In addition to a temperature indicating device, each thermal processing system shall be equipped with at least one temperature/time recording device to provide a permanent record of temperature and time during processing. This recording device may be combined with the steam controller to form a temperature recorder-controller. The temperature/time recorder shall be adjusted to agree as closely as possible with—but in no event higher than—the temperature indicating device. USDA regulations require that the temperature/time recorder be accurate to within 1°F (0.5°C) at the processing temperature. A means of preventing unauthorized changes in adjustment shall be provided. A lock or a notice from management posted at or near the temperature/time recording device warning that only authorized persons are permitted to make adjustments is a satisfactory means for preventing unauthorized changes.

The temperature/time recorder should be used only with the appropriate chart paper for that particular instrument. However, some of the more sophisticated temperature/time recorders are capable of printing their own time-temperature scales. The temperature chart graduations shall not exceed 2°F (1.1°C), within a range of 10°F (5.5°C) of the processing temperature. Each chart shall have a working scale of not more than 55°F per inch (12°C per cm) within a range of 20°F (11.1°C) of the processing temperature. Most instruments produce a continuous line that represents the recorded temperature. Multipoint recorders can be used and, as the USDA regulations indicate, must print at intervals that will assure that the parameters of process time and process temperature have been met. The frequency of recordings should not exceed one-minute intervals.

The location of the temperature recording bulb will vary depending on the type of thermal processing system. The bulb may be installed within a well attached to the retort or located directly within the retort shell. In general, the recorder bulbs are installed adjacent to the temperature indicating device. The specific regulations governing the location of the recorder-controller bulbs will vary and are discussed in the following chapters.

Acidified foods

The USDA requires that atmospheric cookers (pasteurizers) be equipped with at least one temperature/time recording device. Although there are no specific FDA requirements, good manufacturing practice suggests the same principles should apply. For pasteurizers using water as the processing medium, the probe of the temperature recording device should be installed in the hot water discharge or the cold zone in the hot portion of the pasteurizer. If steam is used as the heating medium, the probe should be installed in the cold zone of the unit. The temperature/time recorder provides a continuous permanent record of the processing temperature. The USDA requires that the temperature/time recorder shall meet the same requirements used in low-acid systems.

Temperature Control System

Each retort, shall be equipped with an automatic steam controller to maintain the retort temperature. Retorts or pasteurizers used for acidified foods should also use the same type of control system. Most steam controllers are either air operated or electrically operated. Self-activating controllers responding only to pressure may be found on older installations and are not recommended for general use.

The steam controller may be combined with the temperature/time recorder to form a recorder-controller. The steam control valves in these systems can be either electrically or air operated. *Figures 2* and *3* illustrate the principle of a simple air operated temperature control system, which is the system most commonly used.

The temperature bulb is located in the retort and attached to the Bourdon Tube by means of the thermal tube. As the temperature rises, the Bourdon Tube expands and closes the flapper valve at N, preventing the escape of air. The air pressure expands the diaphragm D, which closes valve S in the pilot valve PV, shutting off the main supply of air to the controller valve. The spring in the air-to-open controller valve then closes the main steam valve. The degree of opening or closing of the valve is determined by balancing the air pressure above the diaphragm against the opposing force of the valve spring.

The temperature to be controlled is set by adjusting the tension on the thermal system. The position of the temperature/time recording pen arm is synchronized with the reading of the temperature indicating device by means of an adjusting screw.

The diaphragm-operated control valve installed in the retort should be the air-to-open type because it is failsafe. If there is a failure in the air supply, these valves automatically close, thus preventing excessive temperature and pressure in the retort.

A compressible packing material is used to prevent leaking of steam or air along the stem of the push rod. These elements must be properly adjusted to always permit free movement of the push rod.

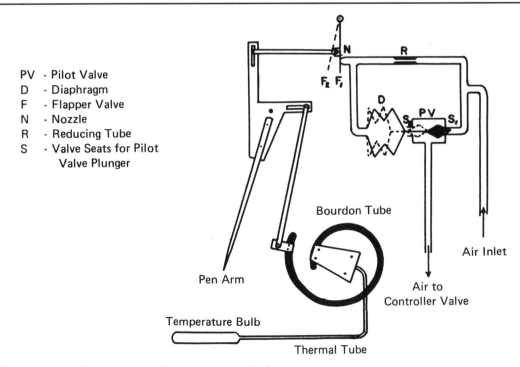

PV - Pilot Valve
D - Diaphragm
F - Flapper Valve
N - Nozzle
R - Reducing Tube
S - Valve Seats for Pilot
Valve Plunger

Figure 2—Diagram of simple, air operated temperature control system.

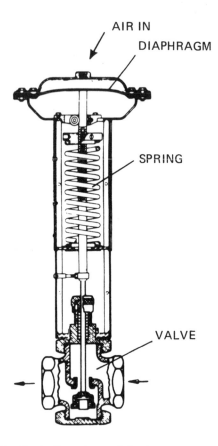

Figure 3—Controller valve and diaphragm actuator mechanism.

Air operated temperature control systems are most often used for thermal processing. When these systems are installed, the thermal tube should be protected from damage with sharp bends or kinks avoided. Damage to the thermal tube could cause erroneous temperatures to be recorded. If an electrical control system is used, it should be installed in a manner that permits accurate operation.

Electronic Control Systems

With the advent of inexpensive microprocessors, electronic controls for thermal processing systems are becoming more prevalent. These control systems can range from a simple, quick responsive temperature control system to a complex system precisely controlling an entire sequence of events. These systems can be programmed to control a complete thermal process—venting, come-up-time, process temperature and time, cooling and overpressure, if required.

Inputs may be made automatically or manually. Items such as initial temperature may be handled by placing a probe in the designated initial temperature container, or items such as fill weight may be manually entered. The

systems would monitor and control the retort(s) based on other information such as retort temperature and the program information stored in the controller. Some systems can, based on operator input, select the proper thermal process for a particular product. These systems also are capable of adjusting the process variables based on the process information collected by the controller in order to compensate for deviations. Some systems will use an alternate process or may be capable of calculating new processes based on appropriate heating factors representing the product heating rate.

A processing authority must be consulted when using these types of control systems to ensure that the system meets all the requirements of the pertinent regulations. FDA does not object to computer-generated thermal processing records in lieu of written records when the software for the system has been reviewed and found to meet the intent of FDA's requirements for recordkeeping. In addition, USDA requires that a PQC program be approved that includes the description and operational details of automatic control systems.

Instrument Air Supply

Air operated control systems should be equipped with adequate filter systems to supply clean, dry air at the proper pressure. Moisture, oil, corrosive liquids or particulates in the air supply eventually will adversely affect the operation of the instrument. Such contaminants are frequently the cause of instrument failure or unreliable operation. A properly maintained system supplied with clean, dry air will operate most effectively.

The air supply system should be designed to supply air at the proper rate and pressure. A dedicated air supply system should be used to supply air to the instrument. A typical air supply system is indicated in *Figure 4*.

Pressure Gauges

Each retort should be equipped with a pressure gauge or other suitable device to monitor pressure within the retort. If a gauge is used, it should be graduated with divisions not to exceed two pounds per square inch. (Some types of packages require a retort pressure greater than the steam pressure during the thermal process or a specific pressure during cooling.) In addition, a pressure gauge can provide the retort operator with useful information during operation and can serve as a safety device by alerting the retort operator to abnormal pressures.

Timing Devices

The use of pocket or wrist watches is not permitted for timing purposes. Analog or digital clocks are permitted and should be accurate to assure that specific times are satisfied. The clock should be located so that it can be easily and accurately read by the operator. If the clock does not indicate seconds, a one-minute safety factor shall be added to each timed function.

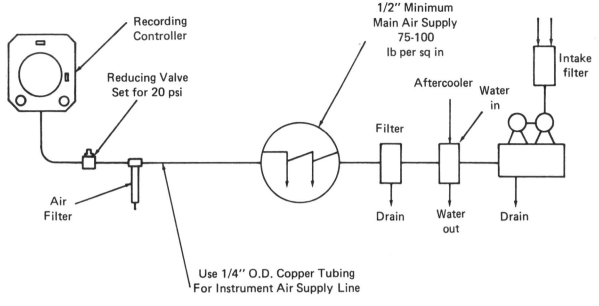

Figure 4—Diagram of the air supply to pneumatic controller.

Maintenance

It is a good practice and a USDA requirement that—upon installation and at any time when proper functioning or accuracy is questioned—all instrumentation be checked. Proper instrument maintenance is essential to provide adequate control and documentation of thermal processing operations.

Equipment

Steam Supply

Steam is the most common heating medium for thermal processing systems. The steam supply to the thermal processing area shall be adequate to bring the retorts to processing temperature and maintain that temperature under normal operating conditions.

Valve Types and Uses

Basically two types of valves are used in thermal processing operations: globe valves, which are better sealing valves, and gate valves, which are full flow type valves (*Figure 5*).

Vents are large valve-controlled openings in retorts used to remove air prior to processing in a steam atmosphere. Globe valves are not recommended for use in vent lines, because they reduce flow through the valve. Vents shall be controlled by a gate, plug cock or other adequate type valve that permits a rapid discharge of air and steam from the retort. (Additional information is included in the following chapters.)

All air lines and water lines connected to a retort shall be equipped with globe valves or other suitable valves to prevent air or water from leaking into the retort. USDA requires that a globe valve or other equivalent type valve be used on all air lines connected to retorts using steam as the processing medium and/or water lines that are intended to be closed during the processing cycle.

Bleeders

Bleeders are small openings in the retort used to provide circulation of a steam heating medium, to remove any air entering the retort with the steam, to provide full

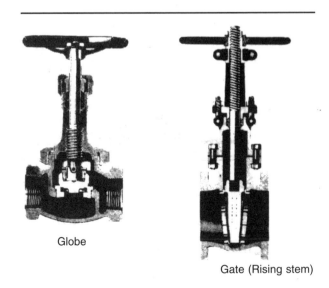

Globe

Gate (Rising stem)

Figure 5—Cross-section of a typical globe and gate valve.

flow of a heating medium past a thermometer bulb, or to remove condensate from the bottom of a retort. Bleeders can range from 1/16-inch openings or larger for a thermometer pocket to 1/4-inch openings on larger processing vessels. All bleeders shall be arranged in such a way that the operator can verify that they are functioning properly. (See chapters on specific processing systems for further information.)

Spreaders

Spreaders are continuations of a steam or water line inside the retort used to provide a uniform distribution of steam or water. Spreaders may also be used for other purposes, such as venting when connected to both vent and water lines. (See chapters on specific processing systems for further information.)

Mufflers

Mufflers may be used on bleeders or vents to reduce the noise level of the escaping steam and air. If mufflers are used, evidence that they do not impede the removal of air or steam or interfere with the temperature uniformity within the retort, shall be maintained by the processor. This information may be in the form of temperature distribution data.

Pasteurizers

Pasteurizers may use either steam, hot water or cascading hot water to provide heat for processing acidified foods. Pasteurizers are maintained at atmospheric pressures. Units using cascading water are the most common and may be a combination pasteurizer/cooler with the first sections using hot water and the remaining sections using cooling water. A continuous belt is used to convey the containers through the pasteurizer and provide a specific residence time based on the speed. Prior to introducing containers into the unit, the proper pasteurization temperature needs to be established, and the belt set to the proper speed. When containers enter the pasteurizer, they should be evenly distributed to ensure that the containers move through the pasteurizer uniformly. Uneven distribution of containers may lead to increased residence time and would be a quality—not a safety—concern.

Both heating and/or cooling sections, if present, need to be maintained to ensure uniform operation and temperature distribution. Steam or water spreaders should be inspected and cleaned periodically to prevent any build-up around nozzles that could restrict the flow. General sanitation and maintenance considerations discussed in this chapter also apply to this equipment.

USDA requires that each atmospheric cooker shall be operated to ensure uniform temperature distribution throughout the processing system. This information needs to be kept on file by the processor and made available to USDA, if requested.

Equipment Maintenance

It is good practice, in addition to being a USDA requirement, that at least once a year each thermal processing system be examined by an individual not directly involved in the daily operations to ensure that the system is functioning properly. In addition, each processing system should be examined thoroughly after a prolonged shutdown. The examination shall include, but is not limited to, an examination of air and water valves for leakage, vent and bleeder mufflers for restrictions that could reduce efficiency, and water spreaders that are used for venting to ensure that the holes are of the intended size. Records shall be kept on file of all maintenance items that could affect the adequacy of the scheduled process. The records shall include the date and type of maintenance performed and the person conducting the maintenance.

Process Room Operation

Company management should perform careful analysis of processing room operations to assure that measures are taken to maintain efficiency and protect product safety. The operators should be thoroughly trained and have a working understanding of the equipment and various steps associated with thermal processing operations.

Posting of Thermal Processes

Operating processes—along with such operating procedures as venting schedules, if applicable—shall be posted in a conspicuous place near the thermal processing equipment or made readily available to the retort operator or duly authorized government inspector. This procedure will help eliminate errors and provide for a reliable operation.

Prevention of Retort Bypass

A system for product traffic control in the retort room shall be established to prevent unretorted product from bypassing the retort process. All retort baskets, trucks, cars or crates containing unretorted product shall be plainly and conspicuously marked by a heat-sensitive indicator or by other effective means. As an alternative, some of the containers on top of each basket shall be marked.

Several marking systems—such as indicator paints, tags or tapes—are available for this purpose. However, a change in the color merely indicates that the steam has been turned on. These indicators must not be relied upon to measure process time or the adequacy of a process. The use of a heat indicator, with the proper temperature/time recorder charts and production records, provides added assurance that each basket was processed at the correct temperature and time.

A visual check shall be performed to determine whether the appropriate change has occurred in the heat-sensitive indicator to ensure that each unit of product has been retorted. A written record of the check should be made. This requirement is intended to prevent unretorted containers from bypassing the retort and going directly from the closing machine to the warehouse.

Retorts should not be closed temporarily during loading. They should be closed *only* when the retort operator is ready to start the process. When several products requiring different processes are being packed at the same time, they should be identified so that each is given the proper process.

Any cans of doubtful status that are found in the cook room or in the bottom of a retort shall be destroyed.

Coding of Containers

Each hermetically sealed container of product shall be marked with an identifying code that will be permanently visible. Codes are most commonly embossed or imprinted directly on the container. When these methods are not possible, the label may be legibly perforated or otherwise marked, providing the label is securely affixed to the product container. FDA requires that the code identify the establishment where packed, the product contained within, and the year, day and period when packed. The period code shall be changed with sufficient frequency to enable ready identification of lots during sale or distribution. Period codes may be changed every four to five hours, at personnel shift changes or when batches are changed, provided that a batch does not exceed a personnel shift.

USDA requires that the code identify, at a minimum, the product (unless the product name is lithographed directly on the container) and the day and year packed. Reasonable manufacturing practice suggests that codes be changed along the lines described above.

The importance of coding is described in detail in Chapter 6. Container coding provides a means to isolate and/or retrieve questionable product. The more information provided in the product code, the more it will assist in accurately locating that product and linking that product with the appropriate production records. The more frequently the code is changed, the better the chance of minimizing the amount of product involved in a product recall.

Temperature/Time Recording Systems

The temperature recording system shall be adjusted to agree as closely as possible with, *but in no event be higher than*, the known accurate temperature indicating device. Most temperature/time recorders are equipped with a screw or dial permitting easy adjustment. If a circular chart is used, the pen arc should match the pen arc on the chart paper during rapid changes in temperature. If the arc does not match, the pen arc should be adjusted or the proper chart paper installed in the temperature/time recorder.

At the start of the day's operations, the temperature/time recorder pen should be set at the proper time of day. USDA requires that the temperature/time recorder correspond to within 15 minutes of the time of day on the written records. It is advisable to verify the accuracy of the temperature/time recording device by checking the time on the recorder and comparing it with the actual time of day.

Initial Temperature

Though often confused with the temperature at which the product is filled into the container, the initial temperature designates the average temperature of the contents of the coldest container to be processed when the sterilization cycle begins. The initial temperature is determined by selecting a container representing the coldest container in the retort load. Just prior to the start of the process, the contents of the container are thoroughly mixed, and the temperature determined. For those retort systems that use water prior to or during processing, provisions shall be made to ensure that the initial temperature is representative of the coldest container or the water in the retort, whichever is colder. The thermal process used must be the process designated for the initial temperature of the retort load. The initial temperature is a critical factor— equally as important as process time, retort temperature and any other critical factors.

Product Incubation

USDA requires that each establishment incubate samples of low-acid and acidified products at $95 \pm 5°F$ ($35 \pm 2.8°C$) for not less than 10 days. The number of samples selected depends on the processing system. The establishment is required to select at least one container per retort load from batch-type retorts. For continuous container handling systems, the establishment shall select at least one container per 1000 containers. Only normal-appearing containers shall be selected. Product may not be shipped before the end of the incubation period unless the establishment has written approval from the USDA-FSIS area supervisor. For written approval to be granted, the plant must assure that shipped product will not reach the retail level before incubation is completed.

In response to a 1988 petition from the National Food Processors Association, USDA-FSIS amended its canning regulations on August 21, 1992, to allow companies with an approved PQC program for finished product inspection to voluntarily follow alternative procedures for incubation and/or handling of abnormal containers. PQC programs deemed by the Agency to provide assurance of finished product safety by equivalent to or greater than the parameters specified in the regulations would be approved. Examples of alternative parameters which would be considered by the Agency include shorter incubation time, different incubation temperature and/or fewer incubation samples.

Process Deviations

A process deviation is defined as a thermal process for which one or more of the critical factors (initial temperature, process time, retort temperature, etc.) specific in the scheduled process have not been satisfied. Deviations involving USDA-regulated products may be handled in accordance with USDA-approved quality control programs. In the absence of such a program, the following procedures shall be used:

If deviations are identified during processing, the product may be immediately given a complete reprocess, an appropriate alternate process established in accordance with USDA regulations, or held for later evaluation by a processing authority. Process deviations identified through records review shall be evaluated by a processing authority. When an evaluation is conducted by a processing authority, a complete description of the deviation, all supporting documentation, a copy of the evaluation report and product disposition recommendations shall be provided to the USDA-FSIS inspector. The inspector will submit this information to the Thermal Processing Branch of USDA-FSIS in Washington, DC for review. No product may be shipped until the USDA has reviewed the submitted information and approved the product disposition actions. If product involved in a deviation is destroyed, destruction shall be conducted in accordance with USDA regulations.

FDA-regulated product deviations shall be handled in accordance with the following requirements: The product may be given a complete scheduled process, a full reprocess, an appropriate alternate process established in accordance with applicable regulations, held for evaluation by a processing authority, or destroyed. If a reprocess is selected, the reprocess must be adequate, under the conditions of manufacture, for the reprocessed product to achieve commercial sterility. In certain products, the original process changes the heating characteristics of the processed product. An example is beans in brine, which after processing are thicker than the unprocessed product and, therefore, heat slower when they are reprocessed. If a reprocess is used, it should be established by a processing authority and should be specific for the product and conditions of use.

Specific regulatory requirements for deviations in continuous rotary retorts may be found in Chapter 12.

The processor shall maintain full records for both the USDA and FDA products regarding the handling of each processing deviation regardless of the seriousness of the deviation. The records should include, at a minimum, the appropriate processing and production records, a full description of the corrective actions, evaluation procedures and results, and disposition of the product. These records shall be maintained in a separate file or in a log detailing the appropriate information. The deviation file shall be made available to USDA or FDA inspectors as requested. Additional information on deviations may be found in Chapter 6 and in chapters on specific processing systems.

Summary

1. The reference instrument for retort temperature during thermal processing operations is the mercury-in-glass thermometer. The USDA allows alternate temperature indicating devices with approval.

2. An accurate temperature/time recording device is required.

3. Each retort should be equipped with a pressure gauge.

4. Pocket or wrist watches shall not be considered satisfactory for timing purposes.

5. Vents shall be installed in such a way that air is removed from the retort before timing of the process is started.

6. Bleeders shall be wide open and continuously emit steam during the entire process, including the come-up-time.

7. Operating processes shall be posted or be readily available to the operator.

8. All retort crates containing unretorted material shall be marked to visually indicate to thermal processing personnel whether each unit has been retorted.

9. Each container shall be coded.

10. All critical factors, including initial temperature, must be adequately determined and recorded for each retort cycle.

11. Process deviations must be handled according to the appropriate regulations.

Chapter 9

STILL RETORTS— PRESSURE PROCESSING IN STEAM

Description of the Retort

A still retort is a batch-type, nonagitating, vertical or horizontal pressure vessel used for processing foods packaged in hermetically sealed containers. Generally, containers are stacked or jumble-loaded into racks, crates, cars, baskets or trays for loading and unloading the retort. However, crateless retorts operate without the use of container support systems.

Since retorts are pressure vessels, they are made of 1/4-inch or thicker boiler plate formed into shape and riveted or welded together. The doors or lids are made of either cast iron or heavy plate. Various lugs and locks are used to secure the doors. These devices are important for worker safety and should always be in satisfactory working condition to prevent the lid or door from blowing off during operation. The pressure inside the retort is tremendous. At 250°F (121°C) with 15 pounds per square inch pressure, approximately 10 tons of force pushes against the lid or door of a retort.

Installation and Operation of Retorts

Proper installation and operation of the retort is essential to achieve satisfactory processing results. The steam supply should be adequate to bring the retort to processing temperature in a reasonable time. If containers are cooled in the retort, the water supply should be sufficient to permit adequate and uniform cooling in a reasonable period of time. The vents shall be designed, installed and operated so that air is removed from the retort before timing of the process begins. Some typical installations are shown in *Figures 1, 2* and *3*.

Instrumentation

Bulb sheaths or probes of the temperature indicating device (mercury-in-glass thermometer) and the temperature/time recording device shall be installed within the retort or in an external well attached to the retort. An external well shall be connected to the retort through at least a 3/4-inch diameter opening and shall have a 1/16-inch or larger bleeder opening located to provide a constant flow of steam past the length of the bulb or probe. The external well bleeder shall emit steam continuously during the entire processing period. The bulb of the time/temperature device should be located adjacent to the temperature indicating device except in still vertical retort installations, which may use steam or water as the processing medium. (Further information may be found in the instrumentation section of Chapter 10 which follows.)

Steam Header and Supply

Steam should be supplied to the processing room through a header large enough to provide adequate steam to all the retorts in use. Insufficient steam supply is indicated by the inability to meet vent requirements, longer times to reach process temperature, and temperature fluc-

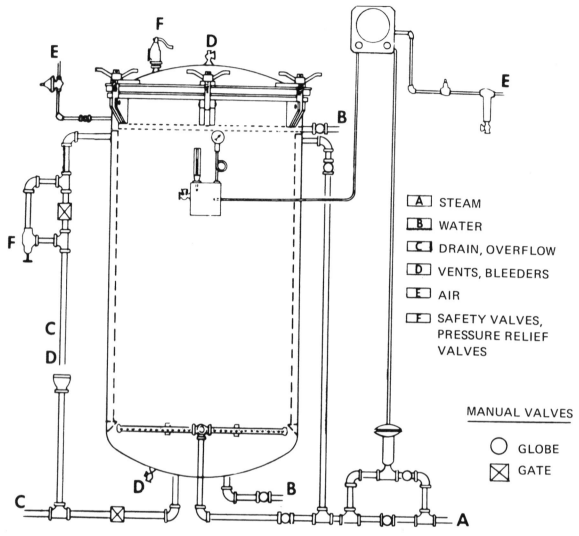

Figure 1—Vertical retort.

A	STEAM
B	WATER
C	DRAIN, OVERFLOW
D	VENTS, BLEEDERS
E	AIR
F	SAFETY VALVES, PRESSURE RELIEF VALVES

MANUAL VALVES

○ GLOBE

⊠ GATE

tuations on retorts in use when additional retorts are being vented.

Steam Inlet

The steam inlet to each still retort shall be large enough to provide sufficient steam for proper operation of the retort, and it shall enter at a point to facilitate air removal during venting. Although steam may enter the top or the bottom of the retort, FDA and USDA require that the steam inlet be located opposite the vent.

Steam Controller and Bypass

Still retorts shall be equipped with an automatic steam controller to maintain the retort temperature. This device may be a recording-controlling instrument when com-

bined with a temperature/time recording device. The details of the control system are described in Chapter 8.

The use of a smaller-sized control valve than the steam inlet pipe may have the advantage of controlling the process temperature with less fluctuation than occurs when a larger-sized valve is used. However, a control valve that is the same size as the inlet pipe is a desirable safety feature when one operator has several retorts to watch, because the retort can be brought up rapidly without using a steam controller bypass.

When a bypass is used, the operator should stay with the retort during the come-up period to prevent an excessive build up of pressure in the retort. As the retort reaches the processing temperature, the bypass valve should be closed slowly to avoid a sudden drop in temperature. Retorts equipped with a bypass can be operated manually

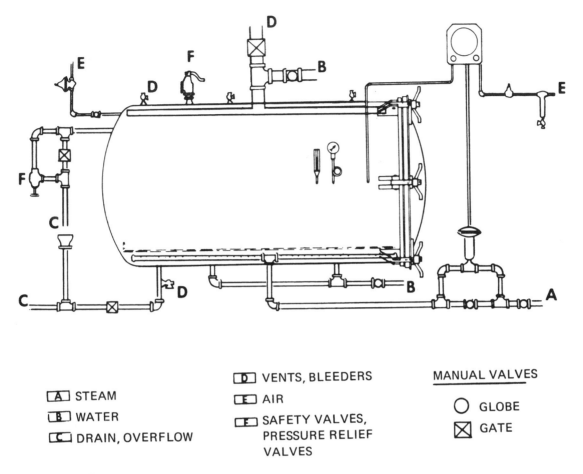

A STEAM	**D** VENTS, BLEEDERS
B WATER	**E** AIR
C DRAIN, OVERFLOW	**F** SAFETY VALVES, PRESSURE RELIEF VALVES

MANUAL VALVES

○ GLOBE

⊠ GATE

Figure 2—Horizontal retort.

in the event of a controller failure. The operator should know how to manually operate the retort.

Steam Spreaders

Steam spreaders are continuations of the steam line inside the retort that promote steam circulation. Perforated spreaders that extend the full length of the retort are required in horizontal still retort installations. For still retorts over 30 feet long, it is desirable to have two inlets connected to the spreader, as shown in *Figure 4*.

Perforations in the spreader for horizontal still retorts should be along the top 90° of this pipe. They should not be directed down against the retort shell, because the steam would tend to flow around the shell and exit through the vents without driving out the air. In addition, when the steam is jetted against the shell, it will gradually erode a hole through the shell.

Spreaders are not required in vertical retort installations, but they may be used, if desired. In vertical still retorts, the spreaders, if used, preferably should be in the form of a cross with perforations along the top or sides of the pipe. A vertical retort can be vented satisfactorily

without a spreader when the steam enters through a single opening at either end of the retort.

The number of perforations in the spreader should be such that the total cross-sectional area of the perforations is equal to one and one-half to two times the cross-sectional area of the smallest part of the steam inlet line. *Table 1* may be used as a guide.

Vents

Vents are large valve-controlled openings in retorts, used for eliminating air during the venting period. They shall be located in that portion of the retort opposite the steam inlet and designed, installed and operated in such a way that air is adequately removed from the retort before timing of the process is started.

Vents shall be controlled by gate, ball or a similar type of full-flow valve which shall open fully to permit rapid discharge of air from the retort during the venting period. Globe valves of the same size as the vent pipe are not recommended, because they reduce the efficiency of the venting due to the resistance of steam and air flow through the valves.

77

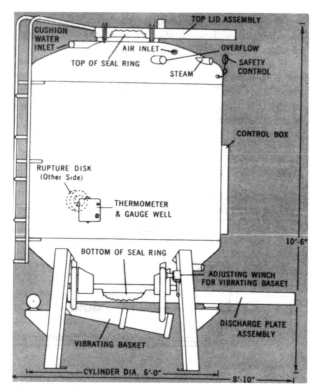

Figure 3—Crateless retort.

Vents shall not be connected directly to a closed drain system without an atmospheric break in the line. Exceptions are made for other systems, provided adequate documentation is provided by a processing authority. In crateless retorts with top steam entry, the drains are connected to a manifold header and used as vents after the cushion water has been drained from the retort. Operating procedures for venting these retorts or other retorts with unusual piping arrangements should be obtained from a processing authority.

Where a retort vent manifold connects several vent pipes from a single still retort, it shall be controlled by a gate, ball or other full-flow valve. The retort manifold shall be of such a size that the cross-sectional area of the pipe is larger than the total cross-sectional area of all connecting vents. The manifold shall not be connected directly to a closed drain system without an atmospheric break in the line.

A vent manifold header connecting vents or manifolds from several still retorts shall lead to the atmosphere. The vent manifold header shall not be controlled by a valve, and it shall be of such a size that the cross-sectional area is at least equal to the total cross-sectional area of all connecting retort manifold pipes or vents from all retorts venting simultaneously.

Bleeders

Bleeders are small openings in the retort used to remove air entering the retort with the steam and to provide circulation of steam in the retort. Bleeders shall be wide open and continuously emitting steam during the entire process, including the come-up time. A 1/16-inch or larger bleeder shall be used on thermometer wells and a 1/8-inch or larger bleeder shall be used on the retort.

All bleeder openings shall be arranged in such a way that the operator can observe that steam is escaping during the process. In retorts having a steam inlet at the top or above the level of the lowest container, a 1/8-inch or larger bleeder opening shall be installed in the bottom of the retort to completely remove condensate. All bleeders, including the condensate bleeder, shall be arranged so that the operator can observe that they function properly. They shall be checked with sufficient frequency to ensure that they are functioning or that condensate is adequately removed. Visual checks with recorded results are suggested at 15 minute intervals. USDA requires that intermittent condensate removal systems be equipped with an alarm system to serve as a continuous monitor of condensate bleeder functioning. The alarm system shall be tested for proper operation at the beginning of each shift, and the results recorded.

Horizontal still retorts shall have at least one bleeder located within approximately one foot of the outermost location of containers at each end along the top of the

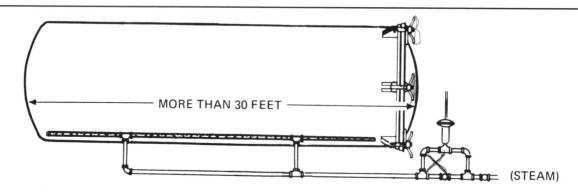

Figure 4—Steam spreader recommended for long retorts.

Table 1—Number of holes in steam spreaders for steam inlet pipe sizes.

Size Holes (inches)	1 inch pipe	1¼ inch pipe	1½ inch pipe	2 inch pipe	2½ inch pipe
3/16	47–62	81–108	111–148	183–224	260–346
1/4	27–36	45–60	62–84	102–137	147–196
3/8	—	21–28	28–37	45–60	66–88
1/2	—	11–15	15–20	26–36	36–48

retort and additional bleeders not more than eight feet apart along the top. Vertical still retorts shall have at least one bleeder at a location opposite steam entry. Bleeders may be installed at positions other than these, as long as there are temperature distribution data or other adequate documentation indicating that they accomplish adequate removal of air and circulation of steam within the retort. This information shall be maintained on file by the processor and must be made available to USDA and FDA personnel as required.

Mufflers

Mufflers are often used on bleeders and vents to reduce the noise created by escaping steam. If mufflers are used, evidence that they do not significantly impede the removal of air shall be kept on file. This evidence may be in the form of temperature distribution data or a letter from the manufacturer, the designer or a processing authority.

Air Supply

Retorts may need a compressed air supply for two reasons:

1. Most retorts are equipped with air-operated, automatic steam controllers.

2. The use of air for pressure cooling of containers in the retort is preferable to the use of steam due to the noncondensable properties of air. This attribute eliminates the possibility of accidentally condensing the steam in the retort, thus reducing the retort pressure and increasing the possibility of containers buckling.

Retorts using air for pressure cooling shall be equipped with a suitable valve (globe valve or the equivalent) on the air line to prevent air leakage into the retort during processing.

Water Supply

Most retorts are piped to supply water to cool the containers partially or completely after processing. The regulations require that retorts using water for cooling be equipped with a suitable valve (globe valve or equivalent) to prevent leakage of water into the retort during processing.

If cooling water enters the top of the retort, care should be taken to prevent condensing the steam remaining in the retort after the process is completed. This condensation can create a partial vacuum in the retort, causing buckling or straining of the can ends. A vacuum breaker may prevent this situation.

Construction of Crates, Cars and Dividers

Crates, cars, gondolas and trays for holding containers are made of strap iron, perforated sheet metal or other suitable materials. When perforated sheet metal is used for the bottoms, the perforations shall (USDA) be one-inch holes on two-inch centers or their equivalent. Other arrangements may be used if adequate temperature distribution is documented by a processing authority. This documentation shall be maintained on file by the processor and made available to FDA or USDA personnel as required. USDA requires that the establishment have documentation on file of venting adequacy whenever divider plates are used between layers of cans.

Processing Considerations

Venting Considerations

No single venting method applies to all still retorts, and, therefore, all venting schedules must be designed by a processing authority. To ensure adequate air removal during the venting period, time, temperature and other requirements specified in the venting schedule for a particular retort installation shall be met. Timing of the process shall not begin until the retort has been properly vented and the processing temperature is reached and maintained.

Before the retort cycle begins, there is a large amount of air in the retort. A horizontal retort fully loaded with cans still has 70 to 80 percent of its space occupied by air. A fully-loaded vertical retort has more than 60 percent of its space occupied by air. It is essential that the air be removed before a steam process begins. For any retort using steam as the heating medium, temperature distribution tests or other suitable tests are used to establish adequate venting schedules.

FDA and USDA regulations specify venting procedures for vertical and horizontal retorts with specific piping arrangements. For retorts with unusual piping, loading or operating procedures, temperature distribution tests must be conducted to establish adequate venting procedures. This information must remain or file and be made available to FDA or USDA as necessary.

Effect of Divider Plates on Venting

When divider plates are used between layers of cans, an increased venting schedule above that used for conventional loading systems may be required for adequate removal of air. Dividers may inhibit the flow of steam among the cans. The venting adequacy should be documented by the processing authority, kept on file and made available to FDA or USDA personnel as necessary.

Initial Temperature

The initial temperature of the coldest container in the retort at the time the sterilizing cycle begins must be determined. The details for determining initial temperature are discussed in Chapter 8.

Process Timing

The timing of a process shall not start until the scheduled venting procedure is completed and the required retort temperature is observed on the temperature indicating device (mercury-in-glass thermometer). Accurate timing devices shall be used to determine process and venting times. Additional information on timing devices can be found in Chapter 8.

Container Cooling

Containers may be partially or completely cooled in the retort. In pressure cooling, pressure is maintained in the retort while containers are cooled sufficiently to reduce their internal pressure to a safe level. Then the containers may be exposed to atmospheric pressure without danger of buckling the containers or straining the seals.

No specific times for pressure cooling can be listed, since they are affected by a number of factors such as product, container size, process temperature, cooling water temperature and the amount of water used. In some instances where low retort temperatures are used, the smaller can sizes may be processed without pressure cooling. As a general rule, cans of 401 diameter or larger require pressure cooling when processed at 240°F (116°C) or higher. Cans smaller than 401 diameter may require pressure cooling, especially when processed at higher than 250°F (121°C).

Containers are completely cooled when the temperature of their contents is reduced to approximately 100°F (38°C). A complete flooding of containers in the retort is suggested since spray-cooling may not produce uniform cooling.

Cooling Water Treatment

FDA requires that container cooling water be chlorinated or otherwise sanitized as necessary for cooling canals and for recirculated water supplies. In addition, there should be a measurable residual of the sanitizer employed at the water discharge point of the container cooler. USDA regulations contain the same basic requirements. However, for systems that reuse or recirculate water, USDA requires that systems be designed to prevent organic build up and be easily cleaned. In addition, information about the recirculation system shall be made available to a USDA representative for review. Also note that only approved chemicals may be added to cooling water in USDA-regulated establishments. For further information on cooling water sanitizers, see Chapter 5.

Record Requirements

All critical factors specified in the scheduled process shall be measured and recorded at intervals of sufficient frequency to ensure that the critical factors remain within the limits specified in the scheduled process. These intervals should not exceed 15 minutes. In addition to the generic record requirements outlined in Chapter 6, the written records for still retorts shall include: time steam on, time vent closed, temperature to which vented, time the process begins, mercury-in-glass thermometer/recorder readings, time steam off, and—as USDA requires and good manufacturing practices suggest—the actual process time.

Summary

1. Vents shall be installed and operated in such a way that air is removed from the retort before the timing of the process begins.

2. The steam inlet in each still retort shall be large enough to provide enough steam for proper operation of the retort.

3. Every retort shall be equipped with a mercury-in-glass thermometer.

4. Each retort shall have an accurate temperature recording device.

5. Divider plates should have perforations equivalent to at least one-inch holes on two-inch centers.

6. Steam spreaders are required in all horizontal retorts.

Chapter 10

STILL RETORTS—
PROCESSING WITH OVERPRESSURE

Introduction

The term "overpressure" refers to the pressure supplied to a retort in excess of that exerted by the heating medium at a given process temperature. In a steam retort, the pressure at 250°F (121.1°C) is 15 psig; (pounds per square inch gauge); any pressure supplied to the retort in excess of that 15 psig is referred to as overpressure.

The retort systems described in this chapter may operate at a pressure of 25-35 psig with a 250°F (121.1°C) retort temperature. Contrary to the operation of still retorts using pure steam, the retorts utilizing a processing medium of water or steam/air mixture to heat the containers can have air or additional steam introduced during the processing cycle to provide overpressure.

Overpressure during processing is required to maintain the integrity of containers that, due to package construction and/or type of closure, have a limited resistance to internal pressure (*Figure 1*). The internal pressure in these containers will be greater than the pressure of pure steam at the process temperature. Some examples of containers processed with overpressure are semirigid plastic containers with heat sealed lids or metal double seamed ends, flexible pouches, metal trays and glass jars.

Description of Retorts

A variety of retort types are designed to provide overpressure during still processing. Steam or air may be used as the source of overpressure in the retort. The processing medium used varies from water in which the containers are totally immersed, to water that cascades over the containers, to a mixture of water sprays and steam/air, or to a steam/air mixture.

Installation and Operation of Retorts

Common Considerations

Proper installation and operation of each retort is essential to achieve satisfactory processing results. The installation considerations for these retort systems vary depending on the type of heating medium—water (total immer-

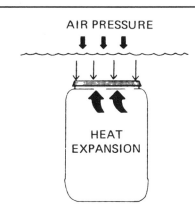

Figure 1—Overriding air pressure prevents container damage or loss of seal during the process.

sion, cascades or sprays) or a steam/air mixture—and the source of overpressure—air or steam. These retorts are equipped with various controls and alarms necessary to monitor the critical factors.

Instrumentation

At least one temperature indicating device (mercury-in-glass thermometer) and a temperature/time recording device are required for each retort. The general specifications for these instruments and information on pressure gauges, timing devices and mufflers may be found in Chapter 8. The placement of the bulbs or probes of temperature indicating devices is dependent on the processing medium and will be discussed in later sections.

Steam controller

Regardless of the processing medium, each retort shall be equipped with an automatic steam controller to maintain retort temperature. This may be a recording-controlling instrument when combined with a temperature/time recording device. The automatic steam controller must respond only to temperature.

Pressure control

Overriding pressure may be supplied in the form of air or steam. Each retort shall have an automatic pressure control unit to control the air or steam entering or leaving the retort to maintain the required overpressure.

USDA requires that each retort system shall be equipped with a pressure recording device, which may be combined with a pressure controller. In addition, each retort should be equipped with a pressure gauge that can be read easily by the operator. USDA also specifies that the required overpressure shall be maintained continuously during the come-up, thermal processing and cooling periods.

When compressed air is used to provide overpressure, a nonreturn (check) valve shall be provided in the air supply line to prevent moisture from entering the system.

Processing medium circulation

No matter which processing medium is used, a means shall be provided to circulate the heating medium in order to ensure uniform temperature distribution within the retort during processing. Adequate temperature distribution shall be documented by a processing authority through temperature distribution tests. The circulation system shall be equipped with a pilot light or signaling device to warn the operator when it is not functioning.

Construction of crates, dividers and racks

Crates, dividers and racks shall be designed to permit uniform circulation of the heating medium around all containers in the retort. The perforation pattern should equal or exceed approximately one-inch holes on two-inch centers or the equivalent. The crates, dividers and/or racks may be made of strap iron, perforated sheet metal or plastic.

Flexible and, where applicable, semirigid plastic containers usually require custom-rack design. USDA specifies that racks for these containers be designed so that the thickness of the filled containers does not exceed that specified in the scheduled process and so that the containers are kept from being displaced—overlapping or nesting on other containers during processing. Containers that become dislodged from the racks could interfere with the heating medium circulation patterns and result in underprocessing. When processing flexible or semirigid containers, care should be taken to prevent puncture or abrasions from worn or sharp metal edges.

Drain valves

Those retorts that require the maintenance of a specific water level shall be equipped with a non-clogging water-tight drain valve. It is recommended practice and an USDA requirement that screens be installed over all drain openings.

Cooling water supply

When these retort systems are used to process glass containers, the cooling water should be introduced so that it does not strike the containers directly in order to minimize breakage due to thermal shock. Cooling water may be added directly into the processing vessel or may be introduced into the suction side of the water circulating pump.

Total Immersion Water Retorts With Air Overpressure

Instrumentation

The bulbs or probes of the temperature indicating device (mercury-in-glass thermometer) shall be located beneath the water throughout the process. For vertical retorts, the bulbs may be installed in a thermometer pocket. The pocket should be designed to permit good circulation of water around the bulb. A hemispherical thermometer pocket is suggested; however, a rectangular pocket of at least 8x8x4 inches may be used. On horizontal retorts, the bulbs or probes shall be inserted directly into the retort shell. In both horizontal and vertical retorts, the bulbs or probes shall extend a minimum of two inches into the processing water without a separable well or sleeve.

The bulb or probe of the temperature/time recording device should be located adjacent to the temperature indicating device (mercury-in-glass thermometer), except in vertical retorts equipped with a combination recorder-controller. In vertical retorts, the recorder-controller bulb shall be located below the lowest crate support in such a position that steam does not strike it directly. In horizontal retorts, the bulb of the temperature recorder-controller shall be located between the water surface and the horizontal plane passing through the center of the retort so that there is no opportunity for direct steam contact with the bulb or probe of the recorder-controller.

Pressure control

Each retort shall have an automatic pressure control unit to introduce compressed air into the retort at the proper rate. There are several system designs to control air overpressure. One design involves introducing air at a constant rate and relieving the pressure when it rises above a certain pressure. Another design involves the introduction of air at the top of the retort above the water level. Automatic control valves control the air entering or leaving the retort to maintain the required overpressure.

Processing medium circulation

There are basically two ways in which adequate circulation can be provided in total immersion water retorts. In vertical retorts, compressed air may be used to promote water circulation and temperature distribution. For both vertical or horizontal retorts, water may be mechanically circulated within the retort to provide adequate temperature distribution (*Figure 2*).

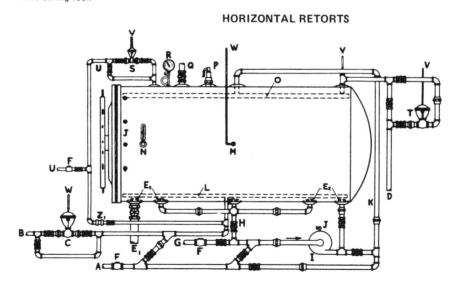

A Water line
B Steam line
C Temperature control
D Overflow line
E_1 Drain line
E_2 Screens
F Check Valves
G Line from hot water storage
H Suction line and manifold
I Circulating pump
J Petcocks
K Recirculating line
L Steam distributor
M Temperature controller bulb
N Thermometer
O Water spreader
P Safety valve
Q Vent valve for steam processing
R Pressure gauge
S Inlet air control
T Pressure control
U Air line
V To pressure control instrument
W To temperature control instrument
X Wing nuts—8 required
Y_1 Crate support
Y_2 Crate guides
Z_1 Constant flow orifice valve used during come-up
Z_2 Constant flow orifice valve used during cook

Figure 2—Basic piping and instrumentation found in total immersion water retorts used for pressure processing with air overpressure.

When air is used to promote circulation, the air shall be introduced into the steam line at a point between the retort and the steam control valve at the bottom of the retort. Air moves into the retort with the steam and usually passes through a spreader at the bottom of the retort. The air provides agitation of the heated water as it rises upward through the crates. Two spreader designs are illustrated in *Figure 3*. It is recommended that crate-centering guides be used to provide a one and one-half inch clearance between the side wall of the crate and the retort shell. This clearance allows space for the water to move downward along the retort wall completing the circulation pattern. Bottom crate supports are required in vertical retorts. Baffle plates are not permitted in the bottom of the retort.

In addition to promoting circulation of the water, air introduced into the steam line also serves to reduce undue vibration (steam knock or hammer) resulting when steam is introduced into cold water. During the come-up-time a greater volume of air is needed to reduce vibration. After the come-up-time is completed, the volume of air may be reduced to that necessary to maintain adequate temperature distribution. Normally, the air supply line is designed to allow air to flow through two orifices: one for the come-up-time air and a smaller one for air during processing.

The air introduced into the steam line will also serve to maintain overpressure. Most vertical retorts are equipped to supply additional air to the retort headspace, since the demand for overpressure may be greater than that supplied through the steam line, especially during the transition from heating to cooling.

In many retorts designed for water immersion processing—such as horizontal retorts—the use of air alone does not ensure adequate temperature distribution. In these retorts, the water is circulated with a pump. The water is drawn from the bottom of the retort through a suction manifold and discharged through a spreader that extends the length of a horizontal retort or through a spreader around the top circumference of a vertical retort. The water spreader holes shall be uniformly distributed along the spreader, and the total cross-sectional area of the holes should not be greater than the cross-sectional area of the outlet of the pump. The retort water suction outlets shall be protected with screens to prevent debris from entering the recirculation system. The pump shall be equipped with a pilot light or signaling device to warn the operator when it is not running. USDA permits the use of a flow-meter alarm system as an alternative for ensuring proper water circulation.

Water level indicator

A means shall be provided to determine the water level in the retort during operation. This requirement may be met by a sight glass or low-water-level alarm (*Figure 4*). Water shall cover all the containers during the entire come-up-time and processing period (minimum recommended depth is six inches above top layer of containers, see *Figure 4*). Water should also cover the top layer of containers during the cooling period.

Cooling water supply

In still vertical retorts, the cooling water should be introduced into the processing water approximately four inches above the top layers of containers. A water spreader may be used for this purpose. Once the containers reach an appropriate temperature, cooling water may be introduced into the bottom of the retort. In retorts using recirculated water as the heating medium, the cooling water should be introduced into the suction side of the pump.

Total Immersion Water Retorts Using Steam for Overpressure

Retorts using total immersion water as the heating medium with steam as a source of overpressure have some unique instrumentation and operating characteristics. A pump is used to circulate the water that is heated by steam in an external heat exchanger. Steam also is introduced at

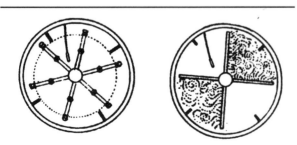

Figure 3—Top view of two types of steam spreaders used in vertical retorts for pressure processing in water.

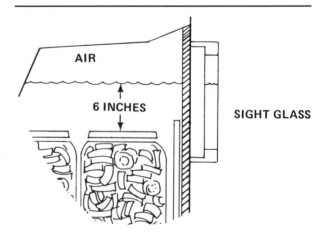

Figure 4—Sight glass for visual check of adequate water level.

the top of the retort, above the water level, to provide the overpressure. Because steam is used both to heat the process water and to provide the source of overpressure, two separate independent steam controllers are needed. The retort may be designed to heat the process water to processing temperature or higher in a separate chamber and transfer the water to the processing vessel at the start of the process.

The location of bulbs or probes of the required temperature indicating device and temperature/time recording device shall meet the same requirements as for total water immersion horizontal retorts.

FDA does not have specific regulations for some of these retort systems but addresses them under the heading of "Other Systems." Many of these systems are designed to provide container agitation, and some specific requirements may be found in these sections of the regulations. The retorts shall be operated in such a manner that commercial sterility is achieved and the critical factors are monitored and recorded.

Steam/Air Retorts

Some retort systems are designed to use a steam/air mixture as the heating medium. The air is the source of overpressure. A fan is located in the back or front of the retort to maintain a uniform mixture of the steam and air and to circulate the mixture among the containers. These retorts shall be operated in such a manner that commercial sterility is achieved and the critical factors are monitored and recorded.

FDA regulations do not directly address the operation of steam/air retorts but instead deal with these systems under the heading "Other Systems." USDA regulations were written more recently and do have some specific requirements. USDA regulations specify that the agency be notified immediately if steam/air retort systems are used.

Instrumentation

The USDA requires that the bulb or probe of the temperature indicating device (mercury-in-glass thermometer) and the bulb of the temperature recorder-controller be inserted directly into the retort shell. The bulbs shall be located so that steam does not strike them directly. The specific location of this instrumentation may vary from system to system.

Pressure control

USDA requires that the retort be equipped with a recording pressure controller to control the air inlet and steam/air mixture outlet. For these systems, pressure must be controlled and recorded. Pressure and temperature are used to ensure that the steam/air ratio meets the scheduled process.

Processing medium circulation

The processing medium is circulated with a fan. The fan shall be equipped with a pilot light or other signaling device to warn the operator when it is not functioning. The efficiency of the circulation system shall be documented by temperature distribution data or other documentation from a processing authority. This data should be maintained in a file by the establishment and made available for inspection by the appropriate regulatory agency.

Cascading Water or Spray Retorts

Some water processing retorts are designed to cascade water over—or to spray water on—the containers during processing. One system uses a water distribution system located at the top of the retort to allow the heating or cooling water to cascade (rain down) over the containers. Air is the source of overpressure. The water is heated externally by a heat exchanger and is pumped through the system. The bulbs of the mercury-in-glass thermometer should be located in the cold zone of the retort, as indicated by temperature distribution studies.

Another system pumps water from the bottom of the retort through water spray nozzles—located at the top and mid-section of the vessel—to heat or cool the containers. The water is heated internally by steam spreaders. A steam/air mixture serves as the source of overpressure. Alternate methods of heating medium circulation may be used provided that adequate temperature distribution data or other documentation is available. These systems shall be operated in such a manner that commercial sterility is achieved, and the critical factors are monitored and recorded.

FDA does not have specific regulations for these types of retort systems, but addresses them under the category of "Other Systems." USDA requires that the water level in the retort be maintained within the range specified by the retort manufacturer or processing authority during the entire come-up, thermal process and cooling periods. The retort operator shall check and record the water level if required by the processing authority. The USDA regulations specify that the agency be notified immediately if these types of retort systems are used.

The location of the temperature indicating device and the recorder-controller bulb(s) may vary depending on the type of system.

Processing Considerations

Overpressure

Overpressure is necessary to maintain container integrity for certain containers and to permit adequate processing. Each different container type may require a different amount of overpressure at different times in the processing and cooling cycles. Too much overpressure initially could panel or permanently distort plastic containers. Insufficient overpressure during processing or the cooling period could cause the flexible containers to swell, which in turn could damage the container seals, affect the heating characteristics of the product and/or interfere with water circulation patterns in the retort. An appropriate pressure profile for a particular container should be recommended by the container supplier or processing authority.

In addition, factors such as product fill temperature, container headspace, container vacuum, entrapped air within the product and processing temperature may influence the overpressure required. These factors will impact the development of internal container pressure and may need to be controlled to adequately process a particular type of container.

Water Level

Retorts that require the maintenance of a specific water level must be monitored and recorded periodically to ensure that the appropriate water level is maintained. In retort systems where the containers must be completely covered by the processing water, if the level of the processing water falls below the top layer of containers, the operator should note the minimum water level. Those containers that were exposed to the atmosphere above the water shall be segregated when the crates are unloaded. This situation is always considered a processing deviation, and segregated containers should be handled accordingly. Water should not be added to the retort unless the practice is recommended by a processing authority.

Initial Temperature

The initial temperature of the coldest container in the retort at the time the sterilizing cycle begins shall be determined. When water is used as a processing medium, the initial temperature used for process selection is the initial temperature of the product or the temperature of the water at the start of the process—whichever is lower.

The details for determining initial temperature are discussed in Chapter 8.

Process Timing

The timing of a process shall not start until the scheduled retort temperature is observed on the temperature indicating device (mercury-in-glass thermometer) and the required retort operating procedures have been completed. Accurate timing devices shall be used in recording process time information. Additional information on timing devices is located in Chapter 8.

Record Requirements

All critical factors specified in the scheduled process shall be measured and recorded at intervals of sufficient frequency to ensure that the critical factors remain within the limits of the scheduled process. These measurements should not exceed 15 minutes. In addition to the generic record requirements outlined in Chapter 6, the written records for retorts using overpressure shall include time steam on, time process begins, overriding pressure and water circulation rate or water level, if they are critical factors.

Summary

1. Processing with overpressure is necessary for flexible, semirigid or rigid containers when these containers or their seals would be damaged in simple steam retorts.

2. The proper pressure shall be controlled by an automatic pressure control unit.

3. The temperature in the retort is controlled independently of the pressure.

4. A means shall be provided to ensure adequate temperature distribution within the retort during processing.

5. When processing in a water immersion system, there shall be a means of determining the water level during operation.

Chapter 11

HYDROSTATIC RETORTS—
CONTINUOUS CONTAINER HANDLING

Introduction

The hydrostatic retort operates at a constant process temperature and has a continuous container-conveyor that transports containers through the retort (*Figure 1*). Thus, there is a constant flow of containers.

Hydrostatic retorts usually operate with steam as the processing medium and with minimal container agitation during processing. However, some hydrostatic retorts use cascading water with overpressure as the processing medium, and others provide container agitation during processing.

The thermal process in hydrostatic retorts occurs in a processing chamber that is maintained at a constant elevated temperature. It is necessary that the processing chamber be under pressure to achieve a process temperature above the boiling point of water. There are no doors or valves separating the processing chamber from the atmosphere; the pressure within the chamber is counterbalanced by the hydrostatic pressure of water. This fact is the basis for the name of these retorts. The container-conveyor enters and exits the processing chamber through water columns of considerable height. It is these water columns that provide the hydrostatic pressure to counterbalance the pressure in the processing chamber.

The higher the retort temperature, the greater the processing pressure in the chamber. A water column of considerable height is required to counterbalance this pressure. For example, the water column height in the feed and discharge legs must be 37 feet above the steam water interface to provide 15 psig pressure in a processing chamber operated at 250°F (121°C). Hydrostatic retorts are limited to a maximum process temperature by the maximum height of the water legs.

Description of System

Container-Conveyor

The container-conveyor is comprised of carriers (flights) that hold the containers (*Figure 2*). The carriers used in hydrostatic retorts permit limited flexibility in the container sizes that may be processed. As an example, for cylindrical cans the carriers may permit a range of container diameters as follows:

- 211 to 303 diameter
- 300 to 404 diameter
- 404 to 603 diameter

Since cylindrical containers are carried end-to-end, there is no limitation regarding container length. The carriers may be custom-made to accommodate containers other than cans, i.e., glass jars, plastic trays and retort pouches.

Hydrostatic retorts may utilize multiple container-conveyors to handle a wider range of container sizes and types at the same time (*Figure 1*). Each conveyor is driven independently so the process time may be set as required by the processing authority for each container size or type.

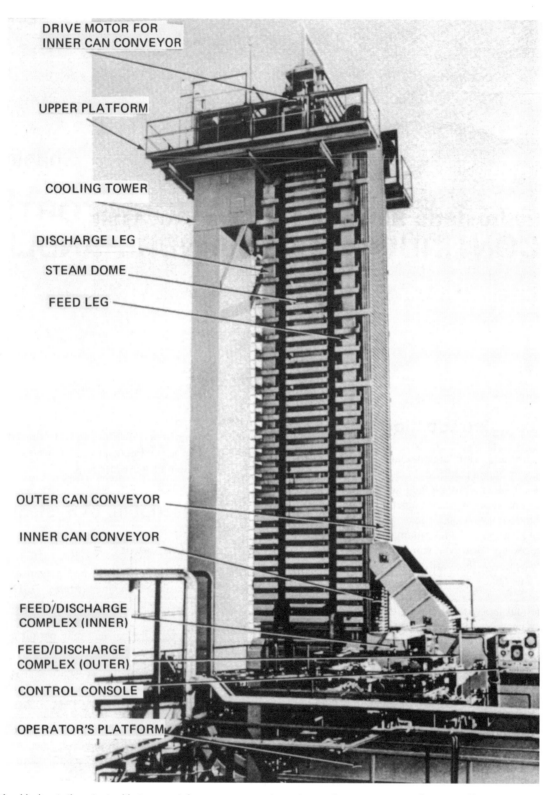

DRIVE MOTOR FOR INNER CAN CONVEYOR

UPPER PLATFORM

COOLING TOWER

DISCHARGE LEG

STEAM DOME

FEED LEG

OUTER CAN CONVEYOR

INNER CAN CONVEYOR

FEED/DISCHARGE COMPLEX (INNER)

FEED/DISCHARGE COMPLEX (OUTER)

CONTROL CONSOLE

OPERATOR'S PLATFORM

Figure 1—Hydrostatic retort with two container-conveyors, two steam dome passes and one cooling tower pass.

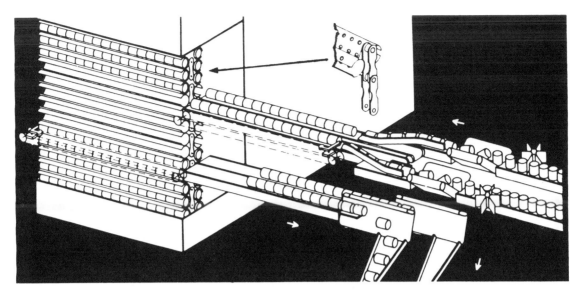

Figure 2—Formation of a stick of cans at a feed station.

Feed and Discharge Stations

A variety of mechanisms are used to load and unload containers from the conveyor. *Figure 2* illustrates the feed and discharge stations of a double-sided, single container-conveyor retort. At the feed station, the containers are formed into a row (stick). The formed stick is fed into a carrier (flight) that holds the containers on the container-conveyor during their trip through the retort. Prior to reaching the feed station, the carrier is opened and the processed, cooled containers are discharged to a conveyor leading to the warehouse.

In-Feed Section

The in-feed section of the container-conveyor extends from the feed station to the point of entry into the first water column. This section is usually covered to protect the containers and minimize the temperature loss before they enter the water.

Feed or Inlet Leg

The feed leg consists of the water filled section of the retort through which containers pass before entering the processing chamber. Usually there is only one water column functioning as a feed leg. However, for applications where overpressure in the processing chamber is required, multiple feed legs may be used.

The water temperature in the feed leg can be independently controlled and may range from ambient to boiling. Steam injection near the base of the feed leg is used to achieve and maintain a desired leg temperature.

Processing Chamber

After passing through the water of the feed leg, the containers enter the processing chamber(s) where they are subjected to the processing medium at the required retort temperature. Temperature within the processing chamber is controlled independently of the water legs. The chamber in steam retorts is referred to as the "steam dome." Hydrostatic retorts using cascading water as the processing medium will have a means of providing and maintaining an overpressure, if necessary.

Discharge or Exit Leg

The containers leave the processing chamber and return to atmospheric pressure through the water of the discharge leg. Like the feed leg, there is usually only one water column but some hydrostatic retorts may have multiple discharge legs.

Water temperature in the discharge leg can be independently controlled. Steam injection at the base of the leg is used to achieve and maintain a desired leg temperature. However, during operation, the hot containers and container-conveyor give up their heat to the discharge leg water, resulting in little or no use of steam to maintain discharge leg temperature.

To recover this heat and conserve energy, many hydrostatic retorts are equipped with a cross-circulation system that pumps hot water from the base of the discharge leg to the base of the feed leg. To complete the circulation, a second pump returns the coolest water from the top of the feed leg to the top of the discharge leg. This system stabilizes the temperatures in the legs (*Figure 3*).

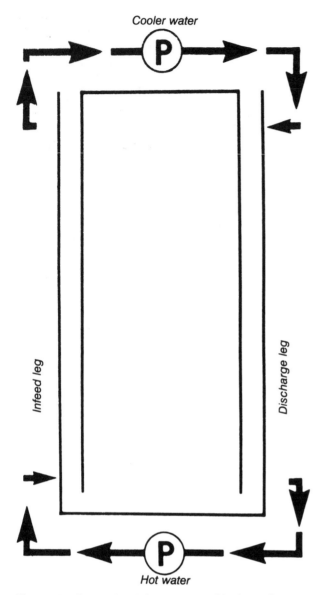

Cooler water

P

Infeed leg

Discharge leg

P

Hot water

Figure 3—Cross-circulation system of hydrostatic retort (P = pump).

When it is desirable to cool the containers as soon as possible after the process, water is pumped from the base of the discharge leg through a heat exchanger to cool the water and is returned to the top of the discharge leg. No cross circulation between the legs is used in this system.

Container Cooling

Container cooling results from water cascading over or being sprayed onto the container-conveyor as it passes through the cooling section. Generally, cooling sections are at atmospheric pressure.

Installation and Operation of Retorts

Instrumentation

At least one temperature indicating device (MIG thermometer) and one temperature/time recording device are required on each processing chamber. The general specifications for these instruments, as well as information on pressure gauges and mufflers, are outlined in Chapter 8.

A temperature indicating device (mercury-in-glass thermometer) shall be installed in the processing chamber near the steam/water interface. A device located approximately three inches above the maximum water level should detect the minimum temperatures in the processing chamber. In addition, the bulb of a temperature/time recorder shall be installed in the processing chamber. The bulb is usually installed adjacent to the temperature indicating device (*Figure 4*).

When the scheduled process specifies maintenance of particular temperatures in the water legs, a temperature indicating device (MIG thermometer) shall be located in each water leg. FDA specifies that a mercury-in-glass thermometer be located at the base of the water leg near the probe of the temperature/time recording instrument. USDA allows alternate locations as long as an accurate measure of water temperature is provided.

Temperature/time recorder probes shall be installed in the water legs if the scheduled process includes maintenance of specific water leg temperatures. A temperature/time recorder probe may be located near the bottom of the water leg and another near the top of the water leg (*Figure 4*).

Steam Controller

Each hydrostatic retort shall be equipped with an automatic steam controller to maintain the process chamber temperature. This may be a recording-controlling instrument when combined with a temperature/time recording device.

Preparation for Processing

Before the start of container processing, the retort shall be operated in accordance with procedures recommended by the retort manufacturer or a processing authority in order to achieve proper temperature distribution in the processing chamber(s). The operating procedures shall be documented by temperature distribution data or other documentation from the manufacturer or processing authority. For steam retorts, the steam dome shall be vented to ensure the removal of air prior to processing.

Bleeders

For steam retorts, a bleeder opening 1/4-inch or larger shall be located in the processing chamber(s) opposite the point of steam entry. Bleeders shall be wide open and shall emit steam continuously during the entire process, including the come-up time. All bleeders shall be arranged in such a way that the operator can observe that they are functioning properly.

Water Level Control

A constant exposure of containers to the processing medium depends on a constant container-conveyor speed and a fixed container-conveyor path in the processing chamber(s). The container-conveyor path is defined by the water level in the base of the processing chamber. This water level will depend on the pressure in the processing chamber and the height of the water legs. This level is called the steam-water interface in steam retorts.

The maximum water level in the base of the processing chamber is established by the manufacturer. Water levels below the maximum provide additional process time, but water levels above maximum shorten the process time. A sight glass should be installed to indicate the water level at the base of the processing chamber, and the maximum level should be clearly marked on the sight glass.

A major cause of water level fluctuation is interruption in the feeding and discharging of containers into the water. As containers are fed into a water leg, they displace water and cause the water level to rise. Conversely, as containers are discharged, they cause the level to fall. A water level control system is usually employed to maintain a constant water height in the water legs and, thus, control the water level in the base of the processing chamber.

Process Timing

Each container-conveyor is independently driven by a variable speed motor. Changing the container-conveyor speed will change the process time. The proper container-conveyor chain speed is determined in the following manner:

1. Calculate the desired carriers-per-minute rate by dividing the desired process time into the number of carriers in the processing chamber.

$$\frac{\text{Number of carriers in processing chamber}}{\text{Process time in minutes}}$$
$$= \text{Carriers-per-minute}$$

2. Calculate the actual carriers-per-minute rate by timing 50 carriers with a stop watch. Divide this time in seconds into 3,000 to get actual carriers-per-minute.

$$\frac{3,000}{\text{Seconds for 50 carriers}} = \text{Carriers-per-minute}$$

3. Adjust speed until actual carriers-per-minute equals the desired carriers-per-minute.

Since process time is a function of container-conveyor speed, the speed setting should be determined with care.

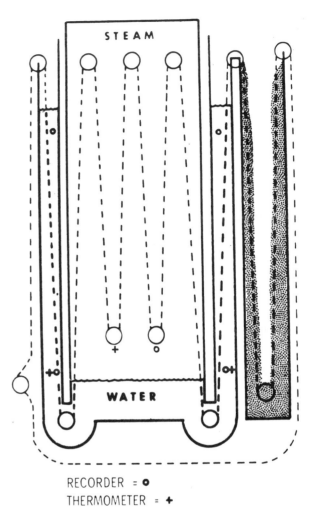

RECORDER = o

THERMOMETER = +

Figure 4—Placement of temperature indicating devices and recorders on a hydrostatic retort.

The container-conveyor speed shall be determined and recorded at the start of processing. USDA and FDA require that the speed be checked and recorded, and it is recommended that the intervals not exceed four hours. The USDA allows the use of continuous recording devices, but the accuracy of the devices shall be manually checked with an accurate stop watch at least once per shift. A means of preventing unauthorized container-conveyor speed changes shall be provided, such as a notice from management or a lock.

Processing Considerations

Feed and Discharge Legs

Because the temperatures within the feed and discharge legs may be independently controlled, the legs may be included as part of the scheduled process. This situation may permit a reduction in the time containers are present in the processing chamber. A feed leg—maintained at an elevated temperature—may heat containers before they enter the processing chamber, and a heated discharge leg may slow the initial cooling of containers. Both situations could result in process time reductions. If either or both of the water legs are included in the scheduled process, the temperatures in the leg(s) must be maintained above that specified in the scheduled process.

Water Level Fluctuation

Should the water level rise above the maximum level at the base of the steam dome, the process time will be shortened. If the water level rises high enough, it will contact the temperature indicating device (mercury-in-glass thermometer) and/or the temperature/time recorder, and they may indicate a temperature drop. If the water continues to rise, it could contact those containers in the bottom loops of the container-conveyor, which may result in underprocessing. An automatic device should be installed to stop the container-conveyor should the water rise above the maximum level.

If the water did not contact the containers in the bottom loops of the container-conveyor, the proper water level may be re-established and the container-conveyor restarted. Those containers that are inside the processing chamber at the time of the container-conveyor stoppage will be exposed to the processing medium for the proper time. If the water contacts the containers in the bottom loops of the container-conveyor, the containers affected shall be segregated and held for evaluation by a processing authority. Each carrier is numbered and a location diagram should be provided to the operator so that the affected containers can be located when discharged.

Initial Temperature

For continuous container handling systems the initial temperature should be measured with sufficient frequency to ensure that the initial temperature of all the containers being processed does not drop below that specified in the scheduled process. If the feed leg is included in the scheduled process, the initial temperature should be measured prior to entry into the leg. If the feed leg is not part of the scheduled process, its temperature should be controlled above the minimum initial temperature of the scheduled process. During line stoppages, the initial temperature should be checked before the line is started.

Record Requirements

All critical factors specified in the scheduled process shall be measured and recorded at intervals of sufficient frequency to ensure that the critical factors remain within the limits specified in the scheduled process. In addition to the generic record requirements outlined in Chapter 6, the written records for hydrostatic retorts shall include the speed of the container chain, the time when containers are in the retort and the temperatures in the water legs, if specified in the scheduled process.

Summary

1. Hydrostatic retorts use water columns to counterbalance the pressure in the steam dome. The water columns allow containers to be moved through the system continuously.

2. Each hydrostatic retort is equipped with at least one mercury-in-glass thermometer, temperature/time recorder and temperature controller. The probes for these devices are located in the steam dome, just above the steam water interface.

3. The water level in the base of the steam dome must be controlled below a maximum level. Water shall not be allowed to contact the containers in the steam dome.

4. For hydrostatic retorts, the process time is dependent on the length of the container chain path in the steam dome and the speed of the conveyor chain.

Chapter 12

AGITATING RETORTS—
CONTINUOUS CONTAINER HANDLING

Introduction

Agitating or rotary retorts with continuous container handling provide intermittent product agitation. This retort system is constructed of at least two cylindrical shells (58 inch diameter) in which processing and cooling take place. The design of the retort is dependent upon several factors, including product, container type and process conditions. The shells can be used for pressure processing in steam, preheating in steam at atmospheric pressure, or cooling with or without pressure. The retort shells can be arranged in various configurations as illustrated in *Figure 1*.

Description of the Retort

The container conveyance system is designed to take sealed containers continuously from the sealing machine.

Inside each shell is a rotating reel with steps to hold the containers. Permanently attached to the inside surface of the shell is a spiral T. The turning of the reel and the leading edge of the spiral T move the containers through the length of the shell (*Figure 2*).

As they advance through a processing shell, containers are subjected to pressurized steam at a constant temperature. When containers reach the end of the processing shell, they are transferred to a cooling shell. Pressurized cooling may be required to prevent container buckling.

Since the shells may be pressurized, containers enter and exit through self-sealing inlet (*Figure 3*) and discharge valves. When multiple pressure shells are used, a transfer valve (*Figure 4*) conveys containers from one shell to another.

This type of retort offers several advantages over still retorts. One advantage is the reduced process time due to intermittent agitation. The agitation occurs when the containers roll on the bottom of a shell. This agitation

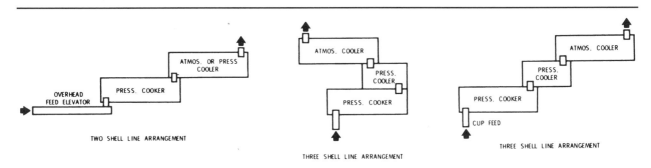

Figure 1—Some typical line and shell arrangements of continuous agitating retorts.

Figure 2—Cut-away view of continuous rotary retort and cooler.

may result in product movement within the container that increases the rate of heat penetration. The product agitation also allows the use of high processing temperatures (up to 280°F (137.8°C)). In some instances, product uniformity and quality are improved. Another advantage is the possibility of reduced production cost through savings in labor and steam.

Some of the possible disadvantages associated with this retort include a large initial investment and additional critical factors to monitor and control. The retorts will accommodate only a limited range of container sizes due to the physical restrictions imposed by the reel steps, spacing of the spiral T, and valve construction.

Installation and Operation of Retorts

Proper installation and operation of each agitating retort with continuous container handling is essential to achieve satisfactory processing results. Some retort systems have more than one pressurized processing shell; each processing shell must be equipped with the required instrumentation and controls. Various controls and alarms that are important for monitoring critical factors can be found on this type of retort system. The general specifications for these instruments and information on pressure gauges and mufflers are outlined in Chapter 8.

Instrumentation

At least one temperature indicating device (mercury-in-glass thermometer) and one temperature/time recording device are required on each processing shell. The bulb or probe of each temperature indicating device (mercury-in-glass thermometer) and each temperature/time recording device shall be installed within the processing shell(s) or in an external well(s) attached to the processing shell(s). External well(s) shall be connected to the processing shell(s) through at least a 3/4-inch diameter opening. External well(s) shall have a 1/16-inch or larger bleeder opening located to provide a constant flow of

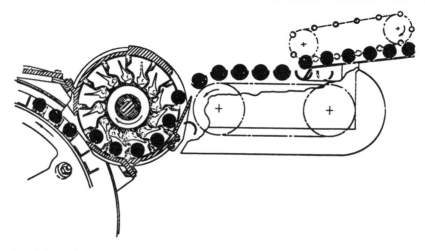

Figure 3—Typical rotary inlet valve.

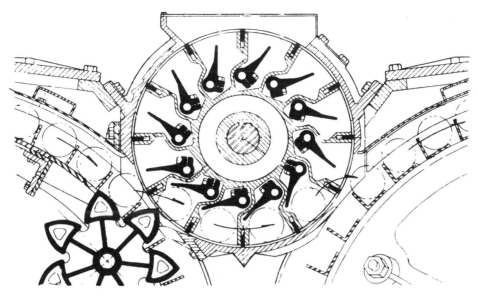

Figure 4—Transfer valve.

steam past the length of the bulbs or probes. The external well bleeder shall emit steam continuously during the entire processing period.

Steam Controller

Each processing shell shall be equipped with an automatic steam controller to maintain the process temperature. This may be a recording-controlling instrument when combined with a temperature/time recording device.

Steam Inlet

Steam entry is accomplished through a manifold with multiple feeder lines that connect to a trough located at the bottom of the shell and running its length. The steam inlet shall be large enough to provide steam for proper operation.

Venting

Vents shall be located in that portion of the processing shell(s) opposite the steam inlet. Usually there are two, 2-inch vents located on the top portion of each processing shell.

The air in each processing shell shall be removed before container processing is started. The venting procedure, which includes time and temperature requirements, shall be documented by temperature distribution data or other documentation from the manufacturer or a processing authority. The retort is usually vented once at the beginning of the day and is not shut down until production is completed.

Bleeders

Bleeders shall be wide open during the entire processing operation, including the come-up-time. All bleeders shall be arranged in such a way that the operator can observe that they are functioning properly. Continuous agitating retorts shall have bleeders which are 1/8-inch or larger installed along the top of each processing shell within approximately one foot of the outermost location of containers at each end of the shell and additional bleeders installed not more than eight feet apart along the top of each shell. Bleeders may be installed at alternate locations as long as there is evidence, such as temperature distribution data, that documents the suitability of these locations.

Condensate Removal

It is required that provisions be made for removal of condensate from the processing shell(s) during the come-up-time and processing time. Failure to remove condensate could allow water to build-up in the bottom of the processing shell and interfere with container rotation. This situation could reduce product agitation and result in underprocessed product.

At the time steam is turned on, the drain shall be open for a sufficient time to remove condensate from the processing shell(s). In addition, a condensate bleeder or automatic condensate removal system shall be installed in the bottom of the processing shell(s) to provide for the continuous removal of condensate during processing.

If a condensate bleeder is used, it shall be arranged to enable the operator to observe it is functioning properly. This observation shall be made and recorded with sufficient frequency (generally, 15 minute intervals) to ensure adequate condensate removal. Automatic systems may be used to provide intermittent condensate removal, provided they are equipped with an automatic alarm system that serves as a continuous monitor that the condensate bleeder is functioning. Automatic alarm systems should be tested to see that they are operating properly at the beginning of each shift and the results recorded. Alarm testing is required by USDA regulations.

Rotational Speed and Process Timing

After the proper come-up-time procedures have been followed and the retort has been brought up to the required processing temperature, the rotational speed of the reel shall be set before containers are introduced. The reel speed is important for two reasons: (1) it determines the residence or process time for the containers; (2) it may affect the agitation of the product, which in turn affects the product heating rate.

The reel speed is adjusted to provide a specific process time. These calculations involve the total container capacity of the processing shells and the number of steps in one turn of the reel (commonly referred to as "reel steps"). The container capacity of each processing shell is normally stamped on the end of the shell's reel shaft. The number of reel steps will depend on the can size and cooker design. *Table 1* may be used as a guide. However, be aware that reels are sometimes altered and the number of steps may be different.

A procedure for checking process time is as follows:

To calculate the desired time for 10 reel revolutions:

Seconds for 10 reel revolutions

$$= \frac{(10 \text{ revs}) \times (60 \text{ sec}) \times \text{reel steps} \times \text{cook time in minutes}}{\text{total container capacity of processing shells}}$$

Example: $\frac{(10 \text{ revs}) \times (60 \text{ sec/min}) \times (36 \text{ cans/rev}) \times (12 \text{ min})}{(2,380 \text{ cans})} =$

108.91 seconds for 10 revolutions

The retort speed is adjusted to provide the correct time on a stop watch, thus providing the correct process time.

When it is desirable to know the cans per minute (CPM) or the reel revolutions per minute (RPM) associated with a process time, the following procedures can be used:

$$\text{CPM} = \frac{\text{total container capacity of processing shells}}{\text{cook time in minutes}}$$

Example: $\frac{2,380 \text{ cans}}{12 \text{ min}} = 198.3 \text{ CPM}$

$$\text{RPM} = \frac{\text{total container capacity of processing shells}}{\text{reel steps} \times \text{cook time in minutes}}$$

Example: $\frac{(2,380 \text{ cans})}{(36 \text{ cans/rev}) \times (12 \text{ min})} = 5.5 \text{ RPM}$

It is important to note that a reel speed faster than that calculated to provide the required process time will result in a short process that may result in an underprocessed product.

Table 1—Number of reel steps for given can sizes.

Can Size	Steps Per Turn of Reel
211	56
300–303	47
307–401	42
404	36
603	24

In addition to process timing, it is important that the reel speed be adjusted properly since it may affect the amount of agitation the product receives. Too slow a speed may provide less agitation and may result in underprocessing. To allow operating flexibility, processes are usually established with data collected at reel speeds that are slower than normally encountered during production. These minimum reel speeds may become critical factors associated with the process.

The reel speed shall be adjusted as specified in the scheduled process. It shall be monitored, recorded and adjusted as necessary: at start up, any time a speed change is made, and at intervals of sufficient frequency (USDA requires four hours or less, FDA suggests four hours or less) to ensure that the reel speed remains as specified in the scheduled process. Alternatively, a recording tachometer may be used to provide a continuous record of reel speed. USDA requires that the accuracy of a recording tachometer be determined and recorded at least once per shift by checking the reel speed with an accurate stopwatch. A means of preventing unauthorized speed changes shall be provided, such as a lock or a notice from management.

Pressure Cooling

Depending on container design and process temperature, pressure cooling may be needed to prevent distortion of the containers when they leave the processing shell. To prevent this problem, the containers are discharged through a transfer valve into a pressure cooling shell or a micro-cool valve where the pressure is maintained by compressed air as the containers move through cooling water. It is recommended that the pressure in the cooler shell or micro-cool valve be maintained at slightly less than the steam pressure in the processing shell, preventing the possibility of air being forced into the processing shell.

After pressure cooling, containers may be transferred to an atmospheric cooler for further cooling. It is recommended that the cooling water be chlorinated or otherwise sanitized.

Processing Considerations

Continuous agitating retorts use the principle of intermittent agitation to provide more rapid product heating and cooling. The container rotation can be divided into three phases consisting of fixed reel, sliding rotation and free rotation (*Figure 5*). The fixed reel and sliding rotation do not provide significant product agitation. During the

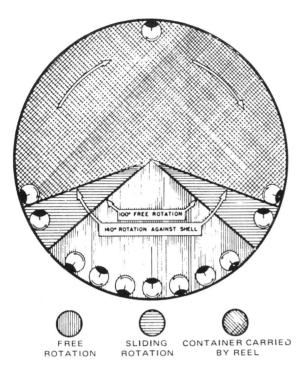

FREE ROTATION

SLIDING ROTATION

CONTAINER CARRIED BY REEL

Figure 5—Diagram showing container rotation phases.

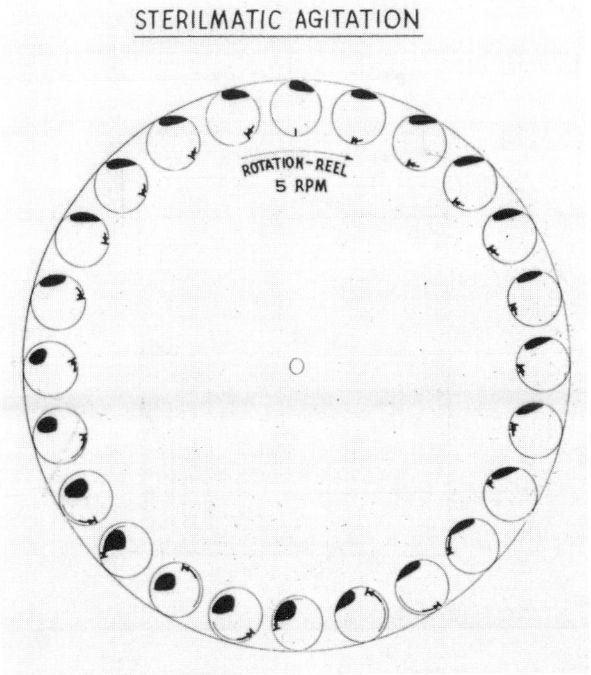

ROTATION~REEL
5 RPM

Figure 6—Product agitation produced by the headspace bubble during rotation.

free rotation phase, the containers roll freely along the inside bottom wall of the shell. The main product agitation occurs during this phase.

Intermittent agitation will affect the rate of heating and cooling only if the product and headspace bubble are able to move within the container during free rotation (*Figure 6*). For example, solid packed items, such as pumpkin, would not benefit from this type of agitation. Brine-packed items (such as peas, green beans and whole kernel corn), thin or slightly thickened sauces (such as cream-style corn, sauces or soups) may have faster heating or cooling rates resulting from this type of agitation. The improved heating rates may allow the use of shorter processes than in still retorting.

Intermittent agitation depends upon several factors—headspace, consistency, reel speed and fill-in weight—to effectively improve heating and cooling rates. If these conditions are critical to the process and are not met, the agitation will be reduced or eliminated, and underprocessing may occur.

Headspace

Headspace is the area inside a container that is void of product. It is measured by one of two methods depending on the character of the product. The net headspace—the space between the inside surface of the lid and the surface of the product—may be determined using net weight measurements. This method may be used only for homogeneous liquid products. Records of the correlation between net weight and net headspace must be maintained.

For products that are not homogeneous liquids, headspace is normally measured as gross headspace (*Figure 7*). Gross headspace is the vertical distance between the level of the product and the top edge of the container. It is measured before or after the filled container is sealed. A straight edge is placed over the top edges of an open container and the distance is measured from the bottom of the straight edge to the top of the product surface. Various instruments are available for the measurement of gross headspace.

Headspace is often a critical factor and must remain within the limits set in the scheduled process.

Consistency

Consistency or viscosity are objective measurements of the thickness of the product. Various instruments are available for making these measurements. If a product is thicker than that specified in the scheduled process, the product may heat slower; therefore, the scheduled process may no longer be adequate. Consistency or viscosity measurements shall be made on product taken from the location specified in the scheduled process.

Initial Temperature

Before containers are introduced into the processing shell and throughout the operation, one or more containers

97

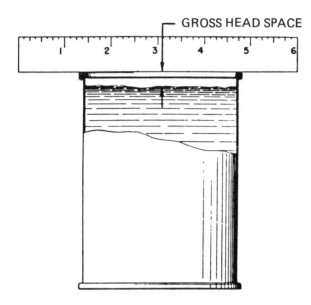

GROSS HEAD SPACE

Figure 7—Method of measuring gross headspace.

should be removed from the line just prior to the inlet valve of the first processing shell. The initial temperature is determined on one of these containers. The initial temperature should be measured with sufficient frequency to ensure that the initial temperature of all the containers being processed does not drop below that specified in the scheduled process. During a line stoppage, the initial temperature should be checked before the line is restarted. The procedure for determining initial temperatures was discussed in Chapter 8.

Handling Process Deviations

Retort jam or breakdown

When a retort jams or breaks down during processing operations, the containers within the retort may not have received a complete process. These containers shall either be reprocessed, repacked and reprocessed, or destroyed. Alternatively, the retort may be operated as a still retort. This alternative is referred to as an emergency still process. When the retort is operated as a still retort, all containers shall be given a full emergency still retort process before the retort is cooled for repairs. If an emergency still process is used, it must be a process recommended by a processing authority.

Any containers in the retort intake valve or transfer valves between processing shells at the time of the breakdown shall be reprocessed, repacked and processed, or discarded.

Both the time the reel was stopped and the time the retort was used as a still retort shall be marked on the temperature/time recording chart and the appropriate entries made on the daily process record form. If any of

the other alternative procedures are followed, the appropriate entries must be made in the processing records to document the disposition of the containers. Unless a filed alternative process is properly applied to render the product commercially sterile, the corrective action taken shall be treated as a process deviation.

Temperature drop

If the retort temperature drops below that specified in the scheduled process while containers are in the processing shell, the reel shall be promptly stopped and container entry to the retort prevented. An automatic device is often used to stop the reel.

The alternative procedures permitted by the regulations when a temperature drop occurs are summarized in *Table 2*.

If the still process alternative is selected, the containers in the processing shell(s) at the time of the temperature drop shall be given a complete scheduled still process recommended by a processing authority. When the retort is used as a still retort, both the time the reel was stopped and the time the retort was used as a still retort should be indicated on the temperature/time recording chart and on other appropriate records. If containers are removed and processed in a still retort, the handling procedures shall be documented in the production records. Complete records must be maintained for the still retort process.

The authorized emergency agitating process alternative may be selected only if the temperature drop is less than 10°F (5.5°C). When this alternative is selected, container entry into the retort shall be stopped and not restarted until the emergency agitating process is completed. The processing procedures used shall be noted in the production records, along with the time container entry was stopped.

A temperature drop below the scheduled process temperature is considered a process deviation and must be treated accordingly unless acceptable corrective action is taken. A description of the complete action taken must be recorded and made part of a separate log or file. If the alternative procedure to destroy the containers is selected, appropriate records must be maintained that verify the number of containers destroyed, the container codes and the method of destruction. For USDA-regulated products,

Table 2—Alternative procedures permitted by USDA and FDA in case of temperature drop.

	Temperature Drop less than 10°F	10°F or more
1. Stop Reel	YES	YES
2. Still Process	YES	YES
3. Evaluate as a Process Deviation	YES	YES
4. Authorized Emergency Agitating Process	YES	NO
5. Destroy	YES	YES

the resident inspector should be notified prior to destruction of the product.

Record Requirements

Due to the additional critical factors associated with continuous agitating retorts, additional records are required for this type of processing system. All critical factors specified in the scheduled process shall be measured and recorded at intervals of sufficient frequency to ensure that they remain within the limits specified. These measurements should not exceed 15 minutes. Both agencies require that the records include the approximate number of containers processed, product initial temperature, time steam on, time and temperature vent closed (if applicable), time the first can enters the retort, time the last can exits the retort, functioning of the condensate bleeder and reel speed. The USDA requires that reel speed be determined and recorded at intervals not to exceed four hours. Also, readings of the temperature indicating device(s) and temperature/time recorder(s) shall be made and recorded when the first container enters the retort and with sufficient frequency (suggest every 30 minutes) to ensure compliance with the scheduled process.

Summary

1. Continuous agitating retorts provide continuous container handling with intermittent container agitation.

2. Provisions shall be made for removal of condensate from the processing shells when the retorts are brought up to temperature and during operation.

3. Venting is just as important for continuous agitating retorts as for still steam retorts.

4. For continuous agitating retorts, the process time is dependent on the capacity of the retort and the speed of the reel.

5. Critical factors—such as minimum headspace, initial temperature, cooker speed, maximum consistency, maximum fill-in weight, vacuum and can specifications—must be carefully controlled to ensure a proper process.

Chapter 13

AGITATING RETORTS— DISCONTINUOUS CONTAINER HANDLING

Introduction

The retorts discussed in this chapter are batch type (discontinuous container handling) pressure vessels that provide continuous product agitation. A variety of retort makes and models that fall into this category are used to sterilize many product types in an assortment of containers. The retorts either use steam, water, or a steam/air mixture as the processing medium. Air or steam may be used as a source of overpressure. Two basic types of product agitation will be discussed: end-over-end and side-over-side.

Description of the Retort

One class of agitating retorts rotates the containers end-over-end during the entire processing cycle. The resulting product agitation is illustrated in *Figure 1*. In these retorts the containers are positively held in baskets or racks. The baskets are held within the retort in a rotating framework that provides end-over-end rotation at various speeds. This class of retorts can accommodate a wide range of container types and sizes. The container racks can be custom designed to accommodate specific containers. These retorts may be designed for steam processing, water processing (immersion, cascading or spray) with overpressure, or steam/air processing with overpressure.

Another class of retort provides side-over-side agitation in a pure steam processing environment without overpressure. The containers are loaded automatically into the retort using the same design features discussed in the previous chapter. Containers are loaded through a gate valve onto a rotating reel. A spiral T is affixed to the retort shell to auger the containers through the retort. An automatic device counts the containers entering the retort. When the reel is full, the spiral T is unlocked from the retort shell and locked to the reel, positively holding the containers inside the reel steps. This type of rotational

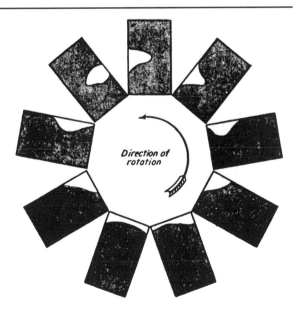

Figure 1—Illustration of end-over-end agitation.

system provides continuous side-over-side product agitation, as illustrated in *Figure 2*. This retort is limited to a narrow range of container sizes.

The advantages of both retort types result from an increased heating rate in certain products due to the continuous agitation. The rotational speeds for these retorts are generally faster than those for continuous container handling retorts, because the containers are positively held in baskets or racks in the retort. Due to the faster speeds and increased rates of agitation, the product process times may be shorter than those for still retorts. For example, a 603 x 700 can of cream-style corn may receive a twenty minute process at 260°F (126.7°C) in one of these retorts, while the process time for cream-style corn in a still retort could be 10 times longer. These shorter processes may improve product quality and uniformity. Some of the possible disadvantages include discontinuous (batch type) container handling, large initial capital investment, and the need to monitor and control additional critical factors.

Installation and Operation of Retorts

Common Considerations

Proper installation and operation of each retort is essential to achieve satisfactory processing results. The installation considerations for these retort systems depend on the heating medium employed—either steam, water (immersion, cascading or spray) or a steam/air mixture—and the source of overpressure, if appropriate. These retorts may be equipped with various controls and alarms, which are important for monitoring critical factors. The general specifications for instruments and information on pressure gauges, timing devices and mufflers are outlined in Chapter 8.

Instrumentation

At least one temperature indicating device (mercury-in-glass thermometer) and a temperature/time recording device are required for each retort.

The location of bulbs or probes of temperature indicating devices and temperature/time recording devices is dependent on the processing medium. The bulbs or probes of these instruments shall be installed either within the retort shell or in external wells attached to the retort.

Steam controller

Regardless of the processing medium, each retort shall be equipped with an automatic steam controller to maintain retort temperature. This may be a recording-controlling instrument when combined with a temperature/time recording device. If the retort is operating with overpressure, the controller must be responsive to temperature only.

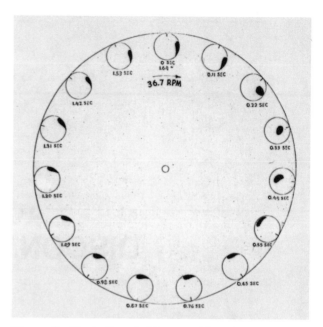

Figure 2—Illustration of side-over-side agitation.

Pressure control

Overriding pressure may be supplied in the form of air or steam. For processes requiring the maintenance of overpressure, the USDA specifies that each retort system shall be equipped with a pressure recording device, which may be combined with a pressure controller. In addition, each retort should be equipped with a pressure gauge that can be read easily by the operator. The specifications for pressure control are discussed in Chapter 10.

If overpressure requirements are specified in the scheduled process, USDA requires that overpressure shall be maintained continuously during the come-up, thermal processing and cooling periods. The retort shall have an automatic pressure control unit to control the air or steam entering or leaving the retort to maintain the required overpressure.

Processing medium circulation

No matter which processing medium is used, a means shall be provided to circulate the heating medium to ensure uniform temperatures within the retort during processing. Adequate temperature distribution shall be documented by temperature distribution data or other documentation from a processing authority. Where applicable, the circulation system shall be equipped with a pilot light or signaling device to warn the operator when it is not functioning.

Rotational speed

The rotational speed of the retort's rotating framework shall be specified in the scheduled process. The speed shall be adjusted, as necessary, to ensure that it remains as specified in the scheduled process, and it shall be checked and recorded for *each* retort load processed. Alteratively, a recording tachometer may be used to maintain a continuous record of speed. The USDA requires that the accuracy of a recording tachometer be determined and recorded at least once per shift by checking the rotational speed using an accurate stopwatch. A means of preventing unauthorized speed changes shall be provided, such as a notice or lock.

Construction of crates, dividers and racks

Retorts that use end-over-end agitation have container racking systems that hold the containers positively in place during processing. These racking systems may be generic or custom designed to hold a specific container, such as a semirigid plastic tray. In addition to positively holding the containers, the racking system must also provide for free movement of the heating medium around the containers. Additional information may be found in Chapter 10. Racks shall be designed to permit uniform circulation of the heating medium around all containers in the retort. The perforation pattern should equal or exceed approximately one-inch holes on two-inch centers or the equivalent. The crates, dividers and/or racks may be made of strap iron or perforated sheet metal or plastic.

Flexible and, where applicable, semirigid plastic containers usually require custom-rack design. USDA specifies that racks for these containers be designed (1) so that the thickness of the filled containers does not exceed that specified in the scheduled process and (2) so that the containers are kept from being displaced, overlapped or rested on other containers during processing. Containers that become dislodged from the racks could interfere with the heating medium circulation patterns and result in underprocessing. When processing flexible or semirigid containers, care should be taken to prevent puncture or abrasions from worn or sharp metal edges.

Drain valve

Those retorts that require the maintenance of a specific water level shall be equipped with a nonclogging watertight drain valve. It is recommended practice and a USDA requirement that screens be installed over all drain openings. These requirements are intended to reduce the risk of water leakage from the retort during the processing period. A low water level may result in underprocessing. Further information, see Chapter 10.

Cooling water supply

When these retort systems are used to process glass containers, the cooling water should be introduced so that it does not strike the containers directly in order to minimize breakage due to thermal shock. Cooling water may be added directly into the processing vessel or introduced into the suction side of the pump.

Water (Total Immersion, Cascading or Sprays) Retorts With Air or Steam Overpressure

These retorts are usually designed to provide end-over-end agitation with water as the heating medium.

Instrumentation

In addition to the general considerations for the temperature indicating device and temperature/time recorder discussed earlier, USDA requires that the bulb or probe of the temperature indicating device extend directly into the water without a separable well or sleeve. The FDA allows the use of external wells attached to the retort. The USDA requires that the temperature recorder-controller probe be located between the water surface and the horizontal plane passing through the center or the retort. The FDA requires that the bulb or probe of the temperature recorder-controller be installed either within the retort shell or in a well attached to the shell. Care must be taken to ensure that steam used to heat the water does not directly strike the bulb or probe of the temperature/time recorder. Due to the wide variety of retort types, alternate locations may be permitted provided the location is acceptable to the regulatory agency.

Pressure control

Each retort shall have an automatic pressure control unit to introduce compressed air or steam into the retort at the proper rate. A nonreturn (check) valve shall be provided in the air supply line to prevent moisture from entering the system. There are several ways overpressure can be controlled. Automatic control valves control the air or steam entering or leaving the retort to maintain the required overpressure. If steam is used to provide overpressure, then an independently controlled steam source is needed for maintenance of the proper overpressure. This steam source is separate from the system used to control processing temperature.

Processing medium circulation

Water retorts (total immersion, cascading or spray) employ a pump to mechanically circulate the water within the retort to provide adequate temperature distribution. The processing water is drawn from the bottom of the retort through a suction manifold and discharged through a manifold spreader or distribution system. The retort water suction outlets shall be protected with screens to prevent debris from entering the circulation system. The pump shall be equipped with a pilot light or signaling device to warn the operator when it is not running. USDA permits the use of a flow-meter alarm system as an alternative for ensuring proper water circulation. Alternate methods of heating medium circulation may be used, provided that adequate temperature distribution or other documentation is available.

Water level indicator

In retort systems where the containers must be completely covered by the processing water, a means shall be provided to monitor the water level in the retort during operation. This requirement may be met by a sight glass or low-water-level alarm. For those systems that require complete immersion of the containers, water shall cover all the containers during the entire come-up-time and processing period. Water should also cover the top layer of containers during the cooling period.

Steam Processing Retorts

Steam retort systems may provide either side-over-side or end-over-end agitation with steam as the processing medium.

Instrumentation

The bulbs of the temperature indicating device and recorder are inserted directly into the shell or in an external well attached to the shell. In addition to the general considerations discussed earlier, the specifications for these instruments and external wells are found in Chapter 9.

Venting

Each retort using steam as the processing medium shall provide for removal of air before process timing begins. The venting procedures shall be documented by temperature distribution data or other documentation from the manufacturer or a processing authority.

Condensate removal

USDA requires that provisions be made for condensate removal. At the time steam is turned on, the drain shall be open for a time sufficient to remove steam condensate from the retort and provisions shall be made for continuing drainage of condensate during the retort operation. The condensate bleeder shall be arranged so the operator can observe proper functioning, and it shall be checked with sufficient frequency (suggest 15-minute intervals) to ensure adequate condensate removal. Automatic systems may be used to provide intermittent condensate removal provided they are equipped with an automatic alarm system that serves as a continuous monitor of condensate bleeder functioning. This alarm system shall be tested for proper functioning at the beginning of each shift and the results recorded. FDA recognizes the importance of condensate removal and recommends that provisions be made for it during the come-up-time and processing time.

Processing medium circulation

Bleeders are required for steam retorts and shall be wide open during the entire processing period, including the come-up-time. All bleeders shall be arranged so the operator can observe proper operation. Further information on the size and placement of bleeders is located in Chapter 9. The requirements are the same as those for horizontal steam retorts.

Steam/Air Retorts

These retorts are usually designed to provide end-over-end container agitation with steam/air as the processing medium.

Instrumentation

In addition to the general considerations for the temperature indicating device and the temperature/time recorder discussed earlier, USDA requires that the bulb or probe of the temperature indicating device (mercury-in-glass thermometer) and the temperature time/recorder (or recorder-controller) be inserted directly into the retort shell and be located so that steam does not strike it directly.

Processing medium circulation

Some system or device, such as a fan, is required to circulate the steam/air heating medium and to maintain uniform temperature distribution. The fan shall be equipped with a device to notify the operator when it is not functioning. Provisions should be made to remove condensate from the retorts. Further information on condensate removal is located in Chapter 9.

USDA regulations specify that the agency be notified immediately if steam/air retort systems are used.

Processing Considerations

In the retorts described in this section, gravitational and centrifugal forces move the product in the containers as they are rotated. Product movement is influenced by its thickness (consistency), the amount of container headspace, and the rotational speed of the retort. For each product, container type and retort type, there is a range of rotational speeds that provides optimum product agitation. It is important to note that minimum headspace, maximum consistency, and rotational speed may be specified as critical factors for agitating processes. If these or other critical factors are not met, product agitation may be reduced or eliminated, resulting in underprocessing.

Headspace

Headspace is normally expressed as gross headspace (*Figure 3*), and it is measured after the container is filled. It may be measured before or after sealing. The measurement is taken by determining the space from the top of the flange or double seam to the product level. This measurement is normally expressed in sixteenths or

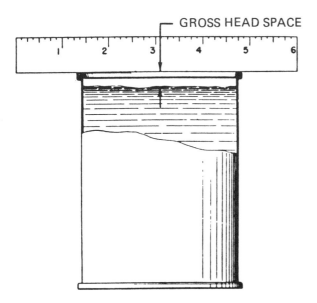

Figure 3—Method of measuring gross headspace.

thirty-seconds of an inch. In making the measurement, a straight edge is placed across the top of the open container, and using a calibrated measuring device held at right angles to the straight edge, a measurement is taken of the space above the product.

Consistency

Consistency is an objective measurement of the thickness of a product. Various instruments are available for this purpose. If the product is thicker than that specified for the scheduled process, the product may be underprocessed.

Initial Temperature

The initial temperature of the coldest can in the retort at the time the processing cycle begins shall be determined and recorded for each retort batch to ensure that the temperature is as specified in the scheduled process. The details for determining initial temperatures are discussed in Chapter 8.

Process Timing

The timing of a process shall not start until the scheduled retort temperature is observed on the temperature indicating device (mercury-in-glass thermometer) and the required retort operating procedures have been completed. Accurate timing devices shall be used in recording processing time information. Additional information on timing devices is located in Chapter 8.

Record Requirements

All critical factors specified in the scheduled process shall be measured and recorded at intervals of sufficient frequency to ensure that the critical factors remain within the limits specified in the scheduled process. The measurements should not exceed 15 minutes—except for rotational speed, which must be measured at least once per retort load unless a recording tachometer is used, in which case its accuracy shall be checked and recorded once per shift.

The written records should include the specific items listed in Chapter 6. Also, it is required that the records include the approximate number of containers processed per retort load, initial temperature, rotational speed, time steam on, venting time/temperature (if applicable), time to reach processing temperature, water level checks (if applicable) and time steam off.

Summary

1. Since the containers are positively held in these retorts, faster rotational speeds are possible resulting in increased product agitation and shorter process times.

2. Adequate provisions shall be made to ensure the circulation of the processing medium.

3. Product agitation results from the movement of the headspace bubble as the container rotates.

4. Critical factors such as minimum headspace, initial temperature, cooker speed, maximum consistency, vacuum, fill weight and container specification shall be carefully controlled to ensure a proper process.

Chapter 14

ASEPTIC PROCESSING AND PACKAGING SYSTEMS

Introduction

The processing systems described in the last five chapters of this text operate by thermally processing product within a container to achieve commercial sterility. This procedure is commonly called conventional canning. Aseptic processing—the subject of this chapter—achieves the same result but by a different method.

In aseptic processing, packages and food product are sterilized in separate systems. The sterile package is then filled with sterile product, closed and sealed in a sterile chamber.

Since aseptic processing is a continuous operation, the behavior of one part of the system can affect the overall performance of the entire system. As a result, numerous critical factors are associated with aseptic processing and packaging often requiring automated control systems. Process establishment for aseptic systems must consider not only the sterilization of the product, the processing equipment and the downstream piping, but also the sterilization of the packaging material and equipment and the maintenance of sterile conditions throughout the aseptic system.

Definitions

To assist in the discussion of aseptic processing and packaging systems, some definitions are presented below. You should be familiar with these terms and their particular significance to aseptic systems.

Aseptic describes a condition in which there is an absence of microorganisms, including viable spores. In the food industry, the terms aseptic, sterile and commercially sterile are often used interchangeably.

Aseptic system refers to the entire system necessary to produce a commercially sterile product contained in a hermetically sealed container. This term includes the product processing system and the packaging system.

Aseptic processing system refers only to the system that processes the product and delivers it to a packaging system.

Aseptic packaging system refers to any piece of equipment that fills a sterile package or container with sterile product and hermetically seals it under aseptic conditions. These units or systems may also form and sterilize the package.

Basic Aseptic System

Figure 1 is a diagram of a simplified aseptic system. Raw or unprocessed product is heated, sterilized by holding at high temperature for a predetermined amount of time, then cooled and delivered to a packaging unit for packaging. Commercial sterility is maintained throughout the system, from the moment of product heating to the discharge of hermetically sealed containers.

Achieving successful aseptic processing and packaging of foods requires, as a minimum, the following conditions:

1. Equipment that can be brought to a condition of commercial sterility.

2. Commercially sterile product.

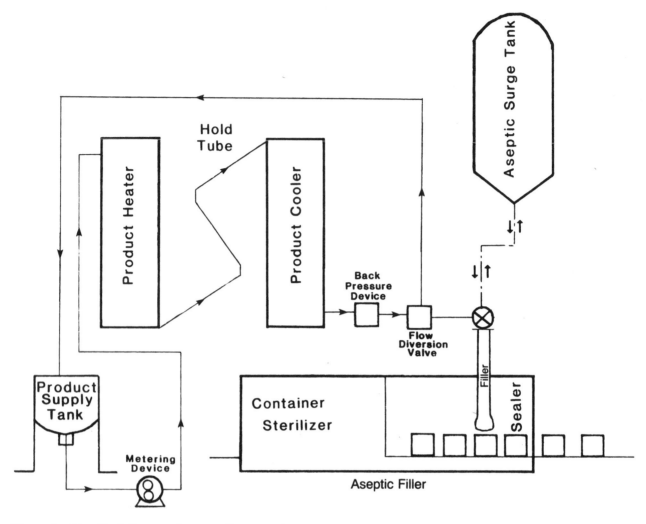

Figure 1—Simplified diagram of an aseptic processing system.

3. Commercially sterile packages.

4. A commercially sterile environment within the packaging machine in which to bring sterile product and packages together and hermetically seal the packages.

5. Monitoring, recording and control of critical factors.

6. Proper handling of finished packages to ensure container integrity.

Aseptic Processing System

Description

Although the equipment for aseptic processing systems varies, all systems have certain common features:

1. A pumpable product.

2. A means to control and document the flow rate of product through the system.

3. A method of heating the product to sterilizing temperatures.

4. A method of holding product at an elevated temperature for a time sufficient for sterilization.

5. A method of cooling product to filling temperature.

6. A means to sterilize the system prior to production and to maintain sterility during production.

7. Adequate safeguards to protect sterility and prevent non-sterile product from reaching the packaging equipment.

Pre-Production Sterilization

Production of a commercially sterile product cannot be assumed unless the processing system and filler have been adequately sterilized before starting production. It is important that the system be thoroughly cleaned before sterilization; otherwise the process may not be effective.

Some systems, or portions thereof, use saturated steam for sterilization. However, for most systems, equipment sterilization is accomplished by circulation of hot water through the system for a sufficient length of time to render it commercially sterile. When water is used, it is heated in the product heater and then pumped through all downstream piping and equipment up to (and generally past) the filler valve on the packaging unit. All product contact surfaces "downstream" from the product heater must be maintained at or above a specified temperature by continuously circulating the hot water for a required period of time.

Surge tanks are generally sterilized with saturated steam rather than hot water due to their large capacity. Although sterilization of surge tanks may occur separately, it is usually conducted simultaneously with hot water sterilization of the other equipment.

In order to control aseptic system sterilization properly, it is necessary that a thermometer or thermocouple be located at the coldest point(s) in the system to ensure that the proper temperature is maintained throughout. Thus, the temperature measuring device is generally located at the most distant point from the heat exchangers. Timing of the sterilization cycle begins when the proper temperature is obtained at this remote location. If this temperature should fall below the minimum, the cycle should be restarted after the sterilization temperature is reestablished. Recording devices are recommended to provide a permanent continuous record to show that the equipment is adequately sterilized before each production run.

Flow Control

Sterilization time or residence time, as indicated in the scheduled process, is directly related to the rate of flow of the fastest moving particle through the system. The fastest moving particle is a function of the flow characteristics of the food. Consequently, a process must be designed to ensure that product flows through the system at a uniform and constant rate so that the fastest moving particle of food receives at least the minimum amount of heat for the minimum time specified by the scheduled process. This constant flow rate is generally achieved with a pump, called a timing or metering pump.

Timing pumps may be variable speed or fixed rate. The pumping rate of the fixed rate pump cannot be changed without dismantling the pump. Variable speed pumps are designed to provide flexibility and allow for easy rate changes. When a variable speed pump is used, it shall be protected against unauthorized changes in the pump speed that could affect the rate of product flow through the system. A lock or a notice from management posted at or near the speed adjusting device warning that only authorized persons are permitted to make adjustments is a satisfactory way to prevent unauthorized adjustments.

Product Heating

A product heater brings the product to sterilizing temperature. There are two major categories of product heaters in aseptic food processing: direct and indirect.

Direct heating, as the name implies, involves direct contact between the heating medium (steam) and the product. Direct heating systems can be one of two types—steam injection or steam infusion.

Steam injection introduces steam into the product in an injection chamber as product is pumped through the chamber (*Figure 2*), while the process of steam infusion introduces product through a steam-filled infusion chamber (*Figure 3*). These systems are currently limited to homogeneous, low viscosity products.

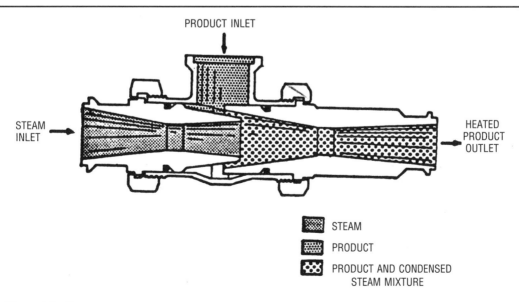

STEAM INLET · PRODUCT INLET · HEATED PRODUCT OUTLET

STEAM
PRODUCT
PRODUCT AND CONDENSED STEAM MIXTURE

Figure 2—Steam injection.

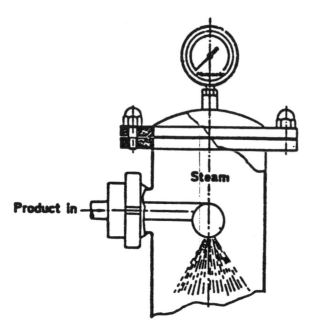

Figure 3—Steam infusion.

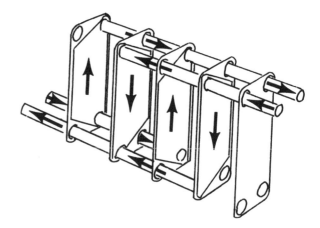

Figure 4—Plate heat exchanger.

Direct heating has the advantage of very rapid heating, which minimizes organoleptic changes in the product. The problems of fouling or ''burn on'' of product in the system may also be reduced in direct heating systems compared to indirect systems. There are also some disadvantages. The addition of water (from the condensation of steam in the product) increases product volume. Since this change in volume increases product flow rate through the hold tube, it must be accounted for when establishing the scheduled process.

Depending on the product being produced, water that was added as steam may need to be removed. Water removal is discussed under product cooling. Steam used for direct heating must be of culinary quality and must be free of non-condensable gases. Thus, strict controls on boiler feed water additives must be followed.

The other major category of product heaters is **indirect heating** units, which have a physical separation between the product and the heating medium. There are three major types of indirect heating units: plate, tubular and swept-surface heat exchangers.

Plate heat exchangers (*Figure 4*) are used for homogeneous liquids of relatively low viscosity. The plates serve both as a barrier and a heat transfer surface with product on one side and the heating medium on the other. Each plate is gasketed, and a series of plates are held together in a press. The number of plates can be adjusted to meet specific needs.

Tubular heat exchangers (*Figure 5*) employ either two or three concentric tubes instead of plates as heat transfer surfaces. Product flows through the inner tube of the double tube style and through the middle tube of the triple tube style, with the heating medium in the other

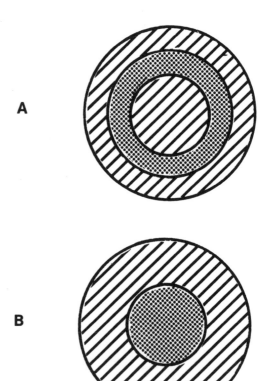

A

B

heating/cooling medium

product

Figure 5—Tubular heat exchanger (A = triple tube, B = double tube).

110

tube(s) flowing in the opposite direction to the product. In a shell and tube heat exchanger (considered a type of tubular exchanger), the tube is coiled inside a shell (*Figure 6*). Product flows through the tube while the heating medium flows in the opposite direction through the shell. Tubular heat exchangers are used for homogeneous products of low to medium viscosity.

Scraped-surface heat exchangers are normally used for processing more viscous products (*Figure 7*). The scraped surface heat exchanger consists of a mutator shaft with scraper blades concentrically located within a jacketed, insulated, heat exchange tube. The rotating blades continuously "scrape" the product off the wall. This scraping reduces buildup of product and "burn on." The heating medium flowing on the opposite side of the wall is circulating water or steam.

Some systems incorporate the use of product-to-product heat exchangers. These devices are either plate or tubular heat exchangers with product flowing on both sides of the plates or through both sets of tubes. This process allows the heat from the hot sterile product to be transferred to the cool, incoming, non-sterile product. Energy and cost savings can be significant by "recycling" the heat from sterile product.

When a product-to-product regenerator is used, it shall be designed, operated and controlled so that the pressure of the sterilized product in the regenerator is at least one psi greater than the pressure of any non-sterilized product in the regenerator. This ratio helps ensure that any leakage in the regenerator will be from sterilized product into non-sterilized product. In addition, an accurate differential pressure recorder shall be installed on the regenerator. One pressure sensor has to be installed at the hot sterilized product outlet and an other at the cooler non-sterilized product inlet. Upon installation the recorder shall be tested against a known accurate standard pressure indicator and shall be retested at least once every three months, or as often as necessary to ensure proper functioning. Pressure differential maintenance and recording is also recommended for heat exchangers employing product-to-water regeneration and may be a requirement in certain instances.

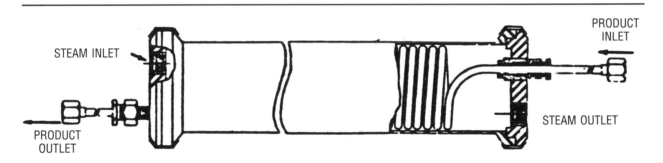

Figure 6—Shell and tube heat exchanger.

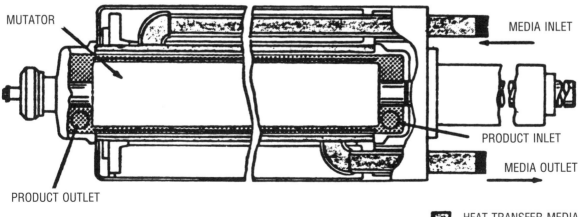

Figure 7—Scraped surface heat exchanger.

Hold Tube

Once the product has been brought to sterilizing temperature in the heater, it flows to a hold tube. The time required for the fastest product particle to flow through the hold tube is referred to as the residence time. The residence time must be equivalent to or greater than the time necessary at a specific temperature to sterilize the product and is specified in the scheduled process. Hold tube volume—which is determined by hold tube diameter and length—combined with the flow rate and flow characteristics of the product, determines the actual residence time of the product in the hold tube. Since the hold tube is essential for ensuring that the product is held at sterilization temperatures for the proper time, certain precautions must be followed:

1. The holding tube shall have an upward slope in the direction of product flow at least 0.25 inch per foot to assist in eliminating air pockets and prevent self-draining.

2. If the holding tube can be taken apart, care should be taken that all parts are replaced and that no parts are removed or interchanged to make the tube shorter or different in diameter. Such accidental alterations could shorten the time the product remains in the tube.

3. If the holding tube can be taken apart, care should be exercised when reassembling to ensure that the gaskets do not protrude into the inner surface. The tube interior should be smooth and easily cleanable.

4. There must be no condensate drip on the tube, and the tube should not be subjected to drafts or cold air, which could affect the product temperature in the holding tube.

5. External heat shall not be applied at any point along the hold tube.

6. The product in the hold tube must be maintained under a pressure sufficiently above the vapor pressure of the product at the process temperature to prevent "flashing" or boiling, since flashing can decrease the product residence time in the hold tube. The prevention of flashing is usually accomplished by use of a back pressure device.

The temperature of the food in the holding tube shall be monitored at the inlet and outlet of the tube. The temperature at the inlet of the tube is monitored with a temperature recorder-controller sensor, which shall be located at final heater outlet and shall be capable of maintaining process temperature in the hold tube. A mercury-in-glass thermometer or other acceptable temperature measuring device (such as an accurate thermocouple-recorder) shall be installed in the product at the holding tube outlet between the holding tube and the cooler inlet. An automatic recording thermometer sensor shall also be located in the product at the holding tube outlet between the holding tube and cooler to indicate the product temperature. The temperature sensing device chart graduations shall not exceed 2°F (1°C) within a range of 10°F (6°C) of the required product sterilization temperature.

Product Cooling

Product flows from the hold tube into a product cooler which reduces product temperature prior to filling. In those systems that use indirect heating, the cooler will be a heat exchanger that may be heating raw product while cooling sterile product. Those systems that use direct heating will typically include a flash or vacuum chamber. The hot product is exposed to a reduced pressure atmosphere within the chamber resulting in product boiling or "flashing." The product temperature is lowered, and a portion or all of the water that was added to the product during heating is removed by evaporation. Upon discharge from the flash chamber, product may be further cooled in some type of heat exchanger.

Maintaining Sterility

After the product leaves the hold tube, it is sterile and subject to contamination if microorganisms are permitted to enter the system. One of the simplest and best ways to prevent contamination is to keep the sterile product flowing and pressurized. A back pressure device is used to prevent product from boiling or flashing, and it maintains the entire product system under elevated pressure. Effective barriers against microorganisms must be provided at all potential contamination points, such as rotating or reciprocating shafts and the stems of aseptic valves. Steam seals at these locations can provide an effective barrier, but they must be monitored visually to ensure proper functioning. If other types of barriers are used, a means must be provided to permit the operator to monitor the proper functioning of the barrier.

Aseptic Surge Tanks

Aseptic surge tanks have been used in aseptic systems to allow the packer to hold sterile product prior to packaging. These vessels, which range in capacity from about one hundred gallons to several thousand gallons, provide flexibility, especially for systems in which the flow rate of a product sterilization system is not compatible with the filling rate of a given packaging unit. If the valving that connects a surge tank to the rest of the system is designed to allow maximum flexibility, the packaging and processing functions can be carried out independently with the surge tank acting as a buffer between the two systems. A disadvantage of the surge tank is that all sterile product is held together, and, if there is a contamination problem, all product is involved. A sterile air or other sterile gas supply system is needed in order to maintain a protective positive pressure within the tank and to displace the contents. This positive pressure must be monitored and controlled to protect the tank from contamination.

Automatic Flow Diversion

An automatic flow diversion device may be utilized in an aseptic processing system to prevent the possibility of potentially unsterile product from reaching the sterile packaging equipment. The flow diversion device must be designed so that it can be sterilized and operated reliably. Past experience has shown that flow diversion valves of the gravity drain type should not be used in aseptic systems due to the possibility of recontamination of sterile product. Since the design and operation of a flow diversion system is critical, it should be done in accordance with recommendations of an aseptic processing authority.

The flow diversion valve should divert product automatically if a deviation occurs. A few examples of situations that may cause a diversion are temperature at the hold tube dropping below the scheduled minimum, inadequate pressure differential in the regenerators, or the packaging unit dropping below minimum operating specifications.

Aseptic Packaging Systems

Basic Requirements

Aseptic packaging units are designed to combine sterile product with a sterile package resulting in a hermetically sealed shelf-stable product. As with aseptic processing systems, there are certain features common to all aseptic packaging systems. The packaging units must:

1. Create and maintain a sterile environment in which the package and product can be brought together.

2. Sterilize the product contact surface of the package.

3. Aseptically fill the sterile product into the sterilized package.

4. Produce hermetically sealed containers.

5. Monitor and control critical factors.

A wide variety of packaging systems are available to satisfy these requirements in many different ways. The following discussion will concentrate on those requirements common to all aseptic packaging systems, using the features previously mentioned as a basis for discussion.

Sterilization Agents

Sterilization agents are used in aseptic packaging units to sterilize the packaging material and the internal equipment surfaces to create a sterile packaging environment. In general, these agents involve either heat, chemicals, high-energy radiation, or a combination of these. For aseptic packaging equipment the sterilization agents used must effectively provide the same degree of protection in terms of microbiological safety that traditional sterilization systems provide for canned foods. This requirement applies to both the food contact surface of the packaging material and the internal machine surfaces that constitute the aseptic or sterile zone within the machine. The safety and effectiveness of these agents must be proven and accepted or approved by regulatory agencies

for packaging commercially sterile low-acid or acidified foods in hermetically sealed containers. Food processors considering use of an aseptic packaging unit should request written assurances that the equipment has passed such testing and that the equipment and sterilizing agents are acceptable to the regulatory agencies for their intended use.

Heat is the most widely used method of sterilization. Steam or hot water is commonly used and referred to as "moist" heat. Superheated steam or hot air may also be used in certain situations and is referred to as "dry" heat. Dry heat is a much less effective sterilization agent than moist heat at the same temperature. Systems that use moist heat operate at elevated pressures compared to dry heat systems, which operate at atmospheric pressures. Other methods may be used to generate heat, such as microwave radiation or infrared light. As new methods are developed, they will have to be evaluated by aseptic processing authorities.

Chemical agents such as hydrogen peroxide are often used in combination with heat as sterilization agents. The FDA regulations specify that a maximum concentration of 35 percent hydrogen peroxide may be used for food contact surfaces. If hydrogen peroxide is used as a sterilant, the packaging equipment must be capable of producing finished packages that also meet FDA requirements for residuals. Not more than 0.5 ppm hydrogen peroxide may be present in tests done with distilled water packaged under production conditions. These regulations apply also to USDA-regulated products.

Other sterilants, such as high energy radiation—UV light, gamma or electron beam radiation—could be used alone or in combination with existing methods. Completely new alternative sterilants may be developed in the future. Whatever methods are developed, they will have to be proven effective in order to protect the public health and will be compared with existing methods.

Aseptic Zones

The aseptic zone is the area within the aseptic packaging machine that is sterilized and is maintained sterile during production. This is the area in which the sterile product is filled and sealed in the sterile container. The aseptic zone begins at the point where the package material is sterilized or where pre-sterilized package material is introduced into the machine. The area ends after the seal is placed on the package and the finished package leaves the sterile area. All areas between these two points are considered part of the aseptic zone.

Prior to production, the aseptic zone must be brought to a condition of commercial sterility analogous to that achieved on the packaging material or other sterile product contact surfaces. This area may contain a variety of surfaces, including moving parts composed of different materials. The sterilant(s) must be uniformly effective and their application controllable throughout the entire aseptic zone.

Once the aseptic zone has been sterilized, sterility must be maintained during production. The area should be constructed in a manner that provides sterilizable physical barriers between sterile and non-sterile areas. Mechanisms must be provided to allow sterile packaging materials and hermetically sealed finished packages to enter and leave the aseptic zone without compromising the sterility of the zone.

The sterility of the aseptic zone can be protected from contamination by maintaining the aseptic zone under positive pressure of sterile air or other gas. As finished containers leave the sterile area, sterile air flows outward, preventing contaminants from entering the aseptic area. The sterile air pressure within the aseptic zone must be kept at a level proven to maintain sterility of the zone. Air or gases can be sterilized using various sterilization agents, but the most common methods are incineration (dry heat) and/or ultrafiltration.

Production of Aseptic Packages

A wide variety of aseptic packaging systems are in use today. These are easily categorized by package type as follows:

1. Preformed rigid and semirigid containers, including:
   A. Metal cans
   B. Composite cans
   C. Plastic cups
   D. Glass containers
   E. Drums
2. Webfed paperboard laminates and plastic containers
3. Partially formed laminated paper containers
4. Thermoform-fill-seal containers
5. Preformed bags or pouches
6. Blow-molded containers

There are a number of different packaging systems represented in these categories. Not all of these systems, however, are being used in the United States for aseptic low-acid product applications.

Containers in these categories may be sterilized by a variety of means. For example, one system using metal cans sterilizes containers with superheated steam. In other systems, preformed plastic cups may be sterilized by hydrogen peroxide and heat or by saturated steam. Systems using containers formed from paperboard laminates also utilize hydrogen peroxide and heat or hydrogen peroxide and ultraviolet irradiation to sterilize packages. Thermoform-fill-seal containers may be sterilized by the heat of extrusion (dry heat) or by hydrogen peroxide and heat. Plastic pouches or bags may be sterilized by gamma irradiation, by the heat of extrusion, or by chemical means such as hydrogen peroxide.

Research is now being conducted to explore alterative sterilization methods for most categories of packaging. Thus, it can be said with some certainty that currently familiar equipment may not be ''state of the art'' tomorrow. Nevertheless, whatever equipment, sterilants or packaging materials are used, the monitoring and control of critical factors will be vital to successful operation.

Incubation

Incubation is defined as the holding of a sample at a specified temperature for a period of time for the purpose of permitting or stimulating the growth of microorganisms that may be present. Routine product incubation programs are recommended as a check on the overall quality and sterility of aseptic products. If the packer is producing an item that is covered by the inspection authority of the USDA (for more information see section on regulations, which follows), routine incubation of samples is mandatory, and the exact program should be established in cooperation with the regulatory representative. Incubation tests should be conducted on a representative sample of containers of product from each packaging code. Records of the incubation tests should be kept.

Record Requirements

Accurate record keeping is essential to successful operation of aseptic systems. Automatic recording and monitoring systems are relied upon more heavily than in traditional processing because of the inherent complexity and numerous critical factors associated with aseptic systems.

The kind of recording or monitoring system used is determined by the variability of individual factors during operation. For example, machine packaging rate is often a pre-set function with relatively little variability. When machine packaging rate is a critical factor, operator monitoring may be sufficient to ensure that the rate stays within critical factor limits. On the other hand, critical factors such as temperature—which could be affected by a variety of other machine functions—can exhibit greater variability. Thus, the need for automatic recording or monitoring of temperature would be greater.

Production records for an aseptic system consist of production logs and recording charts from the aseptic processing system, the aseptic packaging system, and the aseptic surge tank. Recording charts provide a continuous record of the aseptic system's performance. It is necessary that operators mark the charts clearly, in ink, to indicate the time that sterilization and production begin and end. If production is stopped for any reason, such as a drop in process temperature, loss of sterile air pressure, or packaging problems, the time of day that production is stopped and restarted should be noted on the chart.

The production log is a written record of the aseptic system's operation. The operator shall note in the log the time of day that events occur, along with any problems and related corrective action. In addition, the appropriate regulations must be consulted to ensure that all required information is included in the log.

Examples of production log entries may include the following information (*Figure 8*):

Container Size _____ Chart No. _____ Page ___ of ___
Filler Used _____ _____ Date _____
Production Process _____ Lot. No. _____
(Time/Temp.) _____

Product/ Code	Production			CPM/ GPH	HOMO PSI	Holding Tube			Pre-Heat $^\circ$F	Regen. PSIG Diff.	Visual Steam Seal Check
	Start	Stop	Time			Inlet $^\circ$F	Outlet T/C $^\circ$F	Hg $^\circ$F			

Sterilization of Processing System	$^\circ$F	Time	$^\circ$F	Time

COMMENTS: _____
_____
_____

Figure 8—Processing log—product processing system.

1. Temperatures at the hold tube outlet taken from the recorder chart and from the temperature indicating device.

2. Maintenance of a proper pressure differential if a product-to-product regenerator is used.

3. Adequate operation of steam seals.

4. Information relating to additional critical factors.

Although entries for the aseptic packaging system would change according to the type of equipment, the following information could be included (*Figure 9*):

1. Temperature in container sterilizer tunnels (metal containers).

2. Container rate through the packaging unit.

3. Temperature and pressure in the air sterilizer.

4. Temperature of heated air or hydrogen peroxide.

5. Hydrogen peroxide concentration at start and end of production.

6. Any additional critical factors.

For aseptic surge tanks, a record shall be kept to show that the tank has been sterilized and that the sterile air within the tank is maintained at the proper pressure. If the air is sterilized by heat, a record of the incinerator temperature is necessary. If the air filter is sterilized, a record shall show that the filter and sterile air supply system were sterilized at the required temperature and time. The record shall also show that other applicable critical factors were met at the beginning of the operation and that the filter cartridge was changed at proper intervals.

Container Integrity

The integrity of aseptic containers must be ascertained by inspection and testing to ensure that the containers will maintain a hermetic seal during handling, distribution and storage. The concept of maintaining container integ-

| Product/Code | Production | | | Sterile Air | | | H_2O_2 System | | | | | Heating Element |
	Start	Stop	Time	Temp. $^{\circ}F$	Pressure		Level	Low cons.	Wet Guard	PSM		$^{\circ}F$

Sterilization of Filler	Sterile Air Temp. $^{\circ}F$	Heater Draw	Time	H_2O_2 Concentration: _____	COMMENTS:
				Start of Production: _____	_____
				End of Production: _____	_____
					_____

Figure 9—Processing log—aseptic packaging system.

rity is part of good manufacturing practice and an important function of every good quality control and assurance program. Due to the wide variety of containers, the test methodology may be designed for a particular type of package. Both the FDA and USDA require that container integrity be determined through regular inspection procedures.

Government Regulation of Aseptic Processing and Packaging

Three sets of regulatory requirements for food safety are applicable to aseptic food processing and packaging operations. Aseptic systems can fall under the regulatory jurisdiction of either FDA or USDA, and the processor will need to determine which requirements are pertinent. When milk or a milk product—as defined in the Grade A Pasteurized Milk Ordinance (PMO)—is involved, the aseptic operation must comply with the provisions of the PMO in addition to the FDA regulations.

The specific FDA regulations for aseptic processing and packaging systems are covered under 21 CFR 113.40(g). USDA elected to omit aseptic operations when they promulgated their canning regulations in 1986; thus, there is no specific reference to aseptic processing in 318.300 or 381.300. Information on USDA-FSIS requirements for aseptic systems are found in "Guidelines for Aseptic Processing and Packaging Systems in Meat and Poultry Plants," which is available from:

USDA, FSIS, S&T
Facilities, Equipment & Sanitation Division
Washington, DC 20250-3700

These documents are supplemental to the Meat and Poultry Inspection Regulations. In order for a federally inspected meat or poultry establishment to aseptically process and package food products for entry into commerce, the establishment personnel must first submit (1) an "acceptable" proposal to USDA-FSIS and (2) an "acceptable" Partial Quality Control (PQC) program for the operation and maintenance of the accepted system.

Summary

1. "Aseptic" is a term that describes the absence of microorganisms and may be used interchangeably with commercial sterility.

2. An aseptic processing system consists of a timing pump, a means to heat the product, a hold tube and a means to cool the product.

3. The processing system from the hold tube past the fillers is brought to a condition of commercial sterility prior to the introduction of product to the system.

4. The thermal process occurs in the hold tube where flow rate, residence time and temperatures are critical factors.

5. In the event of a process deviation, flow diversion devices are used to prevent potentially non-sterile product from reaching the filler.

6. Aseptic packaging machines create and maintain an aseptic zone (sterile environment) in which sterilized containers are filled and sealed.

7. Sterilization agents such as heat, chemicals, high energy radiation, or a combination of these, can be used to sterilize packages or machine surfaces.

8. Accurate record keeping is essential to successful operation of aseptic processing and packaging operations.

Chapter 15

CONTAINER CLOSURE EVALUATION

Introduction

The primary role of food packaging is to protect the integrity of the product from the time and point of manufacture to the time and point of consumption. Three elements are critical to the performance of a package throughout its shelf-life. They are:

● Adequate package integrity to ensure that the product is contained within the package throughout the distribution and shelf-life of the product. Package integrity prevents the ingress of microorganisms, oxygen, filth or other environmental contaminants that could render the product unfit for consumption or which could simply reduce the quality of the product to a level less than intended.

● Adequate barrier properties to prevent chemical or physical degradation of the product and to prevent inward or outward transfer of flavors and odors.

● Adequate physical strength to withstand the abuse encountered in processing (retorting, aseptic, etc.) and throughout the distribution system.

One of the critical concerns in package integrity is the hermetic seal provided by the closure mechanism. The next three chapters will discuss the technology for evaluating the integrity of closures for metal, glass, semirigid and flexible containers including plastic cans with double seamed metal ends, semirigid containers with heat sealed lids, paperboard packages and flexible pouches.

These chapters emphasize:

1. The critical points in forming the closure for food containers.

2. Frequency rates for sampling and examination of containers.

3. Acceptable and unacceptable variations in closure dimensions, if applicable.

4. Indications of closing or sealing machine malfunction.

5. Corrective measures for closure or sealing defects.

6. Importance of recordkeeping and proper interpretation of recorded results.

This discussion will help readers develop an organizational plan which will ensure that:

1. Inspection and handling of empty containers are adequate to detect and reject unacceptable lots.

2. Frequency and thoroughness of the inspection and maintenance of container closure equipment are adequate to minimize closure problems.

3. Training of operators of closure equipment is adequate to the degree that equipment problems are quickly detected and reported.

4. Employees who evaluate container closures are adequately equipped and trained to perform their assignments.

5. Procedures exist for segregation, retention and evaluation of containers with closures of questionable quality.

Definition of Hermetically Sealed Container

FDA and USDA canning regulations are specific for thermally processed foods packaged in hermetically sealed containers. A hermetically sealed container is defined as a container that is designed and intended to be secure against the entry of microorganisms and to maintain the commercial sterility of its contents during and after processing.

Requirements for Supervisor Training and Closure Examinations

Regulations governing the manufacture and processing of thermally processed low-acid foods packaged in hermetically sealed containers also include requirements dealing with containers and container closures. Regulatory requirements mandate that certain examinations and measurements shall be made and recorded for most common types of containers.

Training of Container Closure Supervisors

The regulations stipulate that all operators of retorts, processing systems, and aseptic processing and packaging systems, plus inspectors of container closures shall be under the operating supervision of a person who has attended a school that is approved by the FDA Commissioner or is generally recognized as adequate for giving instruction in the following areas: retort operations, processing systems operations, aseptic processing and packaging systems operations and container closure inspections. The person shall be identified by that school as having satisfactorily completed the prescribed course of instruction.

Mandatory Examination of Container Closures

A complete discussion of regulatory requirements for closures is found in the following three chapters. The regulations have the following requirements for the types of containers listed.

Rigid Container—*A container that is neither affected by the enclosed contents or deformed by external pressure up to 10 psig (USDA).*

Regular observations shall be made during production runs for gross closure defects. Any such defects shall be recorded along with the corrective action taken. Visual examinations and teardown examinations shall be conducted by a qualified container technician on at least one container from each seaming head or closing machine with sufficient frequency to ensure proper closure. Additional inspections shall be made at the beginning of production, immediately following a jam or after machine adjustments. Visual examinations should not exceed 30 minutes and teardown examinations should not exceed four hours.

Semirigid and Flexible—*A semirigid container is one that is not affected by the enclosed contents but is deformed by an external pressure of 10 psig or less (USDA). A flexible container is one where the shape is significantly affected by the enclosed contents (USDA).*

FDA requires that appropriate inspections be conducted and tests be made by qualified personnel at intervals of sufficient frequency to ensure proper closure. In addition, USDA requires that visual examinations and physical tests be part of this inspection. Physical tests should be made at least every two hours of continuous production. The inspection results, plus any additional information necessary to ensure proper closure, shall be recorded along with any corrective action taken.

The following chapters contain specific information for metal closures, glass closures, plastic containers with double seamed metal ends, plastic containers with heat sealed lids, paperboard containers and flexible pouches. Due to the large variety of closures that may be found on some types of containers (aseptic), it is not possible to discuss all closures. Information on closures not discussed in these chapters may be obtained from the manufacturer or a processing authority.

Chapter 16

CLOSURES FOR METAL CONTAINERS

The metal container is responsible for the success of food canning and its role in providing a year-round supply of high quality, nutritious food within the reach of all the nation's people regardless of location or income. Thus, the can has played and continues to play a vital role in our way of life and standard of living.

Hole and Cap Can

Tin cans were originally known as tin canisters and were invented in 1810 to preserve perishable foods. These containers were constructed with a cylindrical body, a top (ring) and a bottom (disc). The edges of the top and bottom were flanged 90 degrees and then snapped over

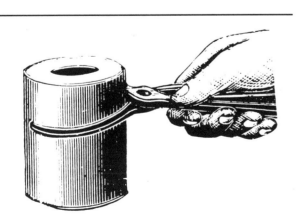

Figure 1—Hole and cap can used until 1900.

the openings at each end of the cylinder. The body was rolled, while tilted, through a solder bath to seal and bond one end. Then, it was tilted so that the other end could roll through the solder bath, immersed just enough to let the solder contact and flow into the lap seam (*Figure 1*).

An opening in the ring, which was the top end, was used as a filling hole for the product. Then a small disc with a tiny hole in the center was placed over the filling hole and soldered. After exhausting the headspace by preheating the can and contents, the small hole in the center of the disc was solder-tipped to close the container completely. Then it was heat processed.

Open Top Can

The turn of the century brought with it a new style of can known as the open top can. The side seam was still soldered, but the ends were fastened to the body by crimping—or as it is known today, by double seaming. By 1920 the open top can had replaced the hole and cap can. This technological breakthrough resulted in cans that could be manufactured, filled and closed more quickly. Most importantly, the hermetic double seam was a more reliable closure method.

In recent years, innovations have been made in the open top can. New technologies—such as the welded side seam, three-piece steel can and the seamless two-piece drawn steel and aluminum cans where the body and bottom are formed as a single unit—evolved. These technological advancements have been accompanied by further developments in materials and designs such as the half steam table tray, retort pouches, easy-open ends and the retortable, microwaveable plastic can.

Can Manufacturing Plate

The "tin" can was originally manufactured from steel sheets that had been dipped in molten tin. This "hot dipped" method was gradually replaced by electroplating the tin coating onto the base steel. This new method allowed for the application of lower and more uniform weights of tin as well as differential coating—different weights of tin on each side of the sheet. Also, electrolytically coated plate is produced in a continuous coil rather than from individual sheets.

Today tin-free steel—steel sheet with a light chromium surface treatment but no tin coating—is used extensively for applications where tin is not required to protect against corrosion or to facilitate the side seam welding process. For instance, tin-free steel is widely used for ends and for the manufacture of drawn two-piece cans.

Certain characteristics of the plate used in can manufacture affect the characteristics of the finished double seams. Depending on the can's size and strength requirements, different thicknesses of metal can be used. For steel containers, the thickness of the metal is indicated by specifying the theoretical weight in pounds per base box instead of actual thickness or gauge. A base box is a unit of area amounting to 31,360 square inches or 217.78 square feet. It corresponds to the area covered by 112 sheets, each 14 × 20 inches. The relationship of base weight to plate thickness is shown by the following formula:

$$\text{Base Weight} = \frac{\text{Plate Thickness (in inches)}}{.00011}$$

When dealing with materials other than steel—such as aluminum or plastic—thickness is specified directly in inches or millimeters.

The temper of tinplate or tin-free steel, usually designated by a number such as T1, T2, T3, etc, indicates the forming properties or hardness of tinplate (T1 = dead-soft; T5 = very hard). Double cold-reduced (2CR) or double-reduced (DR) tinplate or tin-free steel are steel-tin mill products that are given a partial cold reduction to near final gauge and then given another cold reduction to final gauge. The resulting plate is stiffer, harder and stronger than conventional tinplate and enables the use, wherever applicable, of lower base weights for container components.

Neither base weights nor tempers can be attained in tinplate without some variation. Those characteristics can only be controlled within a range, with the nominal value somewhere in the middle of that range. Obviously, with some variability in the basic materials used in can manufacture, double seam characteristics can also reflect similar degrees of variability.

Container Structure

The container structures that help form and become a part of the finished double seam are the body flange and the end curl.

Flange

The flange is the edge of the body cylinder that is flared outward resulting in a rim or ledge. The flange is formed into the body hook during double seaming and becomes interlocked with the cover hook. The width and radius of the flange are determined by can manufacturers to meet the requirements of forming a proper body hook during the double seaming operation (*Figure 2*).

End Curl

The end curl—sometimes referred to as cover curl—is designed to provide sufficient metal to form a good cover hook. Important in the design are proper curl, a proper base for sealing compound application and easy feeding of end units into the closing machine (*Figure 3*).

Sealing Compound

To aid in forming a sound double seam, a rubber-based gasket or sealing material called sealing compound is

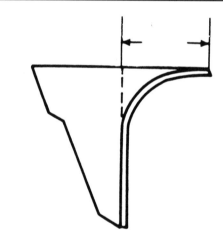

Figure 2—The outward flare of the body cylinder is called a flange.

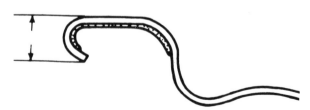

Figure 3—The end curl forms the cover hook and is the area where the sealing compound is placed.

necessary. Can manufacturers jet- or nozzle-apply the sealing compound into the annular groove of the can ends (*Figure 4*). The amount of compound used depends upon the type of compound, the can diameter, the type of sterilization method used and the style of the container. The type of compound depends upon the product and the method of sterilization. Lack of compatibility between compound and product can cause softening, smearing and oozing, resulting in reduced sealing efficiency.

Although the application of sealing compound to the ends is a relatively precise operation, equipment capability may provide variances in the placement and amount of sealing compound. As in the case of tinplate variability, the amount of sealing compound in the ends must also fall within a range of acceptability.

The Double Seam

A double seam is that part of the can formed by joining the body of the can and the end (sometimes referred to as the cover). The body flange and the curl of the end interlock during the double seaming operation to form a strong mechanical structure. Each double seam consists of three thicknesses of the can end and two thicknesses of the can body with an appropriate sealing compound distributed through the folded metal forming a hermetic seal (*Figure 5*).

The can double seam is generally formed in two operations referred to as first operation and second operation—hence the name double seam. Each station of the closing machine has a base plate, a seaming chuck, at least one first operation roll and one second operation roll. The base plate of the machine supports the can body. The snug fitting seaming chuck holds the can end in place and acts as a back-up for the double seaming roll pressure (*Figure 6*).

First Operation

In the first operation, the curl of the end is interlocked (sometimes referred to as engaged) with the flange of the can body. The actual interlocking is performed with a roll having a specially contoured groove. The first operation seam should not be too loose or too tight, since there is no way to correct a faulty first operation seam during the remaining seaming steps. A good quality first operation seam has the body hook approximately parallel to the cover hook, the edge of the flange of the body (which becomes the body hook) well tucked down in the cover hook radius, and the curl of the cover adjacent to, if not actually touching, the body wall of the can (*Figure 7*). The first operation seam will usually be made properly if the following conditions are met:

1. Correct pin gauge height, which is the distance between the bottom of the seaming chuck lip and the top surface of the base plate.

2. Correct base plate pressure.

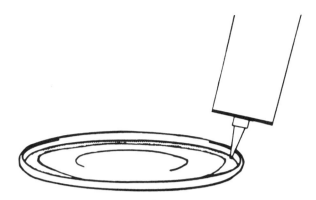

Figure 4—Application of sealing compound to can end.

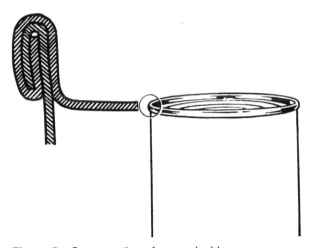

Figure 5—Cross section of a can double seam.

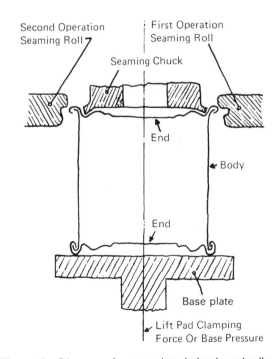

Figure 6—Diagram of seamer head chuck and rolls.

123

3. Correct alignment of seaming rolls to seaming chuck.

4. Correct tightness of the first operation roll.

When the first operation seam is completed, the first operation roll is retracted and no longer contacts the can end.

Second Operation

The second operation roll has a flatter groove profile than the first operation roll. The flatter profile is designed to press the preformed hooks together, to iron out wrinkles in the cover hook, to distribute sealing compound in the seam, and, specifically, to develop double seam tightness (*Figure 8*).

The tightness or compactness of the finished double seam is a function of the adjustment of the second operation roll, its profile and its condition. The second operation roll can be adjusted to tighten the finished double seam. If the correct roll profiles are not used, or the rolls are worn excessively, the desired seam structure and tightness cannot be achieved.

During the double seaming operation, considerable pressure is exerted on the can end, the can body and the sealing compound. The compound should be enclosed by the double seam. The compression by the seaming rolls will cause the sealing compound to flow and fill voids in the seam, thereby blocking potential leakage paths.

The Hermetic Seal

The sealing compound and the mechanically interlocked can end and body work together to make the double seam a hermetic seal (*Figure 8*). Neither the sealing compound nor the interlocked can body and end, by themselves, are able to seal a container hermetically. They must complement each other. The double seam must be correctly formed. The compound, notwithstanding its

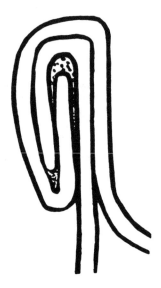

Figure 8—Normal second operation. (Note the compound fills the voids.)

resilience and ability to fill voids in the double seam, cannot compensate for an improperly formed seam.

Double Seam Structure

The quality of a finished first or second operation double seam may be judged by measuring and evaluating the specific structures comprising the seam. Seam dimension guidelines are normally furnished by the supplier of the can body and end being used. Two sets of dimensions may be provided for each attribute measured. The aim is an ideal starting dimension used for set up. The adjustment tolerance or operating limits set the range for good practice. When the adjustment limits are exceeded for critical dimensions, corrective action must be taken.

It is extremely important to understand that seam measurements by themselves cannot be used for determining the quality of a double seam. The seam dimension guidelines are provided for use in setting up the double seam initially and to assist in maintaining acceptable seams during production. The final judgment of the double seam can only be made by a visual inspection of the torn down seam in conjunction with measurements taken from the double seam component parts.

Some of the dimensions provided in the seam guidelines are determined by the plate weight or thickness. For instance, the thickness of either the first operation or second operation seam will depend to a great extent on the thickness of the can body and end being used. Body hook and cover hook lengths, on the other hand, are not affected by plate thickness unless extreme variations are encountered.

Seam dimensions suggested for given can sizes take into account the fact that the body plate and end plate are subject to inherent variations in thickness and hardness

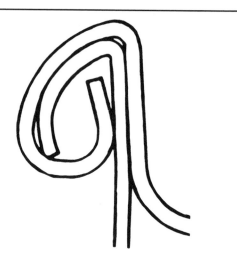

Figure 7—Normal first operation seam.

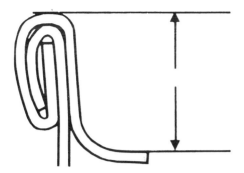

Figure 9—Countersink depth.

(temper). Consequently, the suggested seam dimensions reflect the thickness and tightness necessary for optimum seam integrity.

Seam Measurements

Countersink Depth

The countersink depth is the distance measured from the top of the double seam to the end panel adjacent to the inside wall of the double seam (*Figure 9*).

Seam Thickness

Seam thickness is the maximum distance measured across or perpendicular to the layers of material in the seam. As previously mentioned, there are three layers of the end and two of the body at locations other than the side seam juncture of soldered side seam cans. Thickness is an indication of double seam tightness; however, it should be emphasized that it is only *one* indication of seam tightness (*Figure 10*).

Seam Width (Length or Height)

Seam width, also referred to as seam length or height, is the dimension measured parallel to the hooks of the seam (*Figure 11*). This dimension is somewhat dependent upon the groove contour of the second operation seaming roll.

Body Hook and Cover Hook

The body hook, whose origin was the body flange, and the cover hook, which was formed during the double seaming operation from the end curl, reflect the internal aspects of the double seam. These two structures observed in a cross-section appear in an interlocking relationship to each other (*Figure 12*).

Overlap

The degree of interlock between the body hook and cover hook is known as overlap (*Figure 13*).

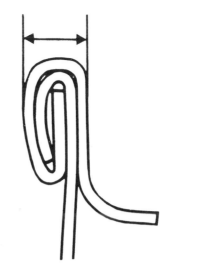

Figure 10—Seam thickness.

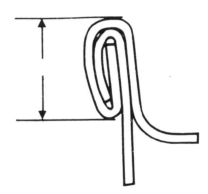

Figure 11—The seam width (length or height).

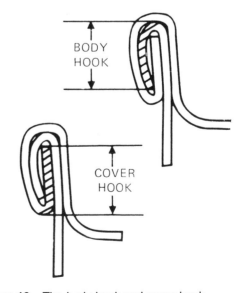

Figure 12—The body hook and cover hook.

Tightness

Seam tightness is judged by the degree of wrinkling of the cover hook. During the first operation, the end curl is guided around and up under the body flange. This process crowds the cut edge of the curl into a small circumference, resulting in a wavy cut edge with accompanying wrinkles around the seam. The function of the second operation roll is to press the preformed first operation cover hook and body hook together to such a degree that the wrinkles may be ironed out sufficiently to ensure a hermetic seal (*Figure 14*).

In a completed double seam, wrinkles may extend from the end curl cut edge downward on the face of the cover hook. The wrinkles help to indicate double seam tightness. Tightness ratio is a numerical designation which indicates the relative freedom from wrinkles—the percentage of smoothness of the cover hook. For additional information, see *Figure 53* and the "Tightness and juncture rating" section later in this chapter.

Juncture Area

The juncture is where the double seam meets and crosses over the side seam area of the can body on a three-piece can. On soldered side seam cans this is a critical area of the double seam, due to the two additional thicknesses of metal at that point (*Figure 15*). On welded side seam cans, the thickness of the weld is only slightly greater than the thickness of the body metal. While a slight impression of the weld is apparent on the face of the cover hook, droop generally is not evident. Some welded cans that are made using a thicker coating over the inside surface of the weld may exhibit slight droops

at the juncture. Two-piece containers have no side seam; therefore, they have no side seam juncture.

Critical Evaluation of the Double Seam

The variability of can-making materials, closing machine adjustments, and/or wear can cause significant variations in the double seam. The shape and conformation of the finished double seam are determined by the contour of the seaming rolls and the taper of the chuck. Roll contours may be changed to accommodate different plate thicknesses. The roll profiles and the pressure adjustments of the rolls and the base plate on the closing machine are the factors that finally determine the shape and integrity of the double seam and its dimensions. Along with visual appearance, the measurements of seam thickness, seam width and countersink depth are quick and easy signals to indicate proper double seam formation.

Although the external shape and conformation of the double seam may appear to be satisfactory, one or more critical internal structures may not be acceptable; as a result, a hermetic seal will not be achieved.

During the examination of double seams, measurements that are outside the recommended guidelines or visual defects may be found. The seriousness of these out-of-normal conditions requires experienced judgment. Whether or not immediate corrective action must be taken depends upon the effect of the seam condition on the soundness of the container seal.

A discussion of seam defects and their possible causes follows.

Excessive Countersink Depth

Excessive countersink depth occurs when the dimension exceeds operating limits and results in shortened cover hooks and overlap (*Figure 16*). Possible causes are:

1. Excessive baseplate pressure.
2. Insufficient (short) pin gauge height.

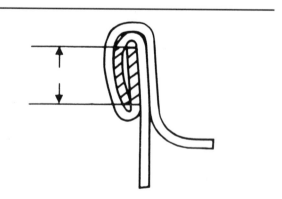

Figure 13—Overlap.

Figure 14—Cover hook wrinkles.

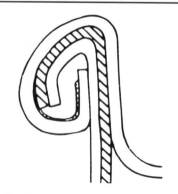

Figure 15—Butting at juncture (first operation).

3. Chuck not fully seated in the end unit.

4. Improper seaming chuck lip height.

5. Improper relation of first operation roll to lip of chuck.

Loose First Operation Seam

When the first operation is too loose, the cover hook will not be in contact with the can body, and there may not be sufficient "tuck up" of the end curl to form a good cover hook and overlap (*Figure 17*). Possible cause of a loose first operation seam may be:

1. First operation seaming roll setting too loose.

2. Worn first operation seaming roll.

3. Worn seaming roll cam, roll pins, bearings or plunger.

4. First operation seaming roll groove profile too wide.

Excessively Tight First Operation Seam

An excessively tight first operation seam will have the bottom of the seam slightly flattened throughout its length, sharp seams and poorly formed cover hooks (*Figure 18*). Possible causes are: (1) first operation seaming roll setting is too tight, and (2) first operation seaming roll groove is too narrow.

Short Body Hooks

When the body hook length is less than the recommended guidelines, the can is said to have short body hooks (*Figure 19*). Possible causes of this condition are:

1. Insufficient lifter pressure.

2. Incorrect pin height setting (seaming chuck set too high in relation to lifter baseplate).

3. First operation seaming roll set too tightly.

4. Second operation seaming roll set too loosely.

5. Improperly formed can flange length or flange radius.

Long Body Hooks

Long body hooks occur when the body hook length is in excess of recommended guidelines (*Figure 20*). Possible causes are:

1. Excessive lifter pressure.

2. Incorrect pin height (pin gauge setting). Seaming chuck too low in relation to lifter baseplate.

3. Improperly formed can flange length, flange radius or mushroomed can flange.

Loose Second Operation Seam

A loose second operation may produce a double seam that leaks because the folds of metal have not been pressed together tightly enough and the compound has not been

Figure 17—Loose first operation seam.

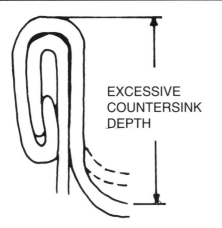

Figure 16—Excessive countersink depth shortens overlap.

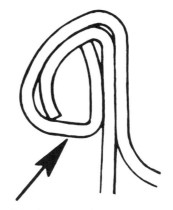

Figure 18—Tight first operation seam.

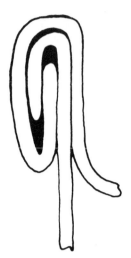

Figure 19—Short body hook.

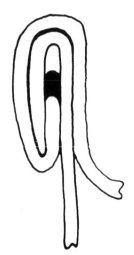

Figure 20—Long body hook.

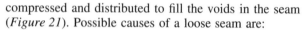

compressed and distributed to fill the voids in the seam (*Figure 21*). Possible causes of a loose seam are:

1. Improper setting of second operation seaming roll.
2. Worn second operation seaming roll.
3. Worn seaming roll cam, roll pins or bearings.
4. Second operation seaming roll groove too wide.

Excessively Tight Second Operation Seam

Excessive pressure in the second operation does not produce a good seam and may stretch the metal, causing an increase in the width (height or length) of the seam and an unhooking or reduction of the overlap (*Figure 22*). An excessively tight second operation seam may also cause sharp seams, as well as compound squeezing out of the seam. A tight seam is more likely to leak than one made with normal pressures. On soldered cans this condition is more pronounced at the side seam lap, so the can is more likely to leak at that point. Possible causes of an excessively tight second operation double seam are:

1. Improper setting of second operation seaming roll.
2. Body and/or end plate abnormally thick.

Short Cover Hook

A cover hook length less than recommended guidelines is known as a short cover hook (*Figure 23*). Possible causes of this condition are:

1. Poorly formed end curls.
2. First operation seaming roll set too loosely.
3. Excessive lifter pressure.
4. Worn first operation seaming roll groove.
5. Excessive countersink depth.

Long Cover Hook

Cover hook length in excess of recommended guidelines indicates a long cover hook condition (*Figure 24*). Possible causes of a long cover hook are: (1) first operation roll set too tightly and (2) poorly formed end curls.

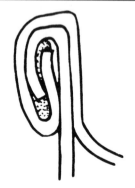

Figure 21—Loose second operation seam.

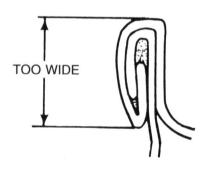

Figure 22—Excessively tight second operation seam.

128

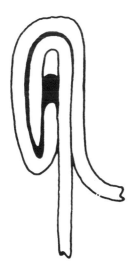

Figure 23—Short cover hook.

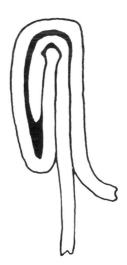

Figure 24—Long cover hook.

Insufficient Overlap

Insufficient overlap exists when the interlock between body hook and cover hook is less than recommended guidelines (*Figure 25*). Possible causes are:

1. Can body flanges out of specifications.
2. Cover end curls out of specifications.
3. Poor adjustment of the closing machine.

Seam Bumps

Seam bumps—most often seen on the packer's end of two-piece cans and three-piece welded side seam cans—are found in a relatively small area of the double seam up to one and one-quarter inches long where seam thickness

suddenly increases by .003 inch to .004 inch or more (*Figure 26*). The increase in thickness is accompanied by a cover hook that is pulled away from the body wall and, when viewed in cross-section, a distorted body hook (*Figure 27*). Possible causes of seam bumps include:

1. Excessively tight finished seams.
2. Long body hooks.
3. Excessive end sealing compound application.

Sprung Seams

Sprung seams is a term used to describe a seam condition that visually appears similar to a seam bump in that the cover hook has pulled away or "sprung back" from its original position and lost contact with the body of the

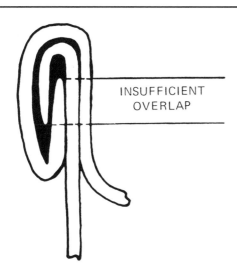

Figure 25—Insufficient overlap.

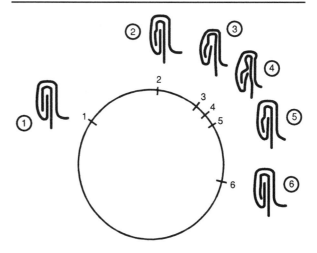

Figure 26—Formation of a seam bump around the double seam. Position 1 indicates a normal double seam and position 4 indicates a fully developed seam bump.

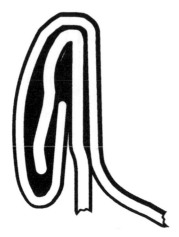

Figure 27—Seam bump cross-section.

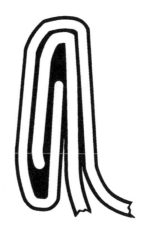

Figure 28—Sprung seam.

can. No internal seam distortion is noted in a seam cross-section. An increase in seam thickness can be noted at that point (*Figure 28*). The existence of this condition is related more to can design and can metals of particular hardness.

Structural Defects

Structural defects are seam abnormalities that are generally serious in nature and may result in loss of the hermetic seal. Observation of any of the following structural defects requires experienced judgement with appropriate corrective action.

Droop

A smooth projection of a double seam below the bottom of a normal seam is identified as a droop. This may occur at any point around the seam. There is commonly a slight droop present where the double seam crosses over the lap (the juncture) of the side seam on soldered cans (*Figure 29*). Possible causes of droop are:

1. Excessive body hook.
2. First operation too loose.
3. Excessive solder in side seam.
4. Worn first operation rolls or roll bearings.
5. Cocked can bodies.
6. Product trapped in seam.
7. Excessive amount or unequal distribution of end seaming compound.
8. Can flange or end curl defect.

Vee or Lip

Vees or lips are irregularities in the double seam due to insufficient and sometimes no overlap of the cover

hook with the body hook, usually in small areas of the seam. The cover hook metal protrudes below the seam at the cover hook radius in one or more "V" shapes (*Figure 30*). Possible causes are the same as for droop.

Sharp Seam

A sharp seam refers to a sharp edge at the top inside portion of the seam, whether at the side seam lap of soldered cans or all the way around the end of any can style. The condition results from a portion of the cover being forced over the top of the seaming chuck lip during double seaming (*Figure 31*). A sharp seam usually can be felt more easily than it can be seen. This condition can be the first indication of a further complication known as a cut-over.

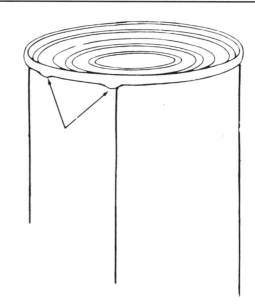

Figure 29—Droop.

130

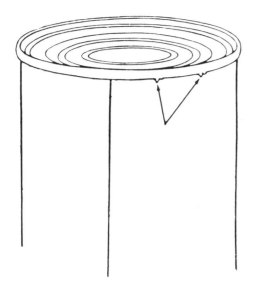

Figure 30—Vee.

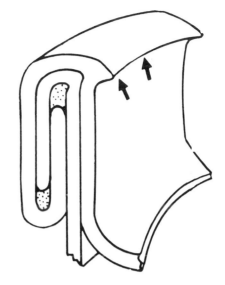

Figure 31—Sharp seam.

Cut-Over

A cut-over is a seam that is sharp enough to fracture the metal at the top inside portion of the seam. This condition is more likely to occur in soldered side seam cans (*Figure 32*). Possible causes of both sharp seams and cut-overs are:

1. Worn seaming chuck.

2. First or second operation seaming rolls set too tight.

3. Worn seaming roll grooves.

4. Excessive solder at the side seam lap.

5. Product in the seam.

6. Vertical play in seaming head assembly.

7. Incorrect alignment of first operation seaming roll to seaming chuck.

8. Excessive vertical play of first operation seaming roll.

9. Excessive base plate pressure.

Jumped Seam or Jump-Over

A jumped seam is a portion of a double seam adjacent to the juncture area of a soldered side seam can that is not rolled tight enough. It is caused by the jumping of the seaming rolls after passing over the lap (*Figure 33*).

Deadhead or Spinner

A deadhead is an incomplete seam caused by the chuck spinning in the countersink of the end during the seaming operation (*Figure 34*). This seam defect is also known as a ''spinner'', ''skidder'' or ''slip''. Possible causes include:

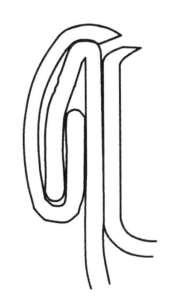

Figure 32—Cut-over.

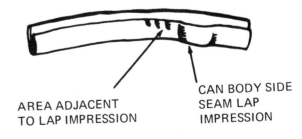

AREA ADJACENT
TO LAP IMPRESSION

CAN BODY SIDE
SEAM LAP
IMPRESSION

Figure 33—Jumped seam.

131

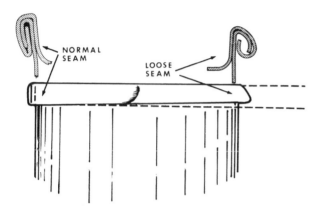

Figure 34—Deadhead or spinner.

1. Incorrect baseplate pressure.
2. Improper end-fit with seaming chuck.
3. Worn seaming chuck.
4. Seaming rolls binding (not freely rotating).
5. Oil or grease on chuck.
6. Excessive vertical play of seaming chuck spindle.
7. Incorrect pin-gauge setting (seaming chuck too high in relation to baseplate).
8. Lifters not rotating freely.

False Seam

A false seam is a seam or portion of a seam that is entirely unhooked and in which the folded cover hook is compressed against the folded body hook (*Figure 35*). A false seam is not always detectable in an external examination. Therefore, a seam section or teardown may be necessary to reveal this defect. Possible causes of false seams are:

1. Bent can flange.
2. Mushroomed flange.
3. Damaged or bent end curls.
4. Misassembly of can and cover.
5. Can not centering on seam chuck.

Other terms may more specifically describe a false seam condition. A **knocked down flange** is usually caused by a bent can flange before double seaming (*Figure 36*). Possible causes of knocked down flanges include:

1. Improper can handling.
2. Out of time end feed and/or can feed settings of the closing machine.

Damaged end curls result when the end curl is flattened in one or more spots, causing the curl to fold back on itself. Possible causes of damaged end curls are:

1. Damage due to improper handling of end units.
2. Improper cover feed or end guide settings.

Can Body Buckling

Can body buckling is a condition found directly under the finished seam where the can appears to have a buckled or twisted condition (*Figure 37*). Possible causes of body buckling are:

1. Excessive baseplate pressure.
2. Improper pin-gauge setting (chuck too low).

Cocked Body

A cocked body occurs when the can body blank was out of square at the time of manufacturing, causing an unevenness at the lap or juncture (*Figure 38*). This is a can manufacturing defect—not a double seam defect—that could result in double seam dimensions that vary excessively around the circumference of the can.

Misassembly

A misassembly, sometimes referred to as a misplaced cover, is the result of the can body and end being improp-

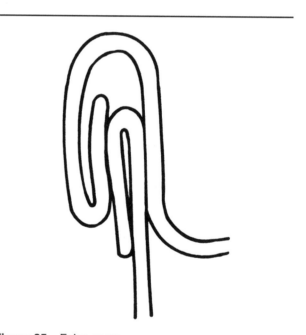

Figure 35—False seam.

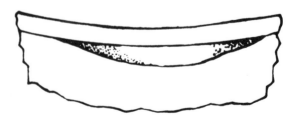

Figure 36—Knocked down flange.

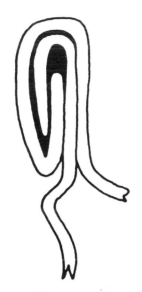

Figure 37—Body buckle.

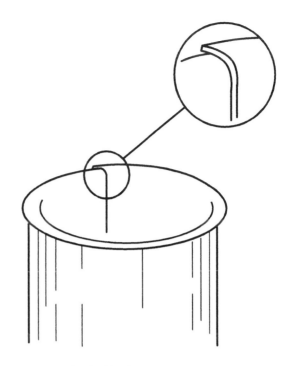

Figure 38—Cocked body.

erly aligned in the closing machine. Therefore, the seam is completely disconnected partway around the can. Possible causes are:

1. Closing machine settings or timing incorrect.
2. Sluggish seaming roll levers.

Cut Seam

A cut seam is a fractured double seam wherein the outer layer of the seam is fractured (*Figure 39*). Possible causes are:

1. Excessively tight seam.
2. Excess solder at the lap of soldered side seam cans.
3. Excessive sealing compound.
4. Defective end plate.

Mushroomed Flange

A mushroomed flange is a can flange that is over-formed, resulting in a long body hook. It may not be possible to see this condition until a cross-section of the seam is cut and examined (*Figure 40*). Possible causes of mushroomed flanges are:

1. Poor can handling practices.
2. Over-flanging.
3. Damage by can filler.

Fractured Embossed/Debossed Codes

Fractured embossed/debossed codes result when the metal of the end has been cut through at the code mark. Fractured embossed/debossed codes may possibly be caused by:

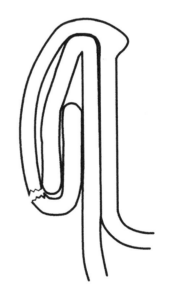

Figure 39—Cut seam.

1. Misalignment of male and female type characters.
2. Misalignment of type holders.
3. Intermixing of new and old types.
4. Improper matching of male and female type.
5. Excessive coder pressure or improper coder setting giving too deep a code mark.

133

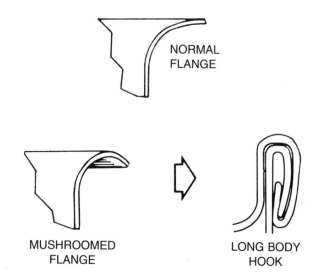

NORMAL FLANGE

MUSHROOMED FLANGE

LONG BODY HOOK

Figure 40—Mushroomed flange.

Broken Chuck

Broken chuck defects occur when a portion of the chuck lip has broken. This results in an excessively loose seam at this point due to lack of backup support for the seaming rolls. Often, an impression of the damaged area of the chuck is made on the end countersink wall. Possible causes for a broken chuck are:

1. Severe jam in the closing machine.

2. Seaming rolls binding on chuck.

3. Improper metal used for chuck or metal fatigue in chuck lip.

4. Prying against chuck to clear a jam.

Evaluation of Double Seam Integrity

It is mandatory that double seams be inspected by a trained closure technician at regular intervals to ensure that satisfactory double seams are being formed throughout daily production. These inspections shall include both visual and teardown examinations. A regular program of seam inspection will minimize the possibility of poorly double seamed containers reaching the consumer. Personnel performing closure examinations shall be under the supervision of a person who has successfully completed a school recognized as adequate for training supervisors of canning operations.

Visual Examinations

A visual examination of double seams formed by each closing machine head is required. The external features of the double seam of each container shall be examined for gross closure defects such as cut-over or sharpness, knock down flanges, false seams, droops and damage to the countersink wall (an indication of a broken seaming chuck).

Additionally, USDA regulations require and good manufacturing practice suggests that these examinations not be limited to double seam defects. Rather they shall include examination of the entire container for product leakage or other obvious defects. When any defects in the double seam or can body or end are observed, the observation along with any corrective action(s) taken shall be recorded.

These examinations shall be conducted as often as necessary to ensure proper closure. Under any conditions, however, the interval between visual inspections should not exceed 30 minutes of continuous closing machine operation. Additional visual examinations shall be made at the beginning of production, immediately following a jam in the closing machine, machine adjustment or a prolonged shut down. It is also recommended that visual examinations follow changes in supply sources for cans and lids and following any changes in container codes.

Teardown Examinations

Tools

The results of double seam examinations are only as reliable as the accuracy of the tools and the care with which the tools are used. All measurements are made and recorded in thousandths of an inch, thus precision tools and measurements are necessary. The person responsible for tearing down seams should be thoroughly schooled in proper measuring techniques. It is important that care be exercised in making the measurements. An inaccurate tool and/or measurement technique may result in the following problems:

1. Failure to detect poorly-formed double seams.

2. Unnecessary retention of product packed in cans with good double seams.

3. Inappropriate adjustment of closing machines.

Given reasonable care, the measuring devices should not need adjustment. However, they should be checked periodically to avoid the possibility of inaccurate measurements.

Seam Micrometer—The seam micrometer has a standard micrometer barrel incorporated onto a suitable stem that has been designed specifically for measurement of double seam dimensions (*Figure 41*). A standard micrometer with a round anvil also can be used. The micrometer is placed over the surface to be measured by balancing it with the index finger at a 90 degree angle to the surface. The micrometer is lowered onto the surface until the anvil touches the surface. The adjustment barrel of the micrometer should then be used to bring the stem in contact with the other side of the surface without exerting excess pressure.

Figure 41—Seam micrometer.

Figure 42—Countersink gauge.

Figure 43—Special can opener.

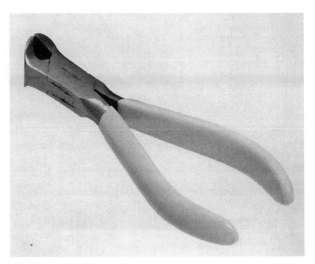

Figure 44—Nippers.

Countersink Gauge—The dial indicator countersink gauge is probably the best (*Figure 42*). However, other types of instruments are less expensive. All are used to measure the countersink depth from the top of the seam to the lowest point adjacent to the countersink wall (away from the side seam crossover).

Can Opener—The special manual can opener is a heavy duty unit commercially available from most container suppliers (*Figure 43*). It is adjustable to the can diameter and removes the center panel of the cover without damaging the seams or the body. The use of a conventional household can opener is discouraged.

Nippers—Nippers are used to tear off the strip of the cover left by the can opener. Most nippers are standard No. 5 nippers available in most hardware stores (*Figure 44*), but other sizes can be used. Experience indicates this size to be the most desirable.

The use of one or more of the following pieces of equipment is optional, but recommended for consistent and more accurate double seam evaluation.

Seam Saw (Optional)—A cross-section of the double seam can be cut with a fine metal saw. A power-driven seam saw is a convenience when many seams are to be inspected (*Figure 45*).

Seam Projector (Optional)—A seam projector is very effective for direct measurement of the seam overlap (*Figure 46*). A small cross-section is first removed from the double seam area of the can. It is then clamped into position, and calipers in the base of the projector permit direct measurement on the projected image of the overlap, cover hook and body hook. The projector allows inspection of the total seam configuration at the same time. Electronic projectors (*Figure 47*) with measurement cursors using a computer interface allow for more precise, consistent, error-free measurement and recording. It should be noted that seam projectors are limited to observing a cross-section of the seam. They do not eliminate the need for seam teardown to make a complete evaluation.

Seam Scope (Optional)—The seam scope is a pencil-like magnifier with an attached light source (*Figure 48*). It contains a visible scale by which the length of the body hook, cover hook and overlap can be read directly in thousandths of an inch on the exposed cross-section of the double seam. Its uses and limitations are similar to those of the seam projector.

Teardown frequency

Double seam teardown examinations shall be performed by a trained closure technician at intervals of sufficient frequency to ensure proper closure. These examinations shall be made on the packer's end double seams using at least one can from each seaming head to ensure maintenance of seal integrity. Teardown examinations should be made at intervals not to exceed four operating hours. The results of teardown examinations,

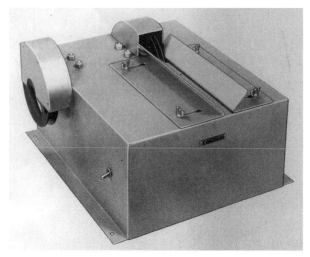

Figure 45—A power-driven seam saw (For illustrative purposes only—the blades on current models are enclosed to prevent injury).

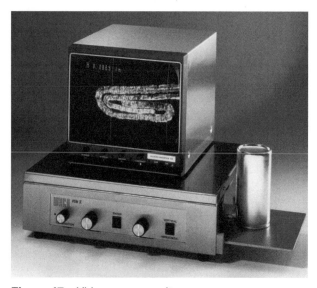

Figure 47—Video seam monitor

Figure 46—A seam projector.

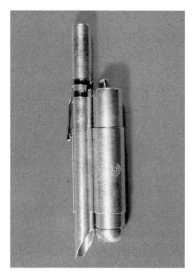

Figure 48—Seam scope.

tainers or when the containers are made nearby and the teardown records from the can manufacturer are available to the USDA representative. USDA also requires that the processor maintain specific guidelines for double seam integrity on file and make them available for review by USDA representatives.

Required measurements

The regulations allow for two methods of double seam teardown examination commonly referred to as the "micrometer" system and the "optical" system.

If a micrometer system is used, measurements are made at three points approximately 120 degrees apart around the double seam, excluding the side seam itself, and at

along with any corrective actions taken, shall be promptly recorded. USDA and good manufacturing practice suggest that these examinations be performed at the beginning of production, immediately following a severe jam or after adjustments/changes to the seaming machine.

In addition to these requirements, the USDA requires that teardown examinations be performed on the can manufacturer's end of at least one container per closing machine at each seam inspection interval, except when teardown examinations are conducted on incoming con-

least one-half inch from the side seam juncture (USDA regulation). USDA requires that at least the maximum and minimum values for each measurement be recorded by the closure technicians. FDA does not have a specific requirement for the manner in which data are recorded; it is recommended that the highest and lowest values be used. Average dimensions derived by calculation from individual measurements of any seam component should not be used.

The following measurement/observations are required (*Figure 49*).

1. Cover hook length.
2. Body hook length.
3. Width (length, height).
4. Tightness (observations for wrinkle).
5. Thickness.
6. Side seam juncture rating (USDA only).

The following determinations are optional with regard to FDA regulation:

1. Overlap (by formula).
2. Countersink.

The formula used to calculate overlap when micrometer measurements are employed is:

theoretical overlap length = CH + BH + T − W

where:
CH = cover hook
BH = body hook
T = end thickness in inches*
W = seam width (height, length)
(*For convenience the end thickness can be assumed to be .010 inches)

If a seam scope or can seam projector (optical system) is used to make the measurements, seam cross-sections should be cut from at least two different locations around the double seam, excluding the side seam juncture.

The following measurements/observations are required:

1. Body hook.
2. Overlap.
3. Tightness (observations for wrinkle).
4. Thickness (by micrometer).
5. Side seam juncture rating (USDA only).

The following are optional by FDA regulation, but should be made:

1. Width (length, height).
2. Cover hook.
3. Countersink.

Teardown measurement procedures

When evaluating the double seam, the applicable external measurements—seam width (length, height), thickness and countersink—are made and recorded first. The thickness and seam width are measured by using a seam micrometer. The measurements should be made without exerting any undue pressure on the adjustment barrel of the micrometer. The countersink dimensions should be taken and recorded by using a suitable depth gauge. Care must be taken to ensure that the point of the depth gauge pin is positioned so that the reading is taken at the base of the countersink radius with the bar of the gauge positioned across the diameter of the end.

To make the internal measurements and observations of the seam, the body and cover hooks must be separated in a special manner to expose the hooks so that they can be accurately measured and/or evaluated for tightness

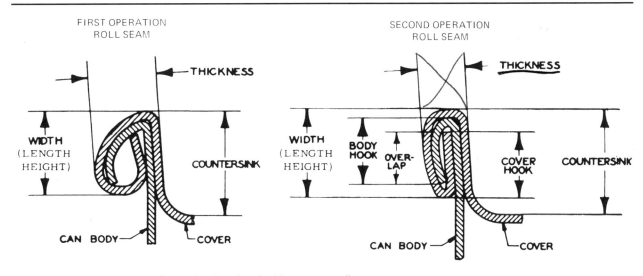

Figure 49—Measurements for evaluating the double seam quality.

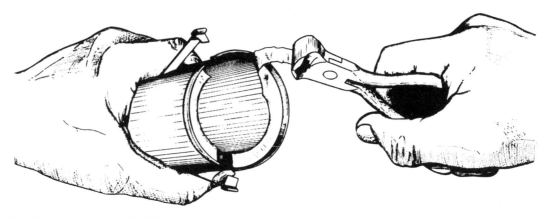

Figure 50—Tearing down the double seam.

and juncture rating. This procedure is commonly referred to as "stripping" or "teardown" (*Figure 50*).

After the cover hook section has been removed from the can, it shall be closely examined for the following (*Figure 51*):

1. Wave or wrinkle condition.
2. Fractures.
3. Condition of juncture area.

If the micrometer system is used, the required cover hook measurements shall be taken around the seam and recorded. The body hook (*Figure 51*), which remains on the can after removing the cover hook, shall also be examined and measured.

Regardless of the measurement system used, the cross-over or juncture area should be carefully examined. Also, the pressure ridge area (*Figure 52*) on the inside wall of the can just opposite the body hook should be examined. The pressure ridge is an impression on the body wall as the result of the pressure applied by the second operation roll in creating seam tightness.

Tightness and juncture rating

When all of the cans in the sample set have been examined and stripped or torn down and the pertinent measurements recorded, the condition of the cover hook shall be rated for tightness and, where appropriate, juncture rating (USDA).

In a completed double seam, any remaining wrinkles help to indicate double seam tightness. Tightness rating is a numerical designation that indicates the relative freedom from wrinkles or smoothness of the cover hook. Several numerical systems are used, as indicated in *Figure 53*. The most commonly used system involves rating tightness from 0 to 100 percent tightness based upon the percentage of freedom from wrinkle. Tightness should be judged not by the number of wrinkles but by the amplitude of the largest wrinkle.

The juncture (crossover) rating for soldered cans indicates the percentage of the cover hook metal available

for overlap when it is interlocked with a body hook (*Figure 54*). In addition to the juncture rating, the seam should be carefully examined for any sign of a looseness wrinkle adjacent to the crossover.

The importance of careful physical measurement and visual examination of the double seam cover hook and body hook cannot be overemphasized. Nothing can replace experience and the good judgment of the closure technician in this part of the double seam evaluation.

Interpretation of Inspection Results

If either the measurements or visual observations are found to be unsatisfactory for one or more of the cans examined, a repeat sampling from the questionable seaming station should be made before any machine adjustments are attempted. If the same unsatisfactory condition is found in the repeat sampling, a decision must be made on whether the nature of the defect is of sufficient magni-

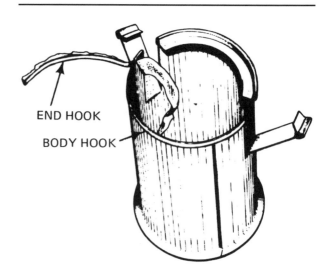

END HOOK
BODY HOOK

Figure 51—Disengaged cover hook.

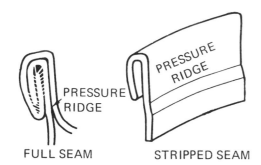

Figure 52—Pressure ridge on inside wall.

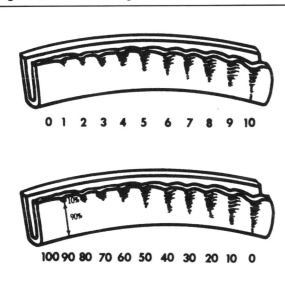

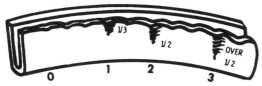

Figure 53—Tightness (cover hook wrinkle) ratings. Several numerical systems are used.

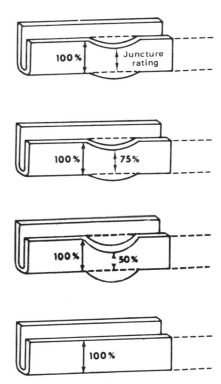

Figure 54—Juncture rating indicates the percentage of cover hook metal at the juncture available for an overlap when it is interlocked with a body hook.

tude to warrant shutting down production immediately, or to continue operating until the end of the production period or next normal down-time. Too frequent or over-adjusting of closing machines can be troublesome and produce defective double seams.

The following examples may be cited as conditions under which production might be continued at little risk until a down-time provides opportunity for adjustment without loss of production.

1. A visual inspection indicates slight sharpness, especially in the juncture area.

2. If the body hook minimum set-up range is .075 inch for the particular can being run and the adjustment tolerance minimum is .072 inch, and inspection reveals that the hooks are running on the low side in the range of .073 to .076 inch, adjustment may be made when convenient.

3. When the thickness adjustment tolerances are .046 to .052 inch and measurements show thickness on the high side up to .053 inch, but the cover hook displays a 100 percent tightness, no immediate adjustment is necessary.

There may at times be pressure on the closing machine operator to continue production until a normal down-time comes, even if abnormal seam conditions are observed. This practice should not be tolerated, since it leads to the production of inferior containers.

If unsatisfactory or questionable double seams are being made or if conditions approximating the following examples are found on visual inspection, the equipment must be shut down and corrections made.

1. Sharp cut-over around periphery of inside of seam or fractures.

2. Heavy cut-over at crossover.

3. Severe droop at crossover.

4. Vees or lips protruding below bottom of double seam.

5. False seam.

6. Distorted or obviously poorly formed seams at the countersink wall or the outside of the seam, which would indicate a probable broken chuck or seaming roll.

7. Skidding or deadheading evidence.

8. Fractured embossed/debossed end code.

If, after teardown, measurements on critical factors beyond the adjustment tolerance limits are found, correction must be made immediately.

Good seam formation cannot be judged by purely mechanical means or measurements. The evaluation requires experience and skill that cannot be quickly imparted. This section has attempted, however, to highlight those factors involved in double seam evaluation that are most essential to good seam formation and to give the supervisor an insight and appreciation of these factors.

Can Seam Evaluation Records

All double seam visual examinations and measurements shall be recorded. The exact nature of any serious defects observed shall be recorded as well as the steps taken for correction. Any marginal or unusual conditions observed should also be recorded. Complete and accurate records are required. The details and examples of forms are contained in Chapter 6.

Chapter 17

CLOSURES FOR GLASS CONTAINERS

The glass package commonly used for low-acid and acidified foods is comprised of two separate elements—the glass container and the metal closure. Both are essential for forming a proper hermetic seal. The characteristics of the glass container and closure (also referred to as cap or lid) will be discussed in this chapter along with the methods for evaluating the closure application.

The Basic Parts of a Glass Container

The three basic parts of a glass container are the finish, the body and the bottom (*Figure 1*). These are formed by the three parts of the glass-container molds in which they are made.

Finish—The finish is the part of the jar that holds the cap or closure, the glass surrounding the opening in the container. In the manufacturing process, it is made in the neck ring or the finish ring. It is so named because, in early hand glass manufacturing, it was the last part of the glass container to be made, hence the term ''finish.''

Body—The body of the container is the portion that is made in the body-mold. It is, in most cases the largest part of the container and lies between the finish and the bottom.

Bottom—The bottom of the container is made in the bottom plate part of the glass-container mold.

The Finish

The finish of glass containers has several specific areas, as follows (*Figure 1*):

Sealing Surface—The portion of the finish that makes contact with the sealing gasket or liner. The sealing surface is usually on the top of the finish, but may be a combination of both top and side seal.

Glass Thread or Lug— One of several horizontal, tapering and protruding ridges of glass around the periphery of the finish that permit specially-designed edges or lugs on the closure to slide between these protrusions and fasten the closure securely with a partial turn. The number of lugs on the closure and their precise configuration is established by the closure manufacturer.

Continuous Thread—A continuous spiral projecting glass ridge on the finish of a container intended to mesh with the thread of a screw-type closure.

Transfer Bead—A continuous horizontal ridge of glass near the bottom of the finish used in transferring the container from one part of the manufacturing operation to another.

Note: Not all glass containers have transfer beads. Some achieve the transfer in manufacturing through different means.

Vertical Neck Ring Seam—A mark on the glass finish resulting from the joint of matching the two parts of the neck ring, also referred to as the **Mold Match** or **Parting Line**.

141

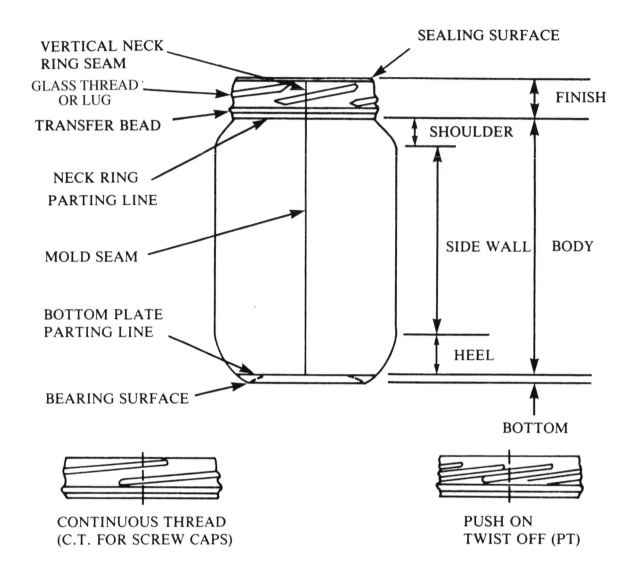

Figure 1—The basic parts of a glass container.

Neck Ring Parting Line —A horizontal mark on the glass surface at the bottom of the neck or finish ring resulting from the matching of the neck ring parts with the body-mold parts.

The Body

The characteristic parts of the body of a glass container are shown in *Figure 1*:

Shoulder—The portion of a glass container in which the maximum cross-section of the body area decreases to join the neck or finish area. The neck area is not shown in *Figure 1* because most glass containers for processed goods have very little neck. Actually, the neck would be any straight area between the shoulder and the bottom

of the bead or, with beadless finishes, the neck ring parting line.

Heel—The heel is the curved portion between the bottom and the beginning of the straight area of the side wall.

Side Wall—The remainder of the body area between the shoulder and the heel.

Mold Seam—A vertical mark on the glass surface in the body area resulting from matching the two parts of the body-mold. The body-mold seam may or may not align with the vertical neck ring seam.

The Bottom

The designated parts of the bottom area are normally those shown in *Figure 1*:

142

Bottom Plate Parting Line—A horizontal mark on the glass surface resulting from the matching of the body-mold parts with the bottom plate.

Bearing Surface—The portion of the container on which it rests. The bearing surface may have a special configuration known as the stacking feature, which is designed to provide some interlocking of the bottom of the jar with the closure of another jar on which it might be stacked for display purposes.

Discussion of the Finish

Many different finishes exist for closing glass containers. *Figure 1* shows only three general types, which may be varied for use with specific closures.

Every type of closure for sealing glass containers has a specific glass finish with which the closure has been designed to function. Attempts to put a lug cap on a jar with a Press-on Twist-off (PT) finish would be futile. Several different types of lug closures are available, each of which has been designed to work best with a specific lug-style finish.

Fortunately, many glass finishes are standardized. For every finish standard designation, a specific set of dimensions, specifications and tolerances have been established by the Glass Packaging Institute, a trade association that works with glass manufacturers and closure manufacturers. Each finish standard drawing has a specific number and may be obtained directly from the Glass Packaging Institute or through the glass manufacturer.

Lubricants or Glass Surface Treatments

Surface treatments or lubricants on glass containers serve the beneficial purpose of easing the smooth flow of containers through conveying systems. They protect the outside surface of the container from abrasion during manufacture and distribution. Many different treatments are used. The use of or change in a surface treatment should be fully discussed with both the glass container and closure suppliers to prevent potential problems. For example, excess surface treatment may effect closure performance or label application.

Definitions of Terms for Glass Closures

Among the terms commonly used for describing parts of metal vacuum closures are the following (*Figure 2*):

Panel—The flat center area in the top of the cap.

Radius or Shoulder—The rounded area at the outer edge of the panel connecting the panel and skirt.

Skirt—The flat, nearly vertical portion on the side of the cap. The skirt may be smooth, knurled or fluted and serves as the gripping surface.

Curl—The rounded or rolled portion at the bottom of the skirt that adds rigidity to the cap and serves to protect the cut edge of the metal.

Lug—A horizontal inward protrusion from the curl that is seated under the thread on the glass finish and holds the cap in position.

Thread—The spiral groove on the skirt of a continuous thread closure that meshes with the thread on the glass finish.

Face—The outside of the cap.

Reverse—The inside of the cap.

Coatings and Lithography—Coatings and inks that are used on the inner and outer surfaces of the cap to protect the metal from attack, adhere gasket materials and decorate the closure.

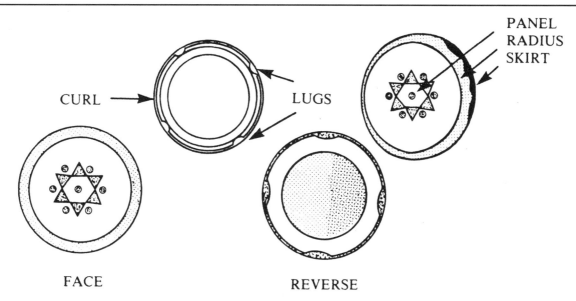

CURL   LUGS   PANEL
                    RADIUS
                    SKIRT

FACE   REVERSE

Figure 2—Parts of metal vacuum closures.

Gasket—The actual sealing member of the cap that must make intimate contact with the glass finish at the proper point to form an effective seal. Gaskets may be made from plastisol compounds.

Plastisols—Suspensions of finely divided resin in a plasticizer, which are usually of two types: (1) flowed-in—used in the standard lug or twist cap, and (2) molded—used in the PT cap. Plastisols are tailored to the product and process. For example, a closure intended for sealing a pasteurized product may not be suitable on a retorted product.

Safety Button or Flip Panel—A raised, circular area in the center of the panel that is used only for vacuum packed products and serves two principal purposes:

1. Dud detection—In the packaging plant it aids in automatic on-line detection of low-vacuum or no-vacuum packages.

2. Consumer indicator—It is an indicator to the consumer that the package is properly sealed when opened in the home. In addition to visual evidence of a disrupted seal, there is also an audible signal.

Role of Vacuum in Obtaining Good Seals

Almost all low-acid and acidified foods packed in glass containers are sealed with vacuum-type closures. The following discussion deals exclusively with this type of closure. The vacuum within the package and the resultant positive pressure on the outside of the cap play an important role in forming and maintaining a good seal. It is important to know how vacuum is formed, what may affect the vacuum level, and how, when, and where it should be measured.

Vacuum Cappers for Glass Containers

Two basic types of cappers apply caps while forming a vacuum in the container—the mechanical vacuum capper and the steam-flow capper. The mechanical vacuum capper is used primarily on dry products and applies the cap to the jar in an evacuated chamber. It is rarely used on low-acid processed foods.

In steam-flow cappers, either straight line or rotary, the container is subjected to a controlled steam atmosphere that displaces the headspace gases from the jar by a flushing action. The steam is trapped in the headspace as the cap is applied, then condenses to form a vacuum that helps hold the closure in place. As an aid to good sealing, the gasket in plastisol-lined caps is softened by steam.

Factors Affecting Vacuum Formation

Four primary factors affect vacuum formation:

1. **Headspace** is an important factor in efficient sealing, particularly in steam-flow cappers. For low-acid food products, sufficient headspace must be allowed to trap adequate steam in the container for forming a vacuum and to accommodate product expansion during retorting. The correct amount of headspace varies with product, processes and product design. However, a rule-of-thumb indicator is that the headspace should be not less than 6 percent of the container volume when measured at the capping temperature. Inadequate headspace can result in displacement or deformation of the closure during retorting. This 6 percent headspace is not as critical with acidified products that are either hot-filled or pasteurized. There still has to be sufficient headspace, however, to allow for vacuum formation, a clean fill and some product expansion during pasteurization.

2. **Product sealing temperature** affects the final vacuum obtained due to the effect of product contraction upon cooling. Other factors being constant, the higher the product temperature at the time of sealing, the higher the final package vacuum. Product temperature may also affect the final vacuum by its interaction with the amount of air in the product. Usually, higher filling temperatures result in less air in the product.

3. **Air in the product**, as mentioned above, can have a direct effect on the final package vacuum and should be kept at a minimum for good sealing, product quality and product appearance. The more air that is trapped in the product, the lower the vacuum.

4. **Capper vacuum efficiency** refers to the ability of the capper to produce vacuum in sealed containers. The most convenient, routine check on the vacuum efficiency of a steam-flow capper is the cold-water vacuum check. It is simple and quick; measurements are made with a vacuum gauge. The cold-water vacuum check shall be made prior to the start-up of actual filling operations or after extended break periods, at change-over from one container size to another, after a major jam, or whenever an unexplained significant change in vacuum level occurs in regular line samples. This check can serve the dual purpose of checking capper vacuum efficiency and cap application with the same jars.

Method of Cold-Water Vacuum Check

A series of jars is filled with cold tap water to the approximate headspace that will be maintained with the commercial product. These are then sealed in the capper after the capper has been allowed to warm up to operating temperature and the normal steam setting attained. The jars are opened and re-run through the capper and then checked for vacuum. The first run through the capper serves to deaerate the water and provide a truer vacuum reading. The vacuum obtained in the jars is then measured by using a standard vacuum gauge. In most instances, the closed gauge vacuum reading obtained should be at least 22 inches, or as recommended by the closure supplier.

The number of jars used to perform the cold-water vacuum check should be as follows:

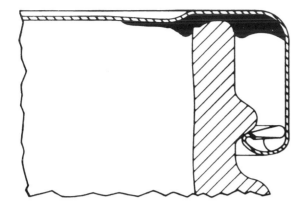

Figure 3—Regular lug or twist cap.

1. Straight-line capper: Four to six containers.
2. Rotary capper: One container for each capping head.

The Principal Vacuum Closure Types

Currently, two types of vacuum closures—lug or twist cap and PT cap—are widely used on low-acid food products. In addition, the plastisol-lined continuous thread (PLCT) closure is used on acidified food products.

Lug or Twist Cap

The lug or twist cap (*Figure 3*) has gained steadily in popularity to become the predominant vacuum-cap type. It is referred to as a convenience or utility closure, because it can be removed without a tool and forms a good reseal for storage.

1. **Structural components**—The lug cap consists of a steel shell and may have from three to six lugs, depending on its diameter; it normally contains a flowed-in plastisol gasket.

2. **Application and seal formation**—The headspace of the glass container is swept by steam the same as the other closure styles. Lug caps are secured to the glass finish by turning or twisting the cap onto the finish to seat the lugs of the cap under the threads on the glass finish. It is desirable, in most instances, that the gasket be softened by heat in the capper to facilitate sealing. Both the lugs and vacuum hold the cap in place on the glass finish, but vacuum is the most important.

PT (Press-on Twist-off) Cap

The Press-on Twist-off or PT cap is in widespread use for baby foods as well as other products (*Figure 4*). It combines the simple application requirements of a press-on closure with the convenience of a lug cap:

1. **Structural components**—The cap consists of a steel shell that has no lugs. The gasket is molded plastisol that covers a sealing area extending from the outer edge of the top panel to the curl of the cap, forming the primary top seal and a secondary long side seal. The standard baby food design contains a safety button or flip panel, as do most other PT caps.

2. **Application and seal formation**—Application requirements call for simply pressing the cap down on the glass finish after flowing steam over the headspace. The PT closure gasket must be properly heated prior to application. The glass threads form impressions in the skirt of the cap gasket that allow the cap to be cammed-off when twisted open. The PT closure is held in place on the finish primarily by vacuum with some assistance from the thread impressions formed in the gasket wall when the cap is heated then cooled.

PLCT (Plastisol-Lined Continuous Thread) Cap

The PLCT cap consists of a metal shell with a threaded skirt that is knurled. It contains a flowed-in plastisol gasket and is applied by screwing the closure onto the glass finish. The PLCT cap may be used in both steam and non-steam applications.

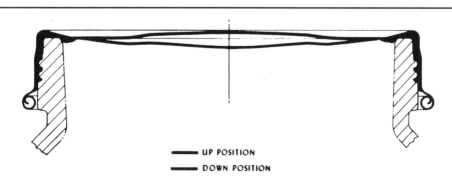

━━ UP POSITION
━━ DOWN POSITION

Figure 4—PT (Press-on Twist-off) cap.

Closure Evaluation

The two general types of closure inspections include: (1) visual, non-destructive, external observations or measurements made at frequent intervals, and (2) cap removal or destructive tests made at less frequent intervals, because the integrity of the seal is destroyed. Both of these tests and observations shall be made at the capper and after processing and cooling. The appropriate tests and observations for each type of closure being considered are listed in *Table 1*.

Tests and Observations for Closure Application and Defects

Cap Tilt—PT caps should be essentially level, not cocked or tilted, and seated well down on the finish. This is judged in relation to the transfer bead or shoulder on the glass container and should not exceed 3/32 of an inch.

Cocked Cap (*Figure 5*)—The term cocked cap is used for both the lug cap and the PLCT cap. It is caused by a lug failing to seat under the glass thread. It occurs on a PLCT cap when the cap and glass threads fail to properly engage. As a result, the cap is cross threaded and becomes cocked.

Crushed Lug (*Figure 6*)—A crushed lug on a lug cap may be visible on external examination. However, it may not be readily apparent, since it does not necessarily result in a tilted cap. It is caused by a lug being forced down over the glass thread by the capper's sealing mechanism.

Stripped Cap (*Figure 6*)—A stripped cap is a lug cap that has been over-applied to the extent that the lugs have been "stripped" off the glass threads on the finish. On visual examination, the lugs appear to be pulled outward.

Vacuum—In most cases, a vacuum will be formed in the package when it comes out of the capper, and the panel of the cap will show a concavity or dished-in appearance indicating the presence of a vacuum.

On PT caps there must be at least five inches of vacuum out of the capper to avoid loose caps. However, a vacuum button, if present, may not be down at this point. After processing and cooling, the button must be down and return to the up position when the cap is removed.

The exact amount of vacuum present is determined with a vacuum gauge and should read within the range for the product being run. This procedure is a destructive test that results in loss of the package integrity.

Temperature—The product temperature should be within the normal range for that product being run and should be recorded in conjunction with vacuum.

Headspace—In most cases, headspace should be not less than 6 percent of the container volume at the sealing temperature. Once the relationship of headspace volume for a specific product is established for a given container, the headspace may be measured with a depth or headspace gauge rather than by volume.

Gasket—After cap removal there should be a visible, even impression in the gasket 360 degrees around the circumference indicating tight contact with the glass finish.

Cut-Thru—Cut-thru occurs when the top of the glass finish has pushed completely through the gasket to the coating on the metal. This problem results in a leaky seal and requires immediate corrective action.

Removal Torque—Removal torque is the force required to remove a cap and can be measured on a standard torque meter. Removal torque should not be used as a measurement for the proper application of lug-style closures, but it may be a valuable quality control tool for measuring removal torque trends. Removal torque, however, is used for the measurement of PLCT cap application. It is suggested that the optimum removal torque should be one-half the diameter of the closure. This is not an absolute rule, and there is flexibility both above and below the optimum removal torque.

Pull-Up—Pull-up, also known as lug position, is a nondestructive method of measuring the engagement of the closure lugs on the threads of the glass finish.

This pull-up or lug position is defined as the distance between the leading edge of the cap lug and the vertical neck ring seam on the glass finish. It is measured in 1/16-inch increments. To measure this position, first find the vertical neck ring seam on the glass finish. There are two vertical seams on the glass finish 180 degrees apart. Remember that the vertical neck ring seams are not always aligned with the body seams. Then simply mea-

Table 1—Recommended tests and observations of vacuum closures for glass containers.

	Type of closure		
	PT	Lug	PLCT
AT CAPPER			
Non-Destructive External Inspection			
Cap Tilt	✔	—	—
Vacuum (cap panel concavity)	✔	✔	✔
Pull-up	—	✔	—
Cocked Cap	—	✔	✔
Crushed Lug	—	✔	—
Destructive Removal Inspection			
Cap Tilt	✔	—	—
Vacuum (gauge)	✔	✔	✔
Temperature	✔	✔	✔
Headspace	✔	✔	✔
Security	—	✔	—
Gasket Impression	—	✔	✔
AFTER PROCESSING AND COOLING			
Non-Destructive External Inspection			
Cap Tilt	✔	—	—
Vacuum (cap panel concavity)	✔	✔	✔
Pull-up	—	✔	—
Cocked Cap	—	✔	✔
Crushed Lug	—	✔	—
Button Position (down)	✔	✔	✔
Destructive Removal Inspection			
Cap Tilt	✔	—	—
Vacuum (gauge)	✔	✔	✔
Temperature	✔	✔	✔
Headspace	✔	✔	✔
Security	—	✔	—
Gasket Impression	✔	✔	✔
Removal Torque (opt.)	✔	✔	✔
Button Position (up)	✔	✔	✔

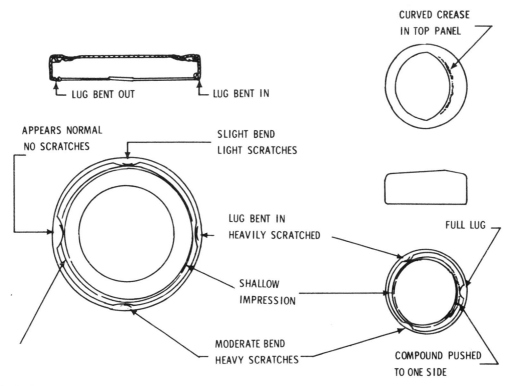

Figure 5—Typical cocked caps.

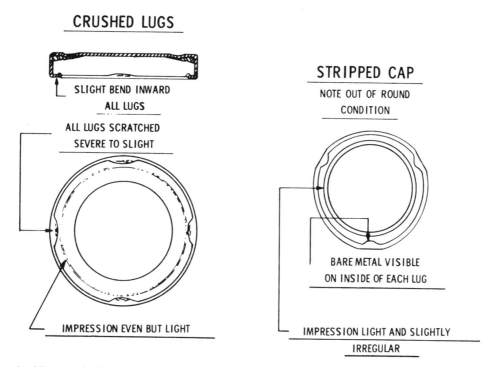

Figure 6—Crushed lugs and stripped caps.

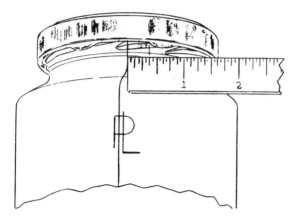

Figure 7—Pull-up measurement of +6.

sure the distance from this vertical line to the leading edge of the cap lug positioned nearest it.

Lug position measurements made on the right side of the parting line as you look at the package are referred to as positive (+), and those to the left side of the parting line as negative (−). Normal pull-up specifications are on the positive side (*Figure 7*). Negative lug positions could indicate over-application of the cap, which, in extreme cases may result in a stripped cap.

It is not recommended that pull-up measurements replace the security measurements described below, but they are very useful once the relationship between pull-up and security has been established for a given lot of glass and caps.

In most cases of proper application, the leading edge of the cap lug will be approximately 4/16 of an inch to the right of the parting line (designated as a + 4 pull-up measurement); however, the distance can vary 4/16 of an inch in either direction—ranging from 0 to + 8—

and still result in good security values within the specified range due to dimensional variations in the glass finish and the cap.

Security—Security values (lug tension of an applied closure) are the most reliable measurement of proper lug cap application. Security value ranges at the capper are specified by the closure manufacturer for good application of three-lug, four-lug, six-lug and eight-lug caps. Values higher than the range specified indicate a secure package with some degree of over-application and should be brought back into the proper range for best overall cap performance. Values that are consistently below the minimums usually indicate under-application, and the condition should be corrected immediately. From time to time, conditions vary to the extent that a deviation from the suggested security numbers is necessary. Variations may be coexistent with the type of plate or the plastisol used in the caps and/or glass surface treatment used by the glass maker. One or a combination of these conditions may dictate a shift of the proper security range in either direction for the specific operation. In some cases, lower security values may be acceptable as long as there is some positive security on packages entering the warehouse.

Because security measurements are destructive tests, there are practical limits to the number of packages that can be tested. The security test on a lug closure is made as follows:

1. With a marking pen or pencil make a vertical line on the cap and a corresponding line on the container (*Figure 8*). (This line has no relationship to the vertical neck ring seam.)

2. Twist closure counter-clockwise only until the vacuum is broken.

3. Reapply closure to container just until the gasket compound touches the glass finish and the closure lug

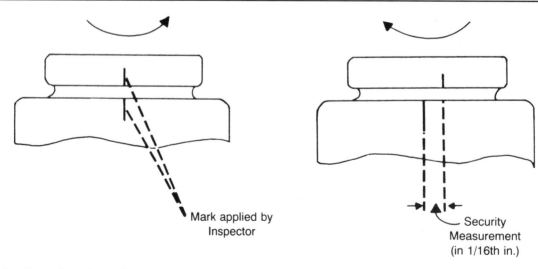

Mark applied by Inspector

Security Measurement (in 1/16th in.)

Figure 8—Illustration of security measurement.

touches the glass thread, or until the closure is just finger-tight (*Figure 8*).

4. Measure the distance between the vertical lines that were made before opening, in 1/16 inch increments (*Figure 8*).

5. Security is considered positive if the line on the cap is to the right of the line on the container. It is negative if the line on the cap is to the left of the line on the container. Negative securities, unless caused by a misapplied closure, should be investigated and corrected immediately.

Security is measured after processing and cooling in the same manner as at the capper, but the range of measurement for normal application will change to a lower value due to gasket compound sink during processing. With heat and pressure, the cap will be pushed further down on the glass finish, changing the lug tension on the glass thread.

Security is not measured on 48mm and smaller diameter lug closures. These small-sized closures use what is called an angle-flat finish, which has a lug stop at the end of the glass thread. For proper application of these closures, it is recommended that the majority of the caps be applied to the stop. For those caps where the cap lugs do not reach the stop, the cap lugs should be no more than one-eighth of an inch away from the stop.

Frequency of Inspection

It is mandatory that closures be inspected by a trained closure technician at regular intervals to ensure that satisfactory closures are being formed throughout the daily production. These inspections shall include both regular visual (nondestructive) and physical (destructive) inspections. A regular program of capper inspection will minimize the possibility of inferior closures reaching the consumer.

Visual Examinations (Non-Destructive)

The external visual examination includes at least one container from each capper. The closure shall be examined for gross closure defects such as the following:

1. Loose or cocked caps.

2. Crushed lugs or stripped caps.

3. Low-vacuum (visual examination of vacuum closure).

USDA regulations require and good manufacturing practice suggests that examinations shall not be limited to specific closure defects and shall include an examination of the entire container for obvious defects, such as fractured or cracked containers. When any defects are observed, the defects along with any corrective action taken shall be recorded. These examinations shall be conducted as often as necessary to ensure proper closure and should not exceed 30 minutes of continuous closing machine operation. Additional visual examinations shall be made at the beginning of production immediately following a container jam, machine adjustments or a prolonged shut down. It is also recommended that visual examinations follow changes in jar or cap supply or jar type.

Due to varying line speeds and conditions, it is not possible to recommend specific sampling frequencies. The following minimum recommendations should be modified by the processor based on specific operating requirements. It is suggested that visual closure inspections on straight-line cappers involve a minimum of six samples taken at random at least once every 30 minutes; on rotary cappers, a minimum of one sample for each capper head at least once every 30 minutes is suggested. Inspections should be conducted with sample jars taken from the capper and after processing and cooling.

Physical Examination (Destructive)

Physical examinations or tests shall be performed by a trained closure technician at intervals of sufficient frequency to ensure proper closure. These examinations should be made at intervals not to exceed four hours of continuous closing machine operation. Any defects shall be recorded along with the corrective action taken. When vacuum closures are used, the FDA requires that capper efficiency shall be checked by measuring cold-water vacuum. This shall be done before actual filling operations and the results shall be recorded.

The USDA requires that at least one container from each closing machine be examined during each regular examination period. Additional closure examinations should be made at the beginning of production, immediately following a jam and after closing machine adjustment. In addition, specification guidelines for closure integrity shall be maintained on file by the processor and made available to USDA representatives upon request.

Due to operating differences, it is not possible to recommend specific sample numbers or frequencies. The following recommendations should be modified by the processor based on specific operating requirements. It is suggested that physical testing for straight line cappers involve a minimum of six samples taken at random at least once every four hours; on rotary cappers, at least one sample for each capper head at least once every four hours is suggested. These examinations should be done with jars that have just been capped and with jars after processing and cooling.

Auxiliary Equipment

The role of auxiliary equipment—headspacers, cocked-cap detectors and ejectors, and dud detectors—that may directly or indirectly affect the sealing of the container should be considered and reviewed by the closure inspection supervisor whether or not these operations fall under his/her direct control and responsibility.

Headspacers

As discussed earlier, headspace is of critical importance in obtaining good seals with certain cap types and is of significant importance with all vacuum caps. Consequently, if a headspacer is incorporated in the production line, the closure inspection supervisor should be sure that it is set properly. Also, product over the finish, which can sometimes result from headspacer operation, may be detrimental to good sealing.

Cocked-Cap Detectors and Ejectors

These devices, usually installed on the capper, can serve to eliminate problem packages before they become mixed with normal packages. They can also serve to signal both the capper operator and quality auditing personnel that a problem exists or is developing.

Dud Detectors

These units, if properly maintained and checked, can monitor the quality of the seals being formed on all packages and, as a consequence, serve as an extremely useful tool to the closure inspection supervisor in checking for defective seals and analyzing sealing problems. It should be part of the closure inspection supervisor's duties to see that these units are checked regularly and maintained in the proper operating condition.

Summary

In evaluating proper sealing of glass containers for low-acid and acidified foods, the following factors play an important role in obtaining good seals:

1. Factors that affect vacuum formation (all cap types):
   A. Headspace
   B. Product temperature
   C. Air in the product
   D. Capper vacuum efficiency

2. Main factors for checking application of all cap types:
   A. Cap is level and seated well down on finish.
   B. Vacuum is adequate.
   C. Impression in gasket is even (particularly after processing).

3. Main factors for checking application of lug caps:
   A. Cap is level and not cocked.
   B. Pull-up is satisfactory.
   C. Security is within specified range.
   D. Vacuum is adequate.
   E. Impression in gasket is good.

4. Main factors for checking application of PT caps:
   A. Cap is level.
   B. Vacuum is adequate.
   C. Proper cam-off exists.
   D. Impression in gasket (after processing) is good.

5. Main factors for checking application of PLCT caps.
   A. Cap is level.
   B. Vacuum is adequate.
   C. Impression in the gasket is good.
   D. Removal torque is in an acceptable range.

6. Act on readings outside desired operating range:
   A. When they persist.
   B. When they are out of operating control limits.
   C. When caps are loose.

Chapter 18

CLOSURES FOR SEMIRIGID AND FLEXIBLE CONTAINERS

Introduction

The first flexible container used for low-acid foods was the retort pouch. This pouch was developed in the early 1960's by the U.S. military as a container for field rations. However, it was not approved for general food use until 1977. Since then, the retort pouch has been in limited commercial use.

It was not until 1981—when hydrogen peroxide was first approved as a sterilant for food contact surfaces of packages—that semirigid and flexible packages could be used for aseptically packaged low-acid foods. More recently the retortable plastic container with a double seamed metal end and the semirigid tray or cup with a heat sealed end have been introduced for retort applications. Currently a large variety of both flexible and semirigid packages are used commercially (*Figure 1*).

Semirigid and flexible packages are primarily composed of single or multi-layers of different types of plastic materials; however, some packages are manufactured with a paperboard component. With the exception of plastic cans with double seamed metal ends, the closure is achieved by some form of heat sealing.

The USDA regulations define semirigid and flexible containers as follows:

Semirigid containers—A container, the shape or contour of which, when filled and sealed, is not significantly affected by the enclosed product under normal atmospheric temperature and pressure, but which can be deformed by external mechanical pressure of less than 10 pounds per square inch gauge.

Flexible container—A container, the shape or contour of which, when filled and sealed, is significantly affected by the enclosed product.

Both FDA and USDA regulations provide specific details on the testing required for double seamed closures. This is not the case for other closures that may be found on flexible and semirigid packages. The technology for producing these closures is varied and constantly evolving. Therefore, specific evaluation methods are not listed in the regulations. This does not mean that the food processor does not need to inspect the closures on these packages. The regulations do require that appropriate inspections and tests be conducted.

As a guide for food processors, industry experts have compiled a list of appropriate test methods for the four

Figure 1—A sample of commercially available semirigid and flexible containers.

151

Table 1—Test methods for semirigid and flexible containers

Test methods	Container type			
	Paperboard	Flexible pouch	Semirigid with heat sealed lid	Plastic with double seamed metal end
Air leak testing	O	O	O	O
Biotesting	O	O	O	O
Burst testing	O	R	R	O
Chemical etching	O	O	O	NA
Compression, squeeze testing	R	R	O	O
Distribution (abuse) test	O	O	O	O
Dye penetration	R	O	R	O
Electester	O	NA	NA	NA
Electrolytic	R	O	R	NA
Gas leak detection	O	O	O	O
Incubation	R	R	R	R
Light	NA	O	O	O
Machine vision	O	O	O	O
Proximity tester	O	O	O	R
Seam scope projection	NA	NA	NA	R
Sound	R	NA	R	R
Tensile (peel) testing	NA	R	R	NA
Vacuum testing	NA	O	R	O
Visual inspection	R	R	R	R

Abbreviations: R, test method is recommended by NFPA Bulletin 41-L, Flexible Package Integrity Bulletin; O, other commercially accepted test method applications; NA, test method is inappropriate for this style package. (Source: *Food and Drug Administration, Bacteriological Analytical Manual.* 7th edition, published by AOAC International, 1992.)

major types of semirigid and flexible containers. As apparent by the scope of the list presented in *Table 1*, testing of semirigid and flexible containers can be very extensive.

The intent of this chapter is to present the unique features of semirigid and flexible containers in relation to the federal regulations and good manufacturing practices—not to serve as a laboratory manual. Therefore, the majority of test methods listed in *Table 1* will not be discussed in detail. For specific testing methods, refer to available publications such as FDA's *Bacteriological Analytical Manual*, NFPA's Bulletin 41-L, USDA Directives and Bulletins, or procedures from equipment manufacturers.

FDA Requirements

The FDA requires that visual examinations be conducted by a qualified container closure inspector at intervals of sufficient frequency to ensure proper closure and to detect any gross closure defects. Containers shall be randomly selected from each sealing or closing head for examination. As with metal cans with double seamed ends, all observations shall be recorded, and any necessary corrective action shall be taken and recorded. Additionally, detailed teardown inspections and tests are required to be conducted by qualified personnel at intervals of sufficient frequency to ensure correct performance of the closing machine and reliable production of the hermetic seal. Records are also required to document these inspections and tests.

Plastic cans with metal double seamed ends are sealed with the same basic mechanism as metal cans with double seamed ends. Therefore, both FDA and USDA require packers who use the plastic cans with metal double seamed ends to meet the testing regulations for metal cans. Any additional measurements specified by the container manufacturer shall also be monitored and recorded.

USDA Requirements

The USDA regulations include more specific details on the evaluation of flexible and semirigid containers. The heat seals shall be visually inspected by a trained closure technician with sufficient frequency to ensure proper closure. These examinations shall be performed before and after thermal processing on representative containers from each sealing head. Corrective action shall be taken when sealing defects are observed. Defects and corrective action shall be promptly recorded. Also, physical test(s), e.g., burst tests, that are considered necessary to assess container integrity must be conducted with sufficient frequency to ensure proper closure.

USDA's regulations require that physical test(s) be performed after the thermal processing operation. Furthermore, USDA recommends that sample containers be tested at least every two hours of production to ensure proper closure. The results of the test(s), including any defects along with corresponding corrective actions, shall be recorded. Acceptance guidelines for the test(s) procedures shall be on file and made available to USDA personnel.

In addition to inspecting and testing the seal of flexible and semirigid containers, the USDA requires and good manufacturing practices suggest that empty containers, closures and container rollstock be inspected, stored, handled and conveyed in a manner to ensure they are clean and free of defects that may affect the product or package integrity.

Along with the USDA canning regulations found in 9 CFR 318 (381), establishments are required to follow applicable FSIS Directives. One such directive—7630.1, revision 3, issued February 1994—requires processors packing low-acid canned foods in semirigid and flexible packages to have an approved quality control program (TQC or PQC) in place that outlines the steps to be taken to adequately process and inspect products in these containers.

Processors who pack product in flexible pouches under military contract will be required to comply with the specific contract requirements. A 100 percent visual inspection of the seals on every pouch produced may be required both before and after thermal processing.

Defect Definitions

The purpose of inspecting and testing flexible and semirigid containers is to ensure that the hermetic condition of the container has not been compromised. A hermetically sealed container has been previously defined as a container that is designed and intended to be secure against the entry of microorganisms and to maintain the commercial sterility of its contents during and after processing. The degree of a container or seal defect may be classified by the impact the defect has on the hermetic condition. Classification of defects are provided below:

Critical defect—A defect that provides evidence that the container has lost its hermetic condition or evidence that there is, or has been, microbial growth in the container's contents.

A critical defect should be considered a potential public health problem. When a critical defect is found, the lot must be set aside and thoroughly inspected and sorted to ensure that containers that have lost their hermetic condition are not distributed.

Major defect—A defect that results in a container that does not show visible signs of having lost its hermetic condition, but the defect is of such magnitude that the container may have lost its hermetic condition.

A major defect may result in the loss of the hermetic condition and lead to spoilage or become a public health problem. Even though a major defect may not be a public health problem by itself, a large number of containers with major defects necessitates more extensive sampling of the lot before distribution. Evidence of a significant number of major defects may be considered a potential public health problem. If the effect of the defect on the hermetic seal appears in question, sampling and examination would be appropriate.

Minor defect—A defect that has no adverse effect on the hermetic condition of the container.

A minor defect may affect only the appearance or saleability—not the safety—of the product. If the effect of the defect on the hermetic seal appears in question, sampling and examination would be appropriate.

The remainder of this chapter discusses the evaluation of package integrity in the four most commonly used types of flexible and semirigid containers: plastic containers with double seamed metal ends, semirigid containers with heat sealed lids, paperboard packages and flexible pouches.

Plastic Containers With Double Seamed Metal Ends

Introduction

The double seamed metal can has provided a means for the food processor to obtain a high level of container integrity and still run at line speeds in excess of 400 cans per minute. Thus, the metal can has been a widely accepted package for shelf-stable low-acid foods. The plastic package with a double seamed end also provides a high level of container integrity. The seam consists of five thicknesses of material: three thicknesses of metal from the end plus the flange and neck of the plastic container (*Figure 2*). These are folded, interlocked and pressed firmly together by the same basic closing machines used for metal cans. The double seamed container is constructed of multiple layers of polypropylene sandwiching a single layer of the oxygen barrier—ethylene vinyl alcohol (EVOH). The newest development by a U.S. manufacturer is a container that has as the primary ingredient high density polypropylene (HDPE) with less than 5 percent EVOH; this has the advantage of easier recycling.

Package terminology

Standard terminology has been developed to define the components of the plastic container with a double seamed metal end (*Figure 3*).

Retortable/microwaveable bowl—Semirigid container made of specific plastic blends and adhesive material.

Height—Distance from the base of the bowl to the body flange.

Width—Diameter of the opening in the bowl.

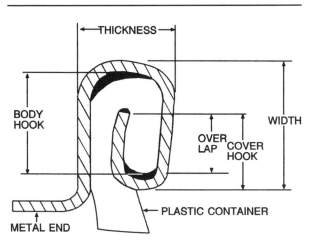

Figure 2—The basic parts of the double seam formed from a metal end and plastic container body.

153

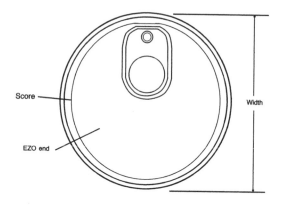

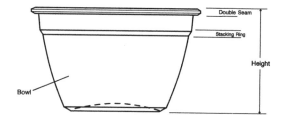

Figure 3—The basic parts of the plastic container with a double seamed metal end.

Table 2—Classification of defects associated with plastic containers with double seamed metal ends.

Defect	Critical	Major	Minor
Abrasion	—	✔	✔
Cuts	✔	—	—
Damaged flanges	✔	—	—
Delamination	—	—	✔
Foreign matter inclusion	—	✔	✔
Gels	—	—	✔
Load damage	—	✔	—
Malformed	—	✔	✔
Short height	✔	—	—
Swollen package	✔	—	—

EZO end—A scored metal end with a pull-tab designed to be removed without a can opener.

Stacking ring—Curved area below the body flange (neck area) where it meets the body of the bowl.

Double seam—Closure formed by interlocking and compressing the curl of the end and the flange of the container body.

Defect Definitions and Classifications

As in the case of metal cans, good double seams on plastic containers are absolutely essential to prevent losses due to spoilage and to ensure consumer public health safety. However, the double seam is not the sole means of protecting a container's hermetic condition. Damage to or defects in the container body itself may have an impact on the integrity of the container and possibly the formation of the double seam. Some common container defects and their causes are listed below. The classifications of the defects are identified in *Table 2*. The magnitude of the defect will determine its classification.

Double seam defects are similar to those discussed in the chapter dealing with metal closures and will not be discussed in this chapter.

Abrasion—Damage to the package surface caused by rubbing or scuffing.

Cuts—A slice or slash that penetrates the package, causing a loss of hermetic integrity.

Damaged flanges—Malformed plastic, too thin, short or long flanges, or bent flanges that impede the double seam operation.

Delamination—Separation of the laminate material which affects appearance but not the hermetic integrity.

Foreign matter inclusion—Matter imbedded in the plastic packaging matter. This will affect the appearance and possibly the integrity of the package.

Gels—Improperly processed plastic included in the packaging material (affects appearance but not integrity).

Load damage—Shift in containers on pallets that damages the containers or shrouds encompassing the containers.

Malformed—Plastic which does not conform to contours as specified.

Short height—Specified dimensions of the package have been altered by manufacturing process or mechanical means (force).

Swollen package—A package which has an altered shape due to gas formation within the package.

Inspection of Double Seam

The same terms that are used to describe an all-metal double seam apply to the metal end/plastic body double seam. Note that sealing compound is also required for double seaming plastic cans and is important to package integrity. From an integrity evaluation viewpoint, the two most important measurements are double seam overlap and tightness. Countersink, cover hook and body hook measurements are generally used as diagnostic inputs providing additional data for evaluating the quality of the double seam when either the overlap or tightness are out of specification.

Overlap—(*Figure 2*) The degree of interlock of the cover hook and body hook is known as the overlap. The integrity of the double seam is dependent on the length of this overlap. Insufficient overlap may result in leakage due to internal pressure formed during thermal processing, vacuum formation during cooling, or disturbance from rough handling.

Theoretical overlap may be calculated for the metal/metal double seam. However, distortion of the plastic body hook during seam teardown of the metal/plastic double seam precludes calculation and requires use of a seam projector or scope to view the seam cross-section and directly measure the overlap. Overlaps must meet the specifications provided by the supplier to ensure adequate interlocking of the cover and body hooks.

Tightness—A properly formed metal/plastic double seam exhibits compression of the plastic components. Therefore, the seam thickness is actually thinner than the sum of the thicknesses of the individual components in the seam: three times the metal end thickness plus the plastic flange and neck thicknesses. This compression ensures good seam tightness. However, there can be too much of a good thing. If the seams are compressed too tightly, the metal end may cut through the plastic neck.

The target thickness for metal can double seams varies with the thicknesses of can body and end. In a similar fashion, thickness of the metal/plastic double seam is a function of the thicknesses of the metal end, plastic flange and neck. This thickness must be determined for each combination of ends and plastic bowls or cans.

There are different methods of determining the relative tightness of the double seam. The main concern is the compression of the plastic body wall. This compression—not the cover hook wrinkle rating—is what defines the tightness. The seam should not be too tight or too loose. The following describes three different methods of deter-mining the relative tightness of the double seam. The processor should use the method recommended by the package supplier.

Method 1 — Body wall compression can be evaluated by determining the actual percentage of the compression. An optical seam projector is essential to accomplish the required visual evaluation. *Figure 4* diagrams these measurements. The acceptable range of compression is 30–50 percent; 20 percent is too loose, and 70 percent is too tight.

Method 2—The tightness may also be evaluated by comparing the actual seam thickness to the calculated thickness of the plastic flange, neck and the three layers of the metal end. The actual seam thickness should be smaller (therefore tighter) than the calculated thickness. The calculated seam thickness can be computed if the thickness of the metal end plate and the thickness of the plastic components are known. The formula is: three times the metal end thickness plus plastic flange thickness plus plastic neck thickness.

Method 3 —The final method of evaluating the tightness of the seam is to inspect the pressure ridge. The pressure ridge reflects the compression of the plastic body wall. The pressure ridge should be visible and continuous (see Chapter 16, *Figure 52*).

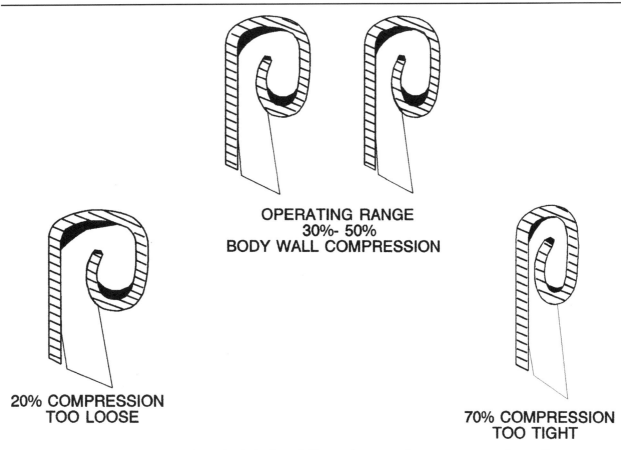

OPERATING RANGE
30%- 50%
BODY WALL COMPRESSION

20% COMPRESSION
TOO LOOSE

70% COMPRESSION
TOO TIGHT

Figure 4—Body wall compression of the plastic body wall. The package supplier may recommend an optimum compression rating.

Frequency of Testing

The regulations require that the container and double seam be inspected and tested to ensure the hermetic seal is not compromised. Representative containers from each seaming head shall be visually inspected for seam defects at a frequency sufficient to ensure proper control. The recommended frequency is every 30 minutes.

Destructive teardown examinations are equally important and are also required to be performed at a frequency sufficient to ensure proper control. The recommended interval is every four hours of continuous production. Because the measurement of seam thickness is nondestructive, this measurement can be made at more frequent intervals—recommend every two hours.

In addition to the double seams, incoming stock of containers and ends should be inspected to ensure compliance with specifications for package height, body wall thickness, flange length and thickness, and visible defects—such as poor flange trim or extraneous plastic.

Semirigid Containers With Heat Sealed Lids

Introduction

Semirigid containers with heat sealed lids are used in retorted, hot-filled, cold-filled and aseptic operations for both high- and low-acid foods. The typical composition of the containers is polypropylene with an oxygen barrier layer, such as EVOH, between the polypropylene layers.

The containers may be purchased from the packaging manufacturer pre-formed, or they may be formed on-line by the food processor in conjunction with the filling operation. Containers may be formed with either of two different methods—blow molding or thermoforming. **Blow molding** involves forcing or air-blowing molten plastic into a mold to form the desired container shape. **Thermoformed** containers are manufactured by pressing the plastic rollstock into a die mold to form the container.

The closures are most commonly composed of foil sandwiched by an outside layer of polyethylene or polyester, and an inside heat sealant layer compatible with the polypropylene sealing layer on the container flange. The foil serves as a barrier to light and oxygen. Depending on the product application, the foil layer may be replaced with silicon oxide or aluminum oxide deposited on a polymer substrate. The closures, which may be pre-cut lids or rollstock, are heat sealed onto the containers.

Sealing methods

Currently, the four different methods of forming a heat seal are induction, impulse, hot bar and ultrasonic sealing. Parameters influencing seal integrity will vary depending on the method of seal formation. Typically pressure, temperature of the seal head, and/or dwell time will be critical factors for forming a good heat seal (*Figure 5*).

Induction sealing employs the generation of a current in an electromagnetic field. The electrical resistance creates heat that fuses the lid to the container flange.

Impulse sealing utilizes rounded sealing bars that are not hot enough to form a seal until after the two sealing surfaces have been pressed together. The resulting heat and pressure applied by the sealing bars cause the polypropylene layers of the lid stock and container to melt and form a fusion seal.

Hot bar sealing also uses sealing bars but instead of gradual heating, the sealing bars are maintained at a constant high temperature.

Ultrasonic sealing employs the generation of ultrasonic wave vibrations. Friction caused by the vibrations generates heat, which forms the fusion seal.

Failure of heat seals

Packaging engineers refer to the separation of the foil lid from the container flange at the seal area as the "failure of the seal." While most people would consider failure of the seal to be undesirable, there is a point when the seal needs to fail—when the consumer peels the lid off the container. The action of peeling the lid actually causes the seal to fail. Obviously a well-fused seal should resist failure until the consumer wants to open the container. The foil lid is separated or peeled from the container by either of two failure methods—adhesive or cohesive bond.

Adhesive failure of seals (*Figure 6*) occurs when the closure peels away from the container flange, usually leaving behind a trace of the sealant. The polypropylene sealing layer of the lid is fusion-sealed to the polypropylene flange of the container. When the lid is peeled, the polypropylene sealing layer of the lid breaks away from

Figure 5—The stereomicrograph on the left represents a good seal while that on the right represents a poor seal. The smooth surface on the seal on the right is an incomplete seal.

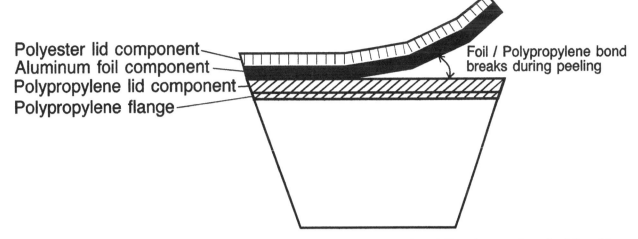

Polyester lid component
Aluminum foil component
Polypropylene lid component
Polypropylene flange

Foil / Polypropylene bond
breaks during peeling

Figure 6—Adhesive failure of the seal occurs when the polypropylene layer of the lid breaks away from the foil and fuses to the container flange.

the foil component of the lid and remains permanently fused to the container flange. The continuous presence of lid polypropylene residues on the flange indicates a well-fused seal.

Cohesive failure of lid stock (*Figure 7*) occurs when the sealant layer of the lid stock splits. The polypropylene sealing layer of the lid is fusion-sealed to the polypropylene flange of the container. When the lid is peeled, the polypropylene sealing layer of the lid breaks within itself and splits—half of the sealing layer is removed with the lid, and about half remains on the flange surface. The frosty material on the sealing surface areas of the lid and flange after peeling is the polypropylene sealing layer of the lid and indicates a well-fused seal.

Defect Definitions and Classifications

Some common defects associated with semirigid containers or their heat seals, along with classifications, are listed below. The defects are classified in *Table 3*.

Abrasion—A scratch partially through the surface layer(s) of the package caused by mechanical, rubbing or scuffing.

Burnt seal—A discolored area of the seal due to overheating.

Channel leaker—A pathway of non-bonding across the width of the seal creating a leaker.

Contaminated seal—Foreign matter in the seal area, such as, but not limited to, water, grease or food.

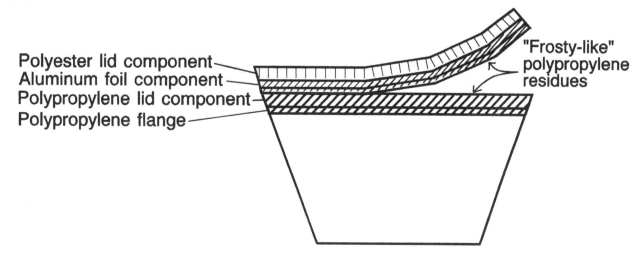

Polyester lid component
Aluminum foil component
Polypropylene lid component
Polypropylene flange

"Frosty-like" polypropylene residues

Figure 7—Cohesive failure occurs when the sealant layer of the lid stock splits.

Table 3—Classification of defects associated with semirigid containers with heat sealed lids.

Defect	Critical	Major	Minor
Abrasion	—	✓	✓
Burnt seal	—	—	✓
Channel leaker	✓	—	—
Contaminated seal	—	✓	—
Crushed	—	✓	✓
Cut	✓	—	—
Delamination	—	—	✓
Flex cracks	—	—	✓
Foreign matter inclusion	—	—	✓
Fracture	✓	—	—
Gels	—	—	✓
Incomplete seal	✓	—	—
Label foldover	—	—	✓
Malformed	—	—	✓
Puncture	✓	—	—
Seal width variation	—	✓	—
Swollen package	✓	—	—
Uneven impression	—	✓	—
Wrinkle	✓	✓	✓

Crushed—Alteration of the package's original dimensions caused by force.

Cut—A mechanical slash or slicing that penetrates the package, causing a loss of hermetic integrity.

Delamination—A separation of the laminate materials.

Flex cracks—Small breaks in one or more layers of the package, due to stressing; not a leaker.

Foreign matter inclusion—Unintended matter imbedded in the plastic.

Fracture—A break through the packaging material.

Gels—Improperly processed plastic included in the packaging material.

Incomplete seal—A portion of the seal that has a lack of adhesion between lid and body.

Label foldover—Label material folded over on itself.

Malformed—Plastic that does not conform to mold contours as designed, or material distribution that does not conform to specifications such as waves, thin spots or discontinuous layers.

Puncture—A mechanical piercing that penetrates the package, causing a loss of hermetic integrity.

Seal width variation—Less than specified seal width.

Swollen package—A package that has expanded due to internal gas formation.

Uneven impression—One that may lead to an out-of-specification seal.

Wrinkle—A fold of material in the seal area.

Inspection of Sealed Containers

Many different non-destructive and destructive examinations may be conducted to ensure the integrity of the heat seal. It is recommended that processors work with the sealing machine and packaging material suppliers to develop a testing protocol. Some examinations that are commonly performed are discussed below.

Non-destructive examinations

Visual examination—Visually inspect sealed containers for alignment of the lid on the cup, appearance of the seal area, sidewall distortion and product on the exterior of the package (*Figure 8*).

Squeeze test procedure—Apply pressure to package sidewalls. The package lid should bulge upwards, as indicated in *Figure 9*. If the package is properly sealed, no headspace gases or product will escape.

Vacuum chamber testing—A vacuum chamber, such as that illustrated in *Figure 10*, can be used to test seal strength. The containers are placed in carriers within the chamber, the chamber is closed, and a vacuum is drawn. The chamber is evacuated to 20'' Hg or other recommended negative pressure. The headspace gases in the containers will expand as the chamber pressure decreases, causing the lid to dome. If the lid does not dome as depicted in *Figure 11*, look for major cuts in the package. Check for any microleakage by watching for deflection of the gauge needle.

Destructive examination

Burst test—The burst test is the principal seal integrity test for retortable plastic containers. It is also a useful diagnostic test to assess consumer peelability for non-retorted containers. In general, a peelable seal which is able to withstand more internal pressure than specified will be difficult for the consumer to remove.

Peel test procedure—Remove the lid by slowly peeling it back at a 45 degree angle as shown in *Figure 12*.

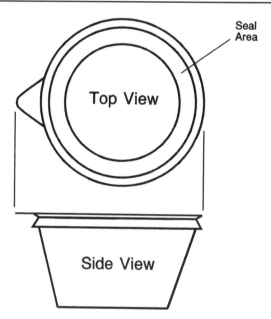

Figure 8—Side and top views of a typical design of a plastic cup with a heat sealed lid. Visually inspect the cup and seal for proper alignment of lid, complete seal and presence of product on exterior.

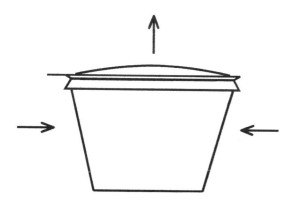

Figure 9—Lid deflection will occur in a properly sealed plastic cup with a heat sealed lid when the container is subjected to pressure by squeezing the sidewalls.

Attention should be paid to the strength and evenness of the peel resistance.

After the lid is removed, visually inspect the seal area for the appearance of the seal on the flange and lid, evenness of the seal, alignment of the seal on the flange and any irregularities (channeling, creases in the lid, or product across the seal) that would compromise package integrity (*Figure 13*).

Dye penetration test—Cut the package open from the bottom in order to keep the heat seal intact. Drain the product and rinse and dry the container.

As depicted in *Figure 14*, a drop of aqueous-based dye (e.g. methylene blue or as recommended by the system manufacturer) is placed on the interior flange-lid surface. The dye should be spread around the entire circumference and allowed to dry completely. A water-based dye should be used since non-aqueous solvent dyes may dissolve into the plastic causing false positives.

Remove the lid and observe the flange area for any dye penetration.

Electroconductivity test—Plastic packages generally do not conduct a flow of low voltage electricity unless a hole is present. A testing apparatus—such as designed by the National Food Processors Association and illustrated in *Figure 15*—can be used to determine the presence of a closed circuit. If voltage is measured, dye or the conductivity meter may be used to determine the location of the hole (*Figure 16*).

Frequency of Testing

Non-destructive and destructive examinations for defects shall be conducted with sufficient frequency to ensure adequate seals. The visual examinations for container defects should be made at least every 15 minutes and results recorded. Every 30 minutes the heat seal on containers from each sealing head should be inspected for completeness.

At the time of start up and a minimum of once every four hours thereafter, at least one container from each sealing head should be squeezed by hand and then the

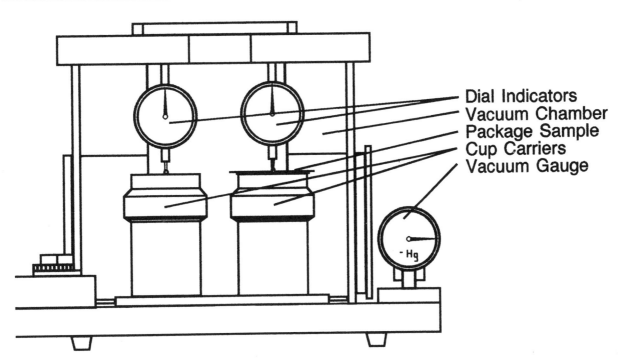

Figure 10—A vacuum test chamber for plastic cups with heat sealed lids. Sealed cups are placed in the cup carriers within the chamber.

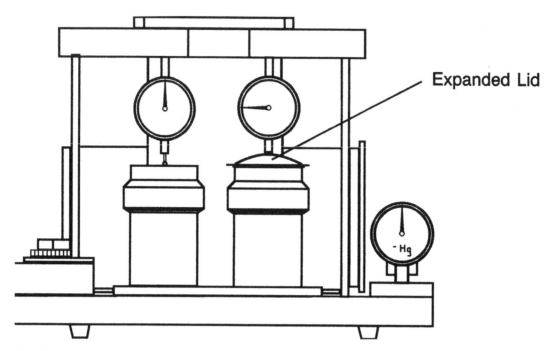

Expanded Lid

Figure 11—The lid on a well-sealed cup will dome as the vacuum in the chamber is pulled. This doming (depicted on the right) is indicated by needle deflection. Absence of needle deflection is an indicator of microleakage.

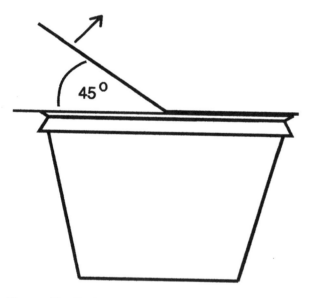

45°

Figure 12—Peel back the lid to simulate the angle of opening by a consumer. Subjectively evaluate the force needed to open the cup.

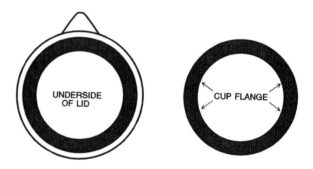

UNDERSIDE OF LID

CUP FLANGE

Figure 13—The shaded areas in the diagram represent the seal areas. Both the lid and the cup flange seal area should be inspected for appearance, evenness, alignment and visible defects.

lid peeled off completely to inspect for acceptable seals. Additionally, at least one package from each sealing head must be peeled open after a splice or lot change of the body and/or lid material.

When there appears to be a questionable seal, a container from that sealing head should be further tested, using such tests as the electroconductivity test or the dye penetration test discussed previously.

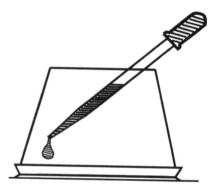

Figure 14—Dye testing the seal area by adding drops of dye to the inside seal area through a hole cut in the bottom of the cup.

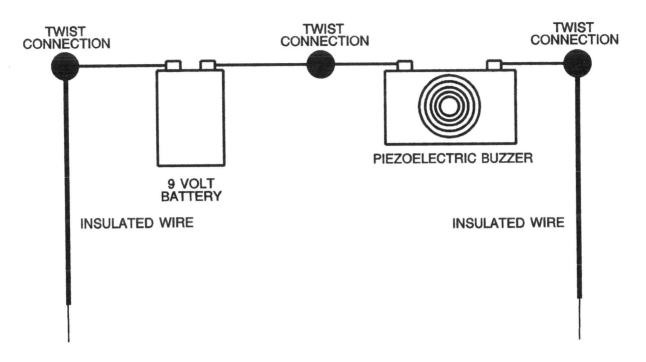

Figure 15—A schematic diagram for an electroconductivity tester.

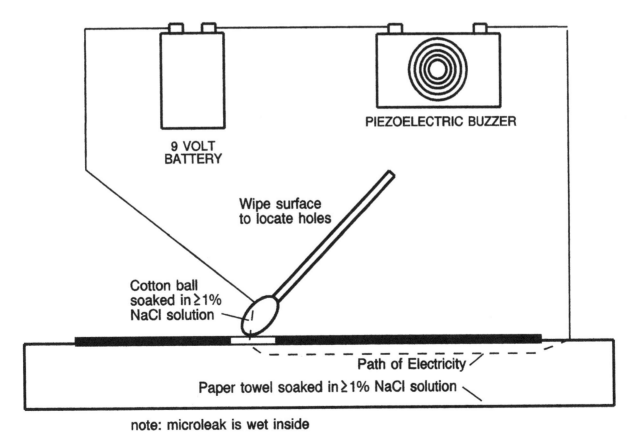

note: microleak is wet inside

Figure 16—An electroconductivity tester can be used to detect microholes in a package. The swab is moved along the surface to detect a break in the package. The buzzer sounds when the swab tip touches the microhole.

Paperboard Packages

Introduction

The basic construction of paperboard packages—whether for cold-filled products or aseptic processing and packaging—is a multilaminate of polymer/paper/polymer. The product contained in the package determines additional layer requirements. For example, the familiar gable-top milk carton consists only of the basic multilaminate, but some juices require foil in the multilaminate to preserve or protect the organoleptic properties of the product by restriction of oxygen. The foil requires Surlyn® on both sides in order to adequately laminate itself to paperboard and/or other polymers. Without the Surlyn® or a similar polymer, the laminated foil sandwich could not be manufactured. *Figure 17* shows a cutaway section of the layers of a typical multilaminated paperboard container.

Paperboard packages will not withstand retorting; therefore, commercially sterile low-acid foods are aseptically packed in paperboard. Paperboard containers may be purchased from the packaging manufacturer as preformed flats, or they may be formed from web stock online in conjunction with the filling operation.

Defect Definitions and Classifications

Common defects associated with the production, filling and sealing of paperboard containers are listed below; their defect classifications are presented in *Table 4*.

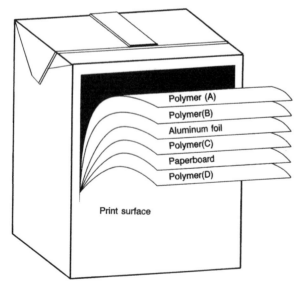

Figure 17—A standard construction of a flexible package with paperboard as the base, foil to block light and keep out air, and polymers to maintain product quality.

Table 4—Classification of defects associated with paperboard packages.

Defect	Critical	Major	Minor
Abrasion	—	✓	✓
Channel leaker	✓	—	—
Corner dent	—	—	✓
Corner leaker	✓	—	—
Crushed	—	✓	✓
Cut	✓	—	—
Loose flap (or ear)	—	—	✓
Misaligned (deformed) seal	—	✓	✓
Perforation leaker	✓	—	—
Pulltab leaker	✓	—	—
Puncture	✓	—	—
Seal leaker	✓	—	—
Swollen package	✓	—	—

Abrasion—Damage to the package caused by mechanically rubbing, scuffing or scratching.

Channel leaker—A patch of non-bonding across the width of the seal, creating a leak.

Corner dent—Dimpling or wrinkling of the corner; caused during manufacture.

Corner leaker—A leak occurring in one of the corners of the package.

Crushed—Alteration of the package's original dimensions caused by force.

Cut—A mechanical slash or slicing that damages the package, resulting in the loss of hermetic integrity.

Loose flap (or ear)—Flap or ear not attached as intended.

Misaligned (deformed) seal—Improper seal position.

Perforation leaker—Leakage through or around perforated area.

Pulltab leaker—Leakage through or around pulltab.

Puncture—A mechanical piercing that damages the package, resulting in the loss of hermetic integrity.

Seal leaker—Product leakage along a seal.

Swollen package—A package that has expanded due to internal gas formation.

Inspection of Sealed Containers

As with the other flexible and semirigid containers, many different destructive and non-destructive examinations may be conducted to ensure the integrity of the heat seals on paperboard packages. Processors are encouraged to work with the sealing machine and packaging material suppliers to develop a testing protocol. Some examinations that are commonly performed are discussed below.

Destructive examination

Teardown procedures—Unfold all flaps as specified by the package supplier and check the integrity and tightness of transverse (top and bottom) and vertical or longitudinal (side) seals by squeezing the package firmly. Evidence of leakage or other critical defect(s) requires immediate remedial action.

162

Puncture the container on the side opposite the side seal and empty the contents. Cut near the fold at each end of the package and down the length of the package opposite the side seal to remove a large rectangular body portion. Observe this body portion for holes, scratches or tears anywhere on the surface. Pay close attention to the corners of the package, particularly directly under end seals and near the straw hole, if present.

Evaluation methods for seal quality differ between package designs, constructions and sealing methods. Specific procedures for a given package should be obtained from the manufacturer.

Seal evaluation usually consists of carefully pulling the seal apart and inspecting the separated seal. In some manufacturers' packages, the seal is good if polymer stretch (continuous presence of stretching polymer film at a point beyond where the paper and laminates have separated) extends the entire length of the seal. In other manufacturers' packages, fiber tear (raw paperboard visible on both sides of the separated seal areas) should be seen the entire length of the seal. This is known as 100 percent fiber tear and is indicative of a good seal.

All seals on the package should be tested. Problems to look for are absence of or a narrow fiber tear, lack of polymer stretch, cold spots (no polymer bond in seal area) and tacking (polymer melt but no stretch or fiber tear).

If a problem is noted, all packages produced since the last acceptable integrity test must be held for reinspection. New packages are to be inspected following correction of the problem.

Frequency of Testing

Non-destructive and destructive examinations shall be conducted with sufficient frequency to ensure adequate seals. Non-destructive visual examinations should be conducted at the time of start-up and a minimum of once every 30 minutes thereafter. At least one package per sealing unit or lane should be torn down and checked for acceptable seals at the time of start-up and a minimum of once every four hours thereafter.

Additionally, for web-fed systems, at least one package per sealing unit or lane should be torn down and checked for acceptable seals (and longitudinal sealing strip if present) immediately after packaging material splicing during filling operations.

At least two consecutive packages should be tested for leaks using a dye leak test, and/or the electroconductivity test, or a suitable alternative. This should be done at the time of start-up and at least every four hours thereafter.

Flexible Pouches

Introduction

Pouches are used for low- and high-acid foods in both aseptic and retort applications. They may be constructed of polyester on the outside for durability and polypropyl-ene on the food contact surface, with an oxygen barrier—polyvinylidene chloride (PVDC or SARAN®), EVOH, or nylon—sandwiched in the middle. The polypropylene can be titanium-tinted to restrict light, or aluminum foil may replace the PVDC as the light-and-oxygen barrier.

Pouch film is supplied to the processor either as rollstock or as pre-formed pouches. If rollstock is used, the pouch forming operation is usually accomplished in the food processing plant by continuous form-fill-seal equipment. Depending on the manufacturer, the form-fill-seal equipment may be configured to form pouches either vertically or horizontally.

Filling pouches is a critical stage in the operation, since it is essential that the pouch is filled to the proper level with product and that the product never contacts the seal area. Overfilling the pouch must be avoided because it not only increases the potential for seal contamination and seal failure but could also lead to under-processing due to the greater thickness. Product dripping from the filler nozzle after the pouch has been filled is a potential seal contamination problem which must be prevented.

Various methods of air evacuation and heat sealing may be used to seal pouches in commercial production. The most commonly used procedures for air evaluation include:

1. Steam flushing of the headspace with saturated or super heated steam.

2. Drawing a mechanical vacuum in a vacuum chamber or by inserting a snorkel tube into the pouch.

3. Mechanically compressing the sides of the pouch to reduce or eliminate the headspace.

4. Hot filling the product to create a vacuum when the product cools.

5. Flushing the headspace with nitrogen gas.

Pouch sealers are generally equipped to apply either hot bar seals or impulse seals. The pouch seal area must be free of contamination and wrinkles in order to form adequate heat seals. Additionally, sealing temperature, pressure and dwell time must be maintained in accordance with the pouch manufacturer's specifications.

Defect Definitions and Classifications

Defects common to pouch production, filling and processing are defined below. *Table 5* denotes the defect classification.

Abrasion/scratch—A scratch partially through the surface layer(s) of the package caused by mechanically rubbing or scuffing. The abrasion will appear as streaks, some darker in color, on the container. Deep scratches that can be felt as indentations are unacceptable. Slight scratches must be tested for acceptability.

Blister—A void within the bonded seal. This defect will appear to resemble a bubble in the sealed area. On a foil pouch, the blister will cause a raised appearance on the seal.

Table 5—Classification of defects associated with flexible pouches.

Defect	Critical	Major	Minor
Abrasion/scratch	—	✔	✔
Blister	—	✔	✔
Burning	—	✔	✔
Channel leaker	✔	—	—
Contamination	—	✔	✔
Convolution	—	—	✔
Crooked seal/short seal	✔	—	✔
Cuts	✔	—	—
Delamination	—	✔	✔
Flex cracks/seal cracking	✔	—	✔
Heat ripples	—	—	✔
Hole/puncture	✔	—	—
Hot fold	—	—	✔
Marks on seal	—	—	✔
Non-bonding	✔	—	—
Seal creep	—	✔	✔
Tear	✔	—	—
Uneven seal juncture	—	—	✔
Waffling	—	—	✔
Wrinkle	✔	✔	✔

Burning—A milky white appearance on the seal is an indication of excess heat/pressure. Some appear as delamination or small blisters on the seal, caused by incorrect heat, pressure or dwell time.

Channel leaker—A patch of non-bonded area across the width of the seal creating a leak. This defect can sometimes be detected visually by the absence of a portion of the seal impression in a seal. If a pouch has a channel leaker, it will usually be detected by applying pressure toward the seal.

Contamination—Foreign matter in the seal area such as, but not limited to, water, grease or food. A pouch with contamination will have a noticeable raised area in the seal where the seal bar has sealed over the contamination. The condition is acceptable if there is a minimum clear seal width of 3/32-inch.

Convolution—A slight visual impression in the seal indented on one side and raised on the other.

Crooked seal/short seal—A seal that is not parallel to the cut edge of the pouch. A hermetic seal that is on an angle with any amount of unsealed material above the closure seal is acceptable. If the seal is on the edge of the pouch with a narrowing on one end, it is acceptable as long as the width is a minimum of 3/32-inch.

Cuts—A mechanical slash or slice that penetrates the package, causing a loss of hermetic integrity. A cut will have a clean appearance on the edges of the material separated.

Delamination—A separation of the laminate materials. Normally this separation is between the foil and the polypropylene layers. Delamination does not affect the hermetic seal, but its presence can affect potential damage in distribution. Some delamination may be present before retorting at the edge of the container. Post-retort delamination wrinkles dramatically; is soft to the touch, or peels away easily. The condition is major when delamination

occurs less than 3/32-inch from the inner seal or in the body of the pouch. Delamination on seals 3/32-inch or greater from the inner seal edge is a minor defect.

Flex cracks/seal cracking—Small breaks in one or more layers of the package, due to flexing, but not a leaker. Will appear as a deep, rough textured wrinkle on a pouch. Cracking in the seal area may not be adjacent to the inner seal and light may not pass through.

Heat ripples—Thin, multiple ripples on a seal caused by heat/tension. Ripples are on the two outer layers and do not affect the inner layer or seal integrity.

Hole/puncture—A mechanical penetration of the package, causing loss of hermetic integrity. A hole or puncture is normally small in size.

Hot fold—A permanent bend in a seal formed after sealing but before the seal area has cooled. This may appear as a large wrinkle or a fold that has been sealed over.

Marks on seal—Flat, unraised marks appearing on one or both sides of a pouch seal. Common causes are plastic build-up on the seal die, a dirty die, or a nick in the die.

Non-bonding—Failure of two sealant films to combine during the sealing process. This can be detected visually by the sealing bar impression on a pouch. If it is in only one area, there will be a faint void in the seal. If it is in the whole seal, the seal impression will be very faint. Applying pressure to the seal area will cause the seal to separate.

Seal creep—Partial opening of the inner border of the seal. This problem normally is detected by applying some pressure upward toward the seal.

Tear—A mechanical rip that penetrates the package, causing a loss of hermetic integrity. A tear will have a jagged appearance on the edges of the separated material.

Uneven seal juncture—Wavy or rough appearance of bonded polymer at the seal juncture. This will appear as small wrinkles but not the fold-over type. The inner seal juncture may also have a wavy appearance.

Waffling—Embossing caused by racks during thermal processing that appears on the surface of the pouch and is easily recognized. The tray rack pattern is embossed on the container causing a "waffling" effect.

Wrinkle—A fold of material in the seal area. This problem is highly visual, since the seal will have a pleated appearance from the foldover of the pouch material and can be seen on the unsealed area above the seal. Unacceptable conditions are foldover wrinkles and deep multiple wrinkles. Single deep wrinkles or flat wrinkles are to be tested for acceptability.

Inspection of Sealed Pouches

As with the other packages covered in this chapter, specific tests and inspection procedures for pouches should be discussed with the pouch supplier. Discussed below are some common tests.

Non-destructive examination

Visual observation and inspection—Check the tightness of both head and side seals by squeezing pouches from each fill tube or sealing lane. Important points are corners and the crossing of the head and side seals. This is a rapid determination of obvious defects. All seals must be accurately torn apart and evaluated for correct integrity of each seal.

Carefully inspect the edges of each head and side seal for any evidence of product in the seal areas. No product should be visible.

Observe the width of each seal area. The width must comply with machine specifications.

Squeeze test—Apply a manual kneading action to force product against the interior seal surface. Examine all seal areas for evidence of product leakage or delamination.

Packages that exhibit delamination of the outer ply on the seal area (but not at product edge) should be further tested by again manually flexing the suspect area 10 times and examining all seal areas for leakage or short-width.

Destructive examination

Teardown procedures—Open packages from each sealing lane or fill tube to check side and top seals. Visually inspect for such defects as misaligned seal, flex cracking, non-bonding and seal creep.

If applicable, tear the seals by doing a seal tensile strength test or a burst strength test. If both tests are used, the burst test must be completed first.

Burst strength test—The burst test to evaluate seal quality may be conducted by methods described in the *AOAC International Bacteriological Analytical Manual*, 7th Edition (1992). Using internal pressure resistance as the measurement to check all seals, apply uniform pressure for 30 seconds under designated test conditions to a level of not less than specified for a material or application. The seals should then be evaluated to ensure that proper closure is still in effect.

Seal tensile strength test—The seal strength test measures the strength of the seal. Procedures for the tensile strength test are available through American Society for Testing and Materials (A.S.T.M.). An acceptable seal should have torn evenly in such a way that the foil and part of the laminated layer from one side of the package tears off adhering onto the seal on the other side of the package. The seal should now appear rough and marbleized. The seal may also be considered to be adequate if the foil is laid bare across the entire length of the seal or as above.

Frequency of Testing

Pouch examinations—both destructive and non-destructive—shall be conducted with sufficient frequency to ensure adequate seals. All pouches across the web or in each sealing lane should be checked for acceptable seals at the time of start-up and a minimum of once every 30 minutes thereafter. Additionally, for web-fed systems, all packages across the web should be checked for acceptable seals after every packaging material splice.

At least one pouch from each fill tube or sealing lane must be tested. All seals on the pouch that are formed by the processor must be tested.

All packages from each fill tube or sealing head should be tested for leaks using the squeeze-test method (see test procedures—squeeze test) at start-up time and at least every 30 minutes thereafter.

Teardown procedures, if applicable, should be conducted at start-up and a minimum of every four hours or more frequently if problems are encountered.

Pouch Handling Procedures

Because flexible pouches are much more susceptible to damage than metal cans, precautions must be taken to avoid pouch damage. Careful handling practices should be followed. The majority of these procedures also apply to other flexible and semirigid containers.

1. Avoid pouch-to-pouch contact. Pouches should not be allowed to fall onto other pouches because sharp pouch corners, sides and other notches can puncture or cut.

2. Avoid excessive handling and manipulation of pouches or other packages with heat seals. This also applies to on-line sampling and inspection stations.

3. Avoid folding of pouches in all operations, particularly in retorting.

4. Prevent pouches from jamming or bunching up on conveyors or other work surfaces.

5. Handle pouches singly rather than in bunches. Avoid tossing pouches onto other pouches.

6. Avoid sliding pouches across conveyor belts, retort racks or other handling surfaces.

7. Place pouches in retort racks in single layers without overlapping. Placement in horizontally oriented racks minimizes the likelihood of pouch damage and should improve productivity. Prevent pouches from overlapping or protruding above the retort racks to avoid damage during loading, processing and unloading.

8. Prevent loaded retort racks from being dropped on other loaded racks. Careful placement avoids damage to both racks and pouches.

9. Regularly inspect retort baskets, racks and trays for damaged and rough spots that could cause abrasions or cuts of flexible pouches.

10. Dry pouches promptly after retorting, using an air knife or in-line dryers rather than wiping dry. The use of surfactants in the cooling water helps in the drying process. Pouches should not be allowed to accumulate in racks after processing and prior to drying.

11. Exercise care when sliding pouches into cartons to ensure that pouches are not damaged by roughened contact surfaces.

12. Prohibit employees and inspectors from wearing jewelry, wrist watches, neckties or other items that could cause either pouch damage or personal injury.

Recordkeeping

Documentation for each routine inspection item listed must be created and maintained as required. Records must be completed at the time of measurement or observation. Regulations require that any defects—along with the necessary corrective action—be documented as well.

The USDA requires that only normal appearing containers be shipped from an establishment. Usually firms develop a condition-of-container sampling plan to inspect the condition of finished product containers. *Figure 18* provides a sample form that may be used for condition-of-container inspections.

Product _____ Code _____ Date _____

Plan Number _____ Lot Size _____ Sample Size _____

Inspected By _____ LOT ACCEPTED REJECTED

Can Size _____

	Defect Count	Major	Critical
Blow, Hard Swell		■	
Flipper Springer		■	
Short Vacuum, Loose Tin		■	
Overstuffed		■	
Punctured		■	
Dents Affecting Score or Seam			■
Seam Cutovers			■
Seam Droops, Lips (Vees)			■
Seam Fractures		■	
False Seams, Spinners, Knock Down Flange		■	
Retort Buckles (Vacuum Retained)			■
Rust Pits			■
Leakers		■	
Dirty			■
Label Missing			■
Label Not Equal to Code		■	
Code Missing			■
Tab Lifted			■
Totals			

Comments:

Figure 18—Sample form that may be used for condition-of-container inspection.

APPENDIX

EMERGENCY PERMIT CONTROL
Code of Federal Regulations
Title 21, Part 108

CONTENTS

21 CFR PART 108—EMERGENCY PERMIT CONTROL

AUTHORITY: Secs. 402, 404, 701 of the Federal Food, Drug, and Cosmetic Act (21 U.S.C. 342, 344, 371).

SOURCE: 42 FR 14334, Mar. 15, 1977, unless otherwise noted.

Subpart A—General Provisions

§ 108.3 Definitions.

(a) The definitions contained in section 201 of the Federal Food, Drug, and Cosmetic Act are applicable to such terms when used in this part.

(b) *Commissioner* means the Commissioner of Food and Drugs.

(c) *Act* means the Federal Food, Drug, and Cosmetic Act, as amended.

(d) *Permit* means an emergency permit issued by the Commissioner pursuant to section 404 of the act for such temporary period of time as may be necessary to protect the public health.

(e) *Manufacture, processing, or packing of food in any locality* means activities conducted in a single plant or establishment, a series of plants under a single management, or all plants in an industry or region, by a manufacturer, processor, or packer.

§ 108.5 Determination of the need for a permit.

(a) Whenever the Commissioner determines after investigation that a manufacturer, processor, or packer of a food for which a regulation has been promulgated in subpart B of this part does not meet the mandatory conditions and requirements established in such regulation, he shall issue to such manufacturer, processor, or packer an order determining that a permit shall be required before the food may be introduced or delivered for introduction into interstate commerce by that person. The order shall specify the mandatory conditions and requirements with which there is a lack of compliance.

　(1) The manufacturer, processor, or packer shall have 3 working days after receipt of such order within which to file objections. Such objections may be filed by telegram, telex, or any other mode of written communication addressed to the Food and Drug Administration, Center for Food Safety and Applied Nutrition (HFF-310), 200 C St. SW., Washington, DC 20204. If such objections are filed, the determination is stayed pending a hearing to be held within 5 working days after the filing of objections on the issues involved unless the Commissioner determines that the objections raise no genuine and substantial issue of fact to justify a hearing.

　(2) If the Commissioner finds that there is an imminent hazard to health, the order shall contain this finding and the reasons therefore, and shall state that the determination of the need for a permit is effective immediately pending an expedited hearing.

(b) A hearing under this section shall be conducted by the Commissioner or his designee at a location agreed upon by the objector and the Commissioner or, if such agreement cannot be reached, at a location designated by the Commissioner. The manufacturer, processor, or packer shall have the right to cross-examine the Food and Drug Administration's witnesses and to present witnesses on his own behalf.

(c) Within 5 working days after the hearing, and based on the evidence presented at the hearing, the Commissioner shall determine whether a permit is required and shall so inform the manufacturer, processor, or packer in writing, with the reasons for his decision.

(d) The Commissioner's determination of the need for a permit constitutes final agency action from which appeal lies to the courts. The Commissioner will not stay a determination of the need for a permit pending court appeal except in unusual circumstances, but will participate in expediting any such appeal.

[42 FR 14334, Mar. 15, 1977, as amended at 54 FR 24891, June 12, 1989]

§ 108.6 Revocation of determination of need for permit.

(a) A permit shall be required only during such temporary period as is necessary to protect the public health.

(b) Whenever the Commissioner has reason to believe that a permit holder is in compliance with the mandatory requirements and conditions established in subpart B of this part and is likely to remain in compliance, he shall, on his own initiative or on the application of the permit holder, revoke both the determination of need for a permit and the permit that had been issued. If denied, the applicant shall, upon request, be afforded a hearing conducted in accordance with § 108.5 (b) and (c) as soon as practicable. Such revocation is without prejudice to the initiation of further permit proceedings with respect to the same manufacturer, processor, or packer should later information again show the need for a permit.

§ 108.7 Issuance or denial of permit.

(a) After a determination and notification by the Commissioner in accordance with the provisions of § 108.5 that a manufacturer, processor, or packer requires a permit, such manufacturer, processor, or packer may not thereafter introduce or deliver for introduction into interstate commerce any such food manufactured, processed, or packed by him unless he holds a permit issued by the Commissioner or obtains advance written approval of the Food and Drug Administration pursuant to § 108.12(a).

(b) Any manufacturer, processor, or packer for whom the Commissioner has made a determination that a permit is necessary may apply to the Commissioner for the issuance of such a permit. The application shall contain such data and information as is necessary to show that all mandatory requirements and conditions for the manufacturer, processing or packing of a food for which regulations are established in subpart B of this part are met and, in particular, shall show that the deviations specified in the Commissioner's determination of the need for a permit have been corrected or suitable interim measures established. Within 10 working days after receipt of such application, (except that the Commissioner may extend such time an additional 10 working days where necessary), the Commissioner shall issue a permit, deny the permit, or offer the applicant a hearing conducted in accordance with § 108.5 (b) and (c) as to whether the permit should be issued. The Commissioner shall issue such a permit to which shall be attached, in addition to the mandatory requirements and conditions of subpart B of this part, any additional requirements or conditions which may be necessary to protect the public health if he finds that all mandatory requirements and conditions of subpart B of this part are met or suitable interim measures are established.

(c) Denial of a permit constitutes final agency action from which appeal lies to the courts. The Commissioner will not stay such denial pending court appeal except in unusual circumstances, but will participate in expediting any such appeal.

§ 108.10 Suspension and reinstatement of permit.

(a) Whenever the Commissioner finds that a permit holder is not in compliance with the mandatory requirements and conditions established by the permit, he shall immediately suspend the permit and so inform the permit holder, with the reasons for the suspension.

(b) Upon application for reinstatement of a permit, the Commissioner shall, within 10 working days, reinstate the permit if he finds that the person is in compliance with the mandatory requirements and conditions established by the permit or deny the application.

(c) Any person whose permit has been suspended or whose application for reinstatement has been denied may request a hearing. The hearing shall be conducted by the Commissioner or his designee within 5 working days of receipt of the request at a location agreed upon by the objector and the Commissioner or, if an agreement cannot be reached, at a location designated by the Commissioner. The permit holder shall have the right to present witnesses on his own behalf and to cross-examine the Food and Drug Administration's witnesses.

(d) Within 5 working days after the hearing, and based on the evidence presented at the hearing, the Commissioner shall determine whether the permit shall be reinstated and shall so inform the permit holder, with the reasons for his decision.

(e) Denial of an application for reinstatement of a permit constitutes final agency action from which appeal lies to the courts. The Commissioner will not stay such denial pending court appeal except in unusual circumstances, but will participate in expediting any such appeal.

§ 108.12 Manufacturing, processing, or packing without a permit, or in violation of a permit.

(a) A manufacturer, processor, or packer may continue at his own risk to manufacture, process, or pack without a permit a food for which the Commissioner has determined that a permit is required. All food so manufactured, processed, or packed during such period without a permit shall be retained by the manufacturer, processor, or packer and may not be introduced or delivered for introduction into interstate commerce without the advance written approval of the Food and Drug Administration. Such approval may be granted only upon an adequate showing that such food is free from microorganisms of public health significance. The manufacturer, processor, or packer may provide to the Commissioner, for his consideration in making any such determination, an evaluation of the potential public health significance of such food by a competent authority in accordance with procedures recognized as being adequate to detect any potential hazard to public health. Within 20 working days after receipt of a written request for such written approval the Food and Drug Administration shall either issue such written approval or deny the request. If the request is denied, the applicant shall, upon request, be afforded a prompt hearing conducted in accordance with § 108.5 (b) and (c).

(b) Except as provided in paragraph (a) of this section, no manufacturer, processor, or packer may introduce or deliver for introduction into interstate commerce without a permit or in violation of a permit a food for which the Commissioner has determined that a permit is required. Where a manufacturer, processor, or packer utilizes a consolidation warehouse or other storage facility under his control, interstate shipment of any such food from the point of production to that warehouse or storage facility shall not violate this paragraph, provided that no further introduction or delivery for introduction into interstate commerce is made from that consolidated warehouse or storage facility except as provided in paragraph (a) of this section.

§ 108.19 Establishment of requirements for exemption from section 404 of the act.

(a) Whenever the Commissioner finds after investigation that the distribution in interstate commerce of any class of food may, by reason of contamination with microorganisms during the manufacture, processing, or packing thereof in any locality, be injurious to health, and that such injurious nature cannot be adequately determined after such articles have entered interstate commerce, he shall promulgate regulations in subpart B of this part establishing requirements and conditions governing the manufacture, processing, or packing of the food necessary to protect the public health. Such regulations may be proposed by the Commissioner on his own initiative or in response to a petition from any interested person pursuant to part 10 of this chapter.

(b) A manufacturer, processor, or packer of a food for which a regulation has been promulgated in subpart B of this part shall be exempt from the requirement for a permit only if he meets all of the mandatory requirements and conditions established in that regulation.

[42 FR 14334, Mar. 15, 1977, as amended at 42 FR 15673, Mar. 22, 1977]

Subpart B—Specific Requirements and Conditions for Exemption From or Compliance With an Emergency Permit

§ 108.25 Acidified foods.

(a) Inadequate or improper manufacture, processing, or packing of acidified foods may result in the distribution in interstate commerce of processed foods that may be injurious to health. The harmful nature of such foods cannot be adequately determined after these foods have entered into interstate commerce. The Commissioner of Food and Drugs therefore finds that, to protect the public health, it may be necessary to require any commercial processor, in any establishment engaged in the manufacture, processing, or packing of acidified foods, to obtain and hold a temporary emergency permit provided for under section 404 of the Federal Food, Drug, and Cosmetic Act. Such a permit may be required whenever the Commissioner finds, after investigation, that the commercial processor has failed to fulfill all the requirements of this section, including registration and filing of process information, and the mandatory portions of §§ 114.10, 114.80(a)(1) and (2), and (b), 114.83, 114.89, and 114.100 (b),(c), and (d) of this chapter as they relate to acidified foods. These requirements are intended to ensure safe manufacturing, processing, and packing processes and to permit the Food and Drug Administration to verify that these processes are being followed. Failure to meet these requirements shall constitute a prima facie basis for the immediate application of the emergency permit control provisions of section 404 of the act to that establishment, under the procedures established in subpart A of this part.

(b) The definitions in § 114.3 of this chapter are applicable when those terms are used in this section.

(c) (1) *Registration.* A commercial processor, when first engaging in the manufacture, processing, or packing of acidified foods in any State, as defined in section 201(a)(1) of the act, shall, not later than 10 days after first so engaging, register and file with the Food and Drug Administration on Form FDA 2541 (food canning establishment registration) information including, but not limited to, the name of the establishment, principal place of business, the location of each establishment in which that processing is carried on, the processing method in terms of acidity and pH control, and a list of foods so processed in each establishment. These forms are available from the Food and Drug Administration, Center for Food Safety and Applied Nutrition, LACF Registration Coordinator (HFF-233), 200 C St. SW., Washington, DC 20204, or at any Food and Drug Administration district office. The completed form shall be submitted to the Food and Drug Administration, Bureau of Foods, Industry Guidance Branch (HFF-342), 200 C St. SW., Washington, DC 20204. Commercial processors presently so engaged shall register within 120 days after the effective date of this regulation. Foreign processors shall register within 120 days after the effective date of this regulation or before any offering of foods for import into the United States, whichever is later. Commercial processors duly registered under this section shall notify the Food and Drug Administration not later than 90 days after the commercial processor ceases or discontinues the manufacture, processing, or packing of the foods in any establishment, except that this notification shall not be required for temporary cessations due to the seasonal character of an establishment's production or by temporary conditions including, but not limited to, labor disputes, fire, or acts of God.

(2) *Process filing.* A commercial processor engaged in the processing of acidified foods shall, not later than 60 days after registration, and before packing any new product, provide the Food and Drug Administration information on the scheduled processes including, as necessary, conditions for heat processing and control of pH, salt, sugar, and preservative levels and source and date of the establishment of the process, for each acidified food in each container size. Filing of this information does not constitute approval of the information by the Food and Drug Administration, and information concerning processes and other data so filed shall be regarded as trade secrets within the meaning of 21 U.S.C. 331(j) and 18 U.S.C. 1905. This information shall be submitted on form FDA 2541a (food canning establishment process filing form for all methods except aseptic). Forms are available from the Food and Drug Administration, Center for Food Safety and Applied Nutrition, LACF Registration Coordinator (HFF-233), 200 C St. SW., Washington, DC 20204, or at Food and Drug Administration district office. The completed form shall be submitted to the Food and Drug Administration, Center for Food Safety and Applied Nutrition, LACF Registration Coordinator (HFF-233), 200 C St. SW., Washington, DC 20204.

(3) *Process adherence and information—*

    (i) *Scheduling.* A commercial processor engaged in processing acidified foods in any registered establishment shall process each food in conformity with at least the scheduled processes filed under paragraph (c)(2) of this section.

    (ii) *Process and pH information availability.* When requested by the Food and Drug Administration in writing, a commercial processor engaged in the processing of acidified foods shall provide the Food and Drug Administration with any process and procedure information that the Food and Drug Administration deems necessary to determine the adequacy of the process. Furnishing of this information does not constitute approval by the Food and Drug Administration of the content of the information filed, and the information concerning processes and other data so furnished shall be considered trade secrets within the meaning of 21 U.S.C. 331(j) and 18 U.S.C. 1905 (to the extent that they qualify under those provisions).

(d) A commercial processor engaged in the processing of acidified foods shall promptly report to the Food and Drug Administration any instance of spoilage, process deviation, or contamination with microorganisms, the nature of which has potential health-endangering significance, where any lot of such food has in whole or in part entered distribution in commerce.

(e) A commercial processor engaged in the processing of acidified foods shall prepare and maintain files on a current procedure for use for products under the processor's control, which that processor will ask the distributor to follow, including plans for recalling products that may be injurious to health; for identifying, collecting, warehousing, and controlling products; for determining the effectiveness of recalls; for notifying the Food and Drug Administration of any recalls; and for implementing recall programs.

(f) All plant personnel involved in acidification, pH control, heat treatment, or other critical factors of the operation shall be under the operating supervision of a person who has attended a school approved by the Commissioner for giving instruction in food-handling techniques, food protection principles, personal hygiene, plant sanitation practices, pH controls, and critical factors in acidification, and who has satisfactorily completed the prescribed course of instruction. The Commissioner will consider students who have satisfactorily completed the required portions of the courses presented under § 108.35 and part 113 of this chapter before March 16, 1979, as having satisfactorily completed the prescribed course of instruction under this section and part 114 of this chapter. The Commissioner will not withhold approval of any school qualified to give such instruction.

(g) A commercial processor engaged in the processing of acidified foods shall prepare, review, and retain at the processing plant or other reasonably accessible location for a period of 3 years from the date of manufacture, all records of processing, deviations in processing, pH, and other records specified in part 114 of this chapter. Upon written demand during the course of a factory inspection under section 704 of the act by a duly authorized employee of the Food and Drug Administration, a commercial processor shall permit the inspection and copying by that employee of these records to verify the pH and the adequacy of processing.

(h) This section shall not apply to the commercial processing of any food processed under the continuous inspection of the meat and poultry inspection program of the Food Safety and Inspection Service of the Department of Agriculture under the Federal Meat Inspection Act (34 Stat. 1256, as amended by 81 Stat. 584 (21 U.S.C. 601 *et seq.*)) and the Poultry Products Inspection Act (71 Stat. 441, as amended by 82 Stat. 791 (21 U.S.C. 451 *et seq.*)).

(i) Wherever the Commissioner finds that any State regulates the commercial processing of acidified foods under effective regulations specifying at least the requirements of part 114 of this chapter, the Commissioner shall issue a notice stating that compliance with such State regulations shall constitute compliance with this section, if the

State through its regulatory agency or each processor of acidified foods in the State files with the Food and Drug Administration the registration information and the processing information prescribed in paragraph (c) of this section.

(j) Imports:

    (1) This section applies to any foreign commercial processor engaged in the processing of acidified foods and offering those foods for import into the United States except that, in lieu of providing for the issuance of an emergency permit under paragraph (a) of this section, the Commissioner will request the Secretary of the Treasury refuse admission into the United States, under section 801 of the act, to any acidified foods which the Commissioner determines, after investigation, may result in the distribution in interstate commerce of processed foods that may be injurious to health as set forth in paragraph (a) of this section.

    (2) Any acidified food so refused admission shall not be admitted until the Commissioner determines that the commercial processor offering the food for import has complied with the requirements of this section and that the food is not injurious to health. To assist the Commissioner in making this determination, a duly authorized employee of the Food and Drug Administration shall be permitted to inspect the commercial processor's manufacturing, processing, and packing facilities.

(k) The following information submitted to the Food and Drug Administration under this section is not available for public disclosure unless it has been previously disclosed to the public as defined in § 20.81 of this chapter or it relates to a product or ingredient that has been abandoned and no longer represents a trade secret or confidential commercial or financial information as defined in § 20.61 of this chapter:

    (1) Manufacturing methods or processes, including quality control information.

    (2) Production, sales, distribution, and similar information, except that any compilation of the information aggregated and prepared in a way that does not reveal information which is not available for public disclosure under this provision is available for public disclosure.

    (3) Quantitative or semiquantitative formulas.

[44 FR 16207, Mar. 16, 1979, as amended at 54 FR 24891, June 12, 1989]

§ 108.35 Thermal processing of low-acid foods packaged in hermetically sealed containers.

(a) Inadequate or improper manufacture, processing, or packing of thermally processed low-acid foods in hermetically sealed containers may result in the distribution in interstate commerce of processed foods that may be injurious to health. The harmful nature of such foods cannot be adequately determined after these foods have entered into interstate commerce. The Commissioner of Food and Drugs therefore finds that, in order to protect the public health, it may be necessary to require any commercial processor, in any establishment engaged in the manufacture, processing, or packing of thermally processed low-acid foods in hermetically sealed containers, to obtain and hold a temporary emergency permit provided for under section 404 of the Federal Food, Drug, and Cosmetic Act. Such a permit may be required whenever the Commissioner finds, after investigation, that the commercial processor has failed to fulfill all the requirements of this section, including registration and the filing of process information, and the mandatory portions of part 113 of this chapter. These requirements are intended to ensure safe manufacture, processing, and packing procedures and to permit the Food and Drug Administration to verify that these procedures are being followed. Such failure shall constitute a prima facie basis for the immediate application of the emergency permit control provisions of section 404 of the act to that establishment, pursuant to the procedures established in subpart A of this part.

(b) The definitions in § 113.3 of this chapter are applicable when such terms are used in this section.

(c) Registration and process filing.

    (1) *Registration.* A commercial processor when first engaging in the manufacture, processing, or packing of thermally processed low-acid foods in hermetically sealed containers in any state, as defined in section 201(a)(1) of the act, shall, not later than 10 days after first so engaging, register with the Food and Drug Administration on Form FDA 2541 (food canning establishment registration) information including (but not limited to) his name, principal place of business, the location of each establishment in which such processing is carried on, the processing method in terms of the type of processing equipment employed, and a list of the low-acid foods so processed in each such establishment. These forms are available from the Food and Drug Administration, Center for Food Safety and Applied Nutrition, LACF Registration Coordinator HFF-233, 200 C St. SW., Washington, DC 20204, or at any Food and Drug Administration district office. The completed form shall be submitted to the Food and Drug Administration, Center for Food Safety and Applied Nutrition, LACF Registration Coordinator HFF-233, 200 C St. SW., Washington, DC 20204. Commercial processors presently so engaged shall register not later than July 13, 1973. Commercial processors duly registered in accordance with this section shall notify the Food and Drug Administration not later than 90 days after such commercial processor ceases or discontinues the manufacture, processing, or packing of thermally processed foods in any

establishment: *Provided*, That such notification shall not be required as to the temporary cessation necessitated by the seasonal character of the particular establishment's production or caused by temporary conditions including but not limited to strikes, lockouts, fire, or acts of God.

(2) *Process filing.* A commercial processor engaged in the thermal processing of low-acid foods packaged in hermetically sealed containers shall, not later than 60 days after registration and prior to the packing of a new product, provide the Food and Drug Administration information as to the scheduled processes including but not limited to the processing method, type of retort or other thermal processing equipment employed, minimum initial temperatures, times and temperatures of processing, sterilizing value (Fo), or other equivalent scientific evidence of process adequacy, critical control factors affecting heat penetration, and source and date of the establishment of the process, for each such low-acid food in each container size: *Provided*, That the filing of such information does not constitute approval of the information by the Food and Drug Administration, and that information concerning processes and other data so filed shall be regarded as trade secrets within the meaning of 21 U.S.C. 331(j) and 18 U.S.C. 1905. This information shall be submitted on the following forms as appropriate: Form FDA 2541a (food canning establishment process filing for all methods except aseptic), or Form FDA 2541c (food canning establishment process filing for aseptic systems). These forms are available from the Food and Drug Administration, Center for Food Safety and Applied Nutrition, LACF Registration Coordinator, HFF-233, 200 C St. SW., Washington, DC 20204, or at any Food and Drug Administration district office. The completed form(s) shall be submitted to the Food and Drug Administration, Center for Food Safety and Applied Nutrition, LACF Registration Coordinator, HFF-233, 200 C St. SW., Washington, DC 20204.

(i) If all the necessary information is not available for existing products, the processor shall, at the time the existing information is provided to the Food and Drug Administration request in writing an extension of time for submission of such information, specifying what additional information is to be supplied and the date by which it is to be submitted. Within 30 working days after receipt of such request the Food and Drug Administration shall either grant or deny such request in writing.

(ii) If a packer intentionally makes a change in a previously filed scheduled process by reducing the initial temperature or retort temperature, reducing the time of processing, or changing the product formulation, the container, or any other condition basic to the adequacy of scheduled process, he shall prior to using such changed process obtain substantiation by qualified scientific authority as to its adequacy. Such substantiation may be obtained by telephone, telegram, or other media, but must be promptly recorded, verified in writing by the authority, and contained in the packer's files for review by the Food and Drug Administration. Within 30 days after first use, the packer shall submit to the Food and Drug Administration, Center for Food Safety and Applied Nutrition, DFCT, HFF-414, 200 C St. SW., Washington, DC 20204 a complete description of the modifications made and utilized, together with a copy of his file record showing prior substantiation by a qualified scientific authority as to the safety of the changed process. Any intentional change of a previously filed scheduled process or modification thereof in which the change consists solely of a higher initial temperature, a higher retort temperature, or a longer processing time, shall not be considered a change subject to this paragraph, but if that modification is thereafter to be regularly scheduled, the modified process shall be promptly filed as a scheduled process, accompanied by full information on the specified forms as provided in this paragraph.

(iii) Many packers employ an ''operating'' process in which retort operators are instructed to use retort temperatures and/or processing times slightly in excess of those specified in the scheduled process as a safety factor to compensate for minor fluctuations in temperature or time to assure that the minimum times and temperatures in the scheduled process are always met. This would not constitute a modification of the scheduled process.

(3) *Process adherence and information.*

(i) A commercial processor engaged in the thermal processing of low-acid foods packaged in hermetically sealed containers in any registered establishment shall process each low-acid food in each container size in conformity with at least the scheduled processes and modifications filed pursuant to paragraph (c)(2) of this section.

(ii) Process information availability: When requested by the Food and Drug Administration in writing, a commercial processor engaged in thermal processing of low-acid foods packaged in hermetically sealed containers shall provide the Food and Drug Administration with any information concerning processes and procedures which is deemed necessary by the Food and Drug Administration to determine the adequacy of the process: *Provided*, That the furnishing of such information does not constitute approval of the information by the Food and Drug Administration, and that the information concerning processes and other data so furnished shall be regarded as trade secrets within the meaning of 21 U.S.C. 331(j) and 18 U.S.C. 1905.

(d) A commercial processor engaged in the thermal processing of low-acid foods packaged in hermetically sealed containers shall promptly report to the Food and Drug Administration any instance of spoilage or process deviation the nature of which indicates potential health significance where any lot of such food has in whole or in part entered distribution.

(e) A commercial processor engaged in thermal processing of low-acid foods packaged in hermetically sealed containers shall promptly report to the Food and Drug Administration any instance wherein any lot of such food, which may be injurious to health by reason of contamination with microorganisms, has in whole or in part entered distribution.

(f) A commercial processor engaged in the thermal processing of low-acid foods packaged in hermetically sealed containers shall have prepared and in his files a current procedure which he will use for products under his control and which he will ask his distributor to follow, including plans for effecting recalls of any product that may be injurious to health; for identifying, collecting, warehousing, and controlling the product; for determining the effectiveness of such recall; for notifying the Food and Drug Administration of any such recall; and for implementing such recall program.

(g) All operators of retorts, thermal processing systems, aseptic processing and packaging systems, or other thermal processing systems, and container closure inspectors shall be under the operating supervision of a person who has attended a school approved by the Commissioner for giving instruction in retort operations, aseptic processing and packaging systems operations or other thermal processing systems operations, and container closure inspections, and has satisfactorily completed the prescribed course of instruction: *Provided,* That this requirement shall not apply in the State of California as listed in paragraph (j) of this section and shall not apply until March 25, 1975 in any other State. The Commissioner will not withhold approval of any school qualified to give such instruction.

(h) A commercial processor engaged in the thermal processing of low-acid foods packaged in hermetically sealed containers shall prepare, review, and retain at the processing plant for a period of not less than one year, and at the processing plant or other reasonably accessible location for an additional two years, all records of processing, deviations in processing, container closure inspections, and other records specified in part 113 of this chapter. If during the first year of the three-year record retention period the processing plant is closed for a prolonged period between seasonal packs, the records may be transferred to some other reasonably accessible location at the end of the seasonal pack. Upon written demand during the course of a factory inspection pursuant to section 704 of the act by a duly authorized employee of the Food and Drug Administration, a commercial processor shall permit the inspection and copying by such employee of these records to verify the adequacy of processing, the integrity of container closures, and the coding of the products.

(i) This section shall not apply to the commercial processing of any food processed under the continuous inspection of the meat and poultry inspection program of the Animal and Plant Health Inspection Service of the Department of Agriculture under the Federal Meat Inspection Act (34 Stat. 1256, as amended by 81 Stat. 584 (21 U.S.C. 601 *et seq.*)) and the Poultry Products Inspection Act (71 Stat. 441, as amended by 82 Stat. 791 (21 U.S.C. 451 *et seq.*)).

(j) Compliance with State regulations:

(1) Wherever the Commissioner finds that any State regulates the commercial thermal processing of low-acid foods in accordance with effective regulations specifying at least the requirements of part 113 of this chapter, he shall issue a notice stating that compliance with such State regulations shall constitute compliance with part 113 of this chapter. However, the provisions of this section shall remain applicable to the commercial processing of low-acid foods in any such State, except that, either the State through its regulatory agency or each processor of low-acid foods in such State shall file with the Center for Food Safety and Applied Nutrition the registration information and the processing information prescribed in paragraph (c) of this section.

(2) The Commissioner finds that the State of California under the laws relating to cannery inspections governing thermal processing of low-acid foods packaged in hermetically sealed containers satisfy the requirements of part 113 of this chapter. Accordingly, processors, who under the laws relating to cannery inspections are licensed by the State of California and who comply with such state regulations, shall be deemed to comply with the requirements of part 113 of this chapter.

(k) Imports:

(1) This section shall apply to any foreign commercial processor engaged in the thermal processing of low-acid foods packaged in hermetically sealed containers and offering such foods for import into the United States except that, in lieu of providing for the issuance of an emergency permit under paragraph (a) of this section, the Commissioner will request the Secretary of the Treasury to refuse admission into the United States, pursuant to section 801 of the act, of any such low-acid foods which the Commissioner determines, after investigation, may result in the distribution in interstate commerce of processed foods that may be injurious to health as set forth in paragraph (a) of this section.

(2) Any such food refused admission shall not be admitted until such time as the Commissioner may determine that the commercial processor offering the food for import is in compliance with the requirements and conditions of this section and that such food is not injurious to health. For the purpose of making such determination,

the Commissioner reserves the right for a duly authorized employee of the Food and Drug Administration to inspect the commercial processor's manufacturing, processing, and packing facilities.

(l) The following data and information submitted to the Food and Drug Administration pursuant to this section are not available for public disclosure unless they have been previously disclosed to the public as defined in § 20.81 of this chapter or they relate to a product or ingredient that has been abandoned and they no longer represent a trade secret or confidential commercial or financial information as defined in § 20.81 of this chapter:

(1) Manufacturing methods or processes, including quality control information.

(2) Production, sales, distribution, and similar data and information, except that any compilation of such data and information aggregated and prepared in a way that does not reveal data or information which is not available for public disclosure under this provision is available for public disclosure.

(3) Quantitative or semiquantitative formulas.

[42 FR 14334, Mar. 15, 1977, as amended at 42 FR 15673, Mar. 22, 1977; 54 FR 24891, June 12, 1989]

CURRENT GOOD MANUFACTURING PRACTICE IN MANUFACTURING, PACKING, OR HOLDING HUMAN FOOD

Code of Federal Regulations
Title 21, Part 110

CONTENTS

21 CFR PART 110—CURRENT GOOD MANUFACTURING PRACTICE IN MANUFACTURING, PACKING, OR HOLDING HUMAN FOOD

AUTHORITY: Secs. 402, 701, 704 of the Federal Food, Drug, and Cosmetic Act (21 U.S.C. 342, 371, 374); sec. 361 of the Public Health Service Act (42 U.S.C. 264).

SOURCE: 51 FR 24475, June 19, 1986, unless otherwise noted.

Subpart A—General Provisions

§ 110.3 Definitions.

The definitions and interpretations of terms in section 201 of the Federal Food, Drug, and Cosmetic Act (the act) are applicable to such terms when used in this part. The following definitions shall also apply:

(a) *Acid foods or acidified foods* means foods that have an equilibrium pH of 4.6 or below.

(b) *Adequate* means that which is needed to accomplish the intended purpose in keeping with good public health practice.

(c) *Batter* means a semifluid substance, usually composed of flour and other ingredients, into which principal components of food are dipped or with which they are coated, or which may be used directly to form bakery foods.

(d) *Blanching*, except for tree nuts and peanuts, means a prepackaging heat treatment of foodstuffs for a sufficient time and at a sufficient temperature to partially or completely inactivate the naturally occurring enzymes and to effect other physical or biochemical changes in the food.

(e) *Critical control point* means a point in a food process where there is a high probability that improper control may cause, allow, or contribute to a hazard or to filth in the final food or decomposition of the final food.

(f) *Food* means food as defined in section 201(f) of the act and includes raw materials and ingredients.

(g) *Food-contact surfaces* are those surfaces that contact human food and those surfaces from which drainage onto the food or onto surfaces that contact the food ordinarily occurs during the normal course of operations. ''Food-contact surfaces'' includes utensils and food-contact surfaces of equipment.

(h) *Lot* means the food produced during a period of time indicated by a specific code.

(i) *Microorganisms* means yeasts, molds, bacteria, and viruses and includes, but is not limited to, species having public health significance. The term ''undesirable microorganisms'' includes those microorganisms that are of public health significance, that subject food to decomposition, that indicate that food is contaminated with filth, or that otherwise may cause food to be adulterated within the meaning of the act. Occasionally in these regulations, FDA used the adjective ''microbial'' instead of using an adjectival phrase containing the word microorganism.

(j) *Pest* refers to any objectionable animals or insects including, but not limited to, birds, rodents, flies, and larvae.

(k) *Plant* means the building or facility or parts thereof, used for or in connection with the manufacturing, packaging, labeling, or holding of human food.

(l) *Quality control operation* means a planned and systematic procedure for taking all actions necessary to prevent food from being adulterated within the meaning of the act.

(m) *Rework* means clean, unadulterated food that has been removed from processing for reasons other than insanitary conditions or that has been successfully reconditioned by reprocessing and that is suitable for use as food.

(n) *Safe-moisture level* is a level of moisture low enough to prevent the growth of undesirable microorganisms in the finished product under the intended conditions of manufacturing, storage, and distribution. The maximum safe moisture level for a food is based on its water activity (a_w). An a_w will be considered safe for a food if adequate data are available that demonstrate that the food at or below the given a_w will not support the growth of undesirable microorganisms.

(o) *Sanitize* means to adequately treat food-contact surfaces by a process that is effective in destroying vegetative cells of microorganisms of public health significance, and in substantially reducing numbers of other undesirable microorganisms, but without adversely affecting the product or its safety for the consumer.

(p) *Shall* is used to state mandatory requirements.

(q) *Should* is used to state recommended or advisory procedures or identify recommended equipment.

(r) *Water activity* (a_w) is a measure of the free moisture in a food and is the quotient of the water vapor pressure of the substance divided by the vapor pressure of pure water at the same temperature.

§ 110.5 Current good manufacturing practice.

(a) The criteria and definitions in this part shall apply in determining whether a food is adulterated (1) within the meaning of section 402(a)(3) of the act in that the food has been manufactured under such conditions that it is unfit for food; or (2) within the meaning of section 402(a)(4) of the act in that the food has been prepared, packed, or held under insanitary conditions whereby it may have become contaminated with filth, or whereby it may have been rendered injurious to health. The criteria and definitions in this part also apply in determining whether a food is in violation of section 361 of the Public Health Service Act (42 U.S.C. 264).

(b) Food covered by specific current good manufacturing practice regulations also is subject to the requirements of those regulations.

§ 110.10 Personnel.

The plant management shall take all reasonable measures and precautions to ensure the following:

(a) *Disease control.* Any person who, by medical examination or supervisory observation, is shown to have, or appears to have, an illness, open lesion, including boils, sores, or infected wounds, or any other abnormal source of microbial contamination by which there is a reasonable possibility of food, food-contact surfaces, or food-packaging materials becoming contaminated, shall be excluded from any operations which may be expected to result in such contamination until the condition is corrected. Personnel shall be instructed to report such health conditions to their supervisors.

(b) *Cleanliness.* All persons working in direct contact with food, food-contact surfaces, and food-packaging materials shall conform to hygienic practices while on duty to the extent necessary to protect against contamination of food. The methods for maintaining cleanliness include, but are not limited to:

(1) Wearing outer garments suitable to the operation in a manner that protects against the contamination of food, food-contact surfaces, or food-packaging materials.

(2) Maintaining adequate personal cleanliness.

(3) Washing hands thoroughly (and sanitizing if necessary to protect against contamination with undesirable microorganisms) in an adequate hand-washing facility before starting work, after each absence from the work station, and at any other time when the hands may have become soiled or contaminated.

(4) Removing all unsecured jewelry and other objects that might fall into food, equipment, or containers, and removing hand jewelry that cannot be adequately sanitized during periods in which food is manipulated by hand. If such hand jewelry cannot be removed, it may be covered by material which can be maintained in an intact, clean, and sanitary condition and which effectively protects against the contamination by these objects of the food, food-contact surfaces, or food-packaging materials.

(5) Maintaining gloves, if they are used in food handling, in an intact, clean, and sanitary condition. The gloves should be of an impermeable material.

(6) Wearing, where appropriate, in an effective manner, hair nets, headbands, caps, beard covers, or other effective hair restraints.

(7) Storing clothing or other personal belongings in areas other than where food is exposed or where equipment or utensils are washed.

(8) Confining the following to areas other than where food may be exposed or where equipment or utensils are washed: eating food, chewing gum, drinking beverages, or using tobacco.

(9) Taking any other necessary precautions to protect against contamination of food, food-contact surfaces, or food-packaging materials with microorganisms or foreign substances including, but not limited to, perspiration, hair, cosmetics, tobacco, chemicals, and medicines applied to the skin.

(c) *Education and training.* Personnel responsible for identifying sanitation failures or food contamination should have a background of education or experience, or a combination thereof, to provide a level of competency necessary for production of clean and safe food. Food handlers and supervisors should receive appropriate training in proper food handling techniques and food-protection principles and should be informed of the danger of poor personal hygiene and insanitary practices.

(d) *Supervision.* Responsibility for assuring compliance by all personnel with all requirements of this part shall be clearly assigned to competent supervisory personnel.

[51 FR 24475, June 19, 1986, as amended at 54 FR 24892, June 12, 1989]

§ 110.19 Exclusions.

(a) The following operations are not subject to this part: Establishments engaged solely in the harvesting, storage, or distribution of one or more ''raw agricultural commodities,'' as defined in section 201(r) of the act, which are ordinarily cleaned, prepared, treated, or otherwise processed before being marketed to the consuming public.

(b) FDA, however, will issue special regulations if it is necessary to cover these excluded operations.

Subpart B—Buildings and Facilities

§ 110.20 Plant and grounds.

(a) *Grounds.* The grounds about a food plant under the control of the operator shall be kept in a condition that will protect against the contamination of food. The methods for adequate maintenance of grounds include, but are not limited to:

   (1) Properly storing equipment, removing litter and waste, and cutting weeds or grass within the immediate vicinity of the plant buildings or structures that may constitute an attractant, breeding place, or harborage for pests.

   (2) Maintaining roads, yards, and parking lots so that they do not constitute a source of contamination in areas where food is exposed.

   (3) Adequately draining areas that may contribute contamination to food by seepage, foot-borne filth, or providing a breeding place for pests.

   (4) Operating systems for waste treatment and disposal in an adequate manner so that they do not constitute a source of contamination in areas where food is exposed.

   If the plant grounds are bordered by grounds not under the operator's control and not maintained in the manner described in paragraph (a) (1) through (3) of this section, care shall be exercised in the plant by inspection, extermination, or other means to exclude pests, dirt, and filth that may be a source of food contamination.

(b) *Plant construction and design.* Plant buildings and structures shall be suitable in size, construction, and design to facilitate maintenance and sanitary operations for food-manufacturing purposes. The plant and facilities shall:

   (1) Provide sufficient space for such placement of equipment and storage of materials as is necessary for the maintenance of sanitary operations and the production of safe food.

   (2) Permit the taking of proper precautions to reduce the potential for contamination of food, food-contact surfaces, or food-packaging materials with microorganisms, chemicals, filth, or other extraneous material. The potential for contamination may be reduced by adequate food safety controls and operating practices or effective design, including the separation of operations in which contamination is likely to occur, by one or more of the following means: location, time, partition, air flow, enclosed systems, or other effective means.

   (3) Permit the taking of proper precautions to protect food in outdoor bulk fermentation vessels by any effective means, including:

      (i) Using protective coverings.

      (ii) Controlling areas over and around the vessels to eliminate harborages for pests.

      (iii) Checking on a regular basis for pests and pest infestation.

      (iv) Skimming the fermentation vessels, as necessary.

   (4) Be constructed in such a manner that floors, walls, and ceilings may be adequately cleaned and kept clean and kept in good repair; that drip or condensate from fixtures, ducts and pipes does not contaminate food, food-contact surfaces, or food-packaging materials; and that aisles or working spaces are provided between equipment and walls and are adequately unobstructed and of adequate width to permit employees to perform their duties and to protect against contaminating food or food-contact surfaces with clothing or personal contact.

   (5) Provide adequate lighting in hand-washing areas, dressing and locker rooms, and toilet rooms and in all areas where food is examined, processed, or stored and where equipment or utensils are cleaned; and provide safety-type light bulbs, fixtures, skylights, or other glass suspended over exposed food in any step of preparation or otherwise protect against food contamination in case of glass breakage.

   (6) Provide adequate ventilation or control equipment to minimize odors and vapors (including steam and noxious fumes) in areas where they may contaminate food; and locate and operate fans and other air-blowing equipment in a manner that minimizes the potential for contaminating food, food-packaging materials, and food-contact surfaces.

   (7) Provide, where necessary, adequate screening or other protection against pests.

§ 110.35 Sanitary operations.

(a) *General maintenance.* Buildings, fixtures, and other physical facilities of the plant shall be maintained in a sanitary condition and shall be kept in repair sufficient to prevent food from becoming adulterated within the meaning of the act. Cleaning and sanitizing of utensils and equipment shall be conducted in a manner that protects against contamination of food, food-contact surfaces, or food-packaging materials.

(b) *Substances used in cleaning and sanitizing; storage of toxic materials.*

   (1) Cleaning compounds and sanitizing agents used in cleaning and sanitizing procedures shall be free from undesirable microorganisms and shall be safe and adequate under the conditions of use. Compliance with this requirement may be verified by any effective means including purchase of these substances under a

supplier's guarantee or certification, or examination of these substances for contamination. Only the following toxic materials may be used or stored in a plant where food is processed or exposed:

    (i)   Those required to maintain clean and sanitary conditions;

    (ii) Those necessary for use in laboratory testing procedures;

    (iii) Those necessary for plant and equipment maintenance and operation; and

    (iv) Those necessary for use in the plant's operations.

  (2) Toxic cleaning compounds, sanitizing agents, and pesticide chemicals shall be identified, held, and stored in a manner that protects against contamination of food, food-contact surfaces, or food-packaging materials. All relevant regulations promulgated by other Federal, State, and local government agencies for the application, use, or holding of these products should be followed.

(c) *Pest control.* No pests shall be allowed in any area of a food plant. Guard or guide dogs may be allowed in some areas of a plant if the presence of the dogs is unlikely to result in contamination of food, food-contact surfaces, or food-packaging materials. Effective measures shall be taken to exclude pests from the processing areas and to protect against the contamination of food on the premises by pests. The use of insecticides or rodenticides is permitted only under precautions and restrictions that will protect against the contamination of food, food-contact surfaces, and food-packaging materials.

(d) *Sanitation of food-contact surfaces.* All food-contact surfaces, including utensils and food-contact surfaces of equipment, shall be cleaned as frequently as necessary to protect against contamination of food.

  (1) Food-contact surfaces used for manufacturing or holding low-moisture food shall be in a dry, sanitary condition at the time of use. When the surfaces are wet-cleaned, they shall, when necessary, be sanitized and thoroughly dried before subsequent use.

  (2) In wet processing, when cleaning is necessary to protect against the introduction of microorganisms into food, all food-contact surfaces shall be cleaned and sanitized before use and after any interruption during which the food-contact surfaces may have become contaminated. Where equipment and utensils are used in a continuous production operation, the utensils and food-contact surfaces of the equipment shall be cleaned and sanitized as necessary.

  (3) Non-food-contact surfaces of equipment used in the operation of food plants should be cleaned as frequently as necessary to protect against contamination of food.

  (4) Single-service articles (such as utensils intended for one-time use, paper cups, and paper towels) should be stored in appropriate containers and shall be handled, dispensed, used, and disposed of in a manner that protects against contamination of food or food-contact surfaces.

  (5) Sanitizing agents shall be adequate and safe under conditions of use. Any facility, procedure, or machine is acceptable for cleaning and sanitizing equipment and utensils if it is established that the facility, procedure, or machine will routinely render equipment and utensils clean and provide adequate cleaning and sanitizing treatment.

(e) *Storage and handling of cleaned portable equipment and utensils.* Cleaned and sanitized portable equipment with food-contact surfaces and utensils should be stored in a location and manner that protects food-contact surfaces from contamination.

[51 FR 24475, June 19, 1986, as amended at 54 FR 24892, June 12, 1989]

§ 110.37 Sanitary facilities and controls.

Each plant shall be equipped with adequate sanitary facilities and accommodations including, but not limited to:

(a) *Water supply.* The water supply shall be sufficient for the operations intended and shall be derived from an adequate source. Any water that contacts food or food-contact surfaces shall be safe and of adequate sanitary quality. Running water at a suitable temperature, and under pressure as needed, shall be provided in all areas where required for the processing of food, for the cleaning of equipment, utensils, and food-packaging materials, or for employee sanitary facilities.

(b) *Plumbing.* Plumbing shall be of adequate size and design and adequately installed and maintained to:

  (1) Carry sufficient quantities of water to required locations throughout the plant.

  (2) Properly convey sewage and liquid disposable waste from the plant.

  (3) Avoid constituting a source of contamination to food, water supplies, equipment, or utensils or creating an unsanitary condition.

  (4) Provide adequate floor drainage in all areas where floors are subject to flooding-type cleaning or where normal operations release or discharge water or other liquid waste on the floor.

  (5) Provide that there is not backflow from, or cross-connection between, piping systems that discharge waste water or sewage and piping systems that carry water for food or food manufacturing.

(c) *Sewage disposal.* Sewage disposal shall be made into an adequate sewerage system or disposed of through other adequate means.

(d) *Toilet facilities.* Each plant shall provide its employees with adequate, readily accessible toilet facilities. Compliance with this requirement may be accomplished by:

    (1) Maintaining the facilities in a sanitary condition.

    (2) Keeping the facilities in good repair at all times.

    (3) Providing self-closing doors.

    (4) Providing doors that do not open into areas where food is exposed to airborne contamination, except where alternate means have been taken to protect against such contamination (such as double doors or positive airflow systems).

(e) *Hand-washing facilities.* Hand-washing facilities shall be adequate and convenient and be furnished with running water at a suitable temperature. Compliance with this requirement may be accomplished by providing:

    (1) Hand-washing and, where appropriate, hand-sanitizing facilities at each location in the plant where good sanitary practices require employees to wash and/or sanitize their hands.

    (2) Effective hand-cleaning and sanitizing preparations.

    (3) Sanitary towel service or suitable drying devices.

    (4) Devices or fixtures, such as water control valves, so designed and constructed to protect against recontamination of clean, sanitized hands.

    (5) Readily understandable signs directing employees handling unprotected food, unprotected food-packaging materials, of food-contact surfaces to wash and, where appropriate, sanitize their hands before they start work, after each absence from post of duty, and when their hands may have become soiled or contaminated. These signs may be posted in the processing room(s) and in all other areas where employees may handle such food, materials, or surfaces.

    (6) Refuse receptacles that are constructed and maintained in a manner that protects against contamination of food.

(f) *Rubbish and offal disposal.* Rubbish and any offal shall be so conveyed, stored, and disposed of as to minimize the development of odor, minimize the potential for the waste becoming an attractant and harborage or breeding place for pests, and protect against contamination of food, food-contact surfaces, water supplies, and ground surfaces.

Subpart C—Equipment

§ 110.40 Equipment and utensils.

(a) All plant equipment and utensils shall be so designed and of such material and workmanship as to be adequately cleanable, and shall be properly maintained. The design, construction, and use of equipment and utensils shall preclude the adulteration of food with lubricants, fuel, metal fragments, contaminated water, or any other contaminants. All equipment should be so installed and maintained as to facilitate the cleaning of the equipment and of all adjacent spaces. Food-contact surfaces shall be corrosion-resistant when in contact with food. They shall be made of nontoxic materials and designed to withstand the environment of their intended use and the action of food, and, if applicable, cleaning compounds and sanitizing agents. Food-contact surfaces shall be maintained to protect food from being contaminated by any source, including unlawful indirect food additives.

(b) Seams on food-contact surfaces shall be smoothly bonded or maintained so as to minimize accumulation of food particles, dirt, and organic matter and thus minimize the opportunity for growth of microorganisms.

(c) Equipment that is in the manufacturing or food-handling area and that does not come into contact with food shall be so constructed that it can be kept in a clean condition.

(d) Holding, conveying, and manufacturing systems, including gravimetric, pneumatic, closed, and automated systems, shall be of a design and construction that enables them to be maintained in an appropriate sanitary condition.

(e) Each freezer and cold storage compartment used to store and hold food capable of supporting growth of microorganisms shall be fitted with an indicating thermometer, temperature-measuring device, or temperature-recording device so installed as to show the temperature accurately within the compartment, and should be fitted with an automatic control for regulating temperature or with an automatic alarm system to indicate a significant temperature change in a manual operation.

(f) Instruments and controls used for measuring, regulating, or recording temperatures, pH, acidity, water activity, or other conditions that control or prevent the growth of undesirable microorganisms in food shall be accurate and adequately maintained, and adequate in number for their designated uses.

(g) Compressed air or other gases mechanically introduced into food or used to clean food-contact surfaces or equipment shall be treated in such a way that food is not contaminated with unlawful indirect food additives.

Subpart D—[Reserved]

Subpart E—Production and Process Controls

§ 110.80 Processes and controls.

All operations in the receiving, inspecting, transporting, segregating, preparing, manufacturing, packaging, and storing of food shall be conducted in accordance with adequate sanitation principles. Appropriate quality control operations shall be employed to ensure that food is suitable for human consumption and that food-packaging materials are safe and suitable. Overall sanitation of the plant shall be under the supervision of one or more competent individuals assigned responsibility for this function. All reasonable precautions shall be taken to ensure that production procedures do not contribute contamination from any source. Chemical, microbial, or extraneous-material testing procedures shall be used where necessary to identify sanitation failures or possible food contamination. All food that has become contaminated to the extent that it is adulterated within the meaning of the act shall be rejected, or if permissible, treated or processed to eliminate the contamination.

(a) *Raw materials and other ingredients.*

    (1) Raw materials and other ingredients shall be inspected and segregated or otherwise handled as necessary to ascertain that they are clean and suitable for processing into food and shall be stored under conditions that will protect against contamination and minimize deterioration. Raw materials shall be washed or cleaned as necessary to remove soil or other contamination. Water used for washing, rinsing, or conveying food shall be safe and of adequate sanitary quality. Water may be reused for washing, rinsing, or conveying food if it does not increase the level of contamination of the food. Containers and carriers of raw materials should be inspected on receipt to ensure that their condition has not contributed to the contamination or deterioration of food.

    (2) Raw materials and other ingredients shall either not contain levels of microorganisms that may produce food poisoning or other disease in humans, or they shall be pasteurized or otherwise treated during manufacturing operations so that they no longer contain levels that would cause the product to be adulterated within the meaning of the act. Compliance with this requirement may be verified by any effective means, including purchasing raw materials and other ingredients under a supplier's guarantee or certification.

    (3) Raw materials and other ingredients susceptible to contamination with aflatoxin or other natural toxins shall comply with current Food and Drug Administration regulations, guidelines, and action levels for poisonous or deleterious substances before these materials or ingredients are incorporated into finished food. Compliance with this requirement may be accomplished by purchasing raw materials and other ingredients under a supplier's guarantee or certification, or may be verified by analyzing these materials and ingredients for aflatoxins and other natural toxins.

    (4) Raw materials, other ingredients, and rework susceptible to contamination with pests, undesirable microorganisms, or extraneous material shall comply with applicable Food and Drug Administration regulations, guidelines, and defect action levels for natural or unavoidable defects if a manufacturer wishes to use the materials in manufacturing food. Compliance with this requirement may be verified by any effective means, including purchasing the materials under a supplier's guarantee or certification, or examination of these materials for contamination.

    (5) Raw materials, other ingredients, and rework shall be held in bulk, or in containers designed and constructed so as to protect against contamination and shall be held at such temperature and relative humidity and in such a manner as to prevent the food from becoming adulterated within the meaning of the act. Material scheduled for rework shall be identified as such.

    (6) Frozen raw materials and other ingredients shall be kept frozen. If thawing is required prior to use, it shall be done in a manner that prevents the raw materials and other ingredients from becoming adulterated within the meaning of the act.

    (7) Liquid or dry raw materials and other ingredients received and stored in bulk form shall be held in a manner that protects against contamination.

(b) *Manufacturing operations.*

    (1) Equipment and utensils and finished food containers shall be maintained in an acceptable condition through appropriate cleaning and sanitizing, as necessary. Insofar as necessary, equipment shall be taken apart for thorough cleaning.

    (2) All food manufacturing, including packaging and storage, shall be conducted under such conditions and controls as are necessary to minimize the potential for the growth of microorganisms, or for the contamination of food. One way to comply with this requirement is careful monitoring of physical factors such as time,

temperature, humidity, a_w, pH, pressure, flow rate, and manufacturing operations such as freezing, dehydration, heat processing, acidification, and refrigeration to ensure that mechanical breakdowns, time delays, temperature fluctuations, and other factors do not contribute to the decomposition or contamination of food.

(3) Food that can support the rapid growth of undesirable microorganisms, particularly those of public health significance, shall be held in a manner that prevents the food from becoming adulterated within the meaning of the act. Compliance with this requirement may be accomplished by any effective means, including:

   (i) Maintaining refrigerated foods at 45°F (7.2°C) or below as appropriate for the particular food involved.

   (ii) Maintaining frozen foods in a frozen state.

   (iii) Maintaining hot foods at 140°F (60°C) or above.

   (iv) Heat treating acid or acidified foods to destroy mesophilic microorganisms when those foods are to be held in hermetically sealed containers at ambient temperatures.

(4) Measures such as sterilizing, irradiating, pasteurizing, freezing, refrigerating, controlling pH or controlling a_w that are taken to destroy or prevent the growth of undesirable microorganisms, particularly those of public health significance, shall be adequate under the conditions of manufacture, handling, and distribution to prevent food from being adulterated within the meaning of the act.

(5) Work-in-process shall be handled in a manner that protects against contamination.

(6) Effective measures shall be taken to protect finished food from contamination by raw materials, other ingredients, or refuse. When raw materials, other ingredients, or refuse are unprotected, they shall not be handled simultaneously in a receiving, loading, or shipping area if that handling could result in contaminated food. Food transported by conveyor shall be protected against contamination as necessary.

(7) Equipment, containers, and utensils used to convey, hold, or store raw materials, work-in-process, rework, or food shall be constructed, handled, and maintained during manufacturing or storage in a manner that protects against contamination.

(8) Effective measures shall be taken to protect against the inclusion of metal or other extraneous material in food. Compliance with this requirement may be accomplished by using sieves, traps, magnets, electronic metal detectors, or other suitable effective means.

(9) Food, raw materials, and other ingredients that are adulterated within the meaning of the act shall be disposed of in a manner that protects against the contamination of other food. If the adulterated food is capable of being reconditioned, it shall be reconditioned using a method that has been proven to be effective or it shall be reexamined and found not to be adulterated within the meaning of the act before being incorporated into other food.

(10) Mechanical manufacturing steps such as washing, peeling, trimming, cutting, sorting and inspecting, mashing, dewatering, cooling, shredding, extruding, drying, whipping, defatting, and forming shall be performed so as to protect food against contamination. Compliance with this requirement may be accomplished by providing adequate physical protection of food from contaminants that may drip, drain, or be drawn into the food. Protection may be provided by adequate cleaning and sanitizing of all food-contact surfaces, and by using time and temperature controls at and between each manufacturing step.

(11) Heat blanching, when required in the preparation of food, should be effected by heating the food to the required temperature, holding it at this temperature for the required time, and then either rapidly cooling the food or passing it to subsequent manufacturing without delay. Thermophilic growth and contamination in blanchers should be minimized by the use of adequate operating temperatures and by periodic cleaning. Where the blanched food is washed prior to filling, water used shall be safe and of adequate sanitary quality.

(12) Batters, breading, sauces, gravies, dressings, and other similar preparations shall be treated or maintained in such a manner that they are protected against contamination. Compliance with this requirement may be accomplished by any effective means, including one or more of the following:

   (i) Using ingredients free of contamination.

   (ii) Employing adequate heat processes where applicable.

   (iii) Using adequate time and temperature controls.

   (iv) Providing adequate physical protection of components from contaminants that may drip, drain, or be drawn into them.

   (v) Cooling to an adequate temperature during manufacturing.

   (vi) Disposing of batters at appropriate intervals to protect against the growth of microorganisms.

(13) Filling, assembling, packaging, and other operations shall be performed in such a way that the food is protected against contamination. Compliance with this requirement may be accomplished by any effective means, including:

   (i) Use of a quality control operation in which the critical control points are identified and controlled during manufacturing.

   (ii) Adequate cleaning and sanitizing of all food-contact surfaces and food containers.

(iii) Using materials for food containers and food-packaging materials that are safe and suitable, as defined in § 130.3(d) of this chapter.

(iv) Providing physical protection from contamination, particularly airborne contamination.

(v) Using sanitary handling procedures.

(14) Food such as, but not limited to, dry mixes, nuts, intermediate moisture food, and dehydrated food, that relies on the control of a_w for preventing the growth of undesirable microorganisms shall be processed to and maintained at a safe moisture level. Compliance with this requirement may be accomplished by any effective means, including employment of one or more of the following practices:

(i) Monitoring the a_w of food.

(ii) Controlling the soluble solids-water ratio in finished food.

(iii) Protecting finished food from moisture pickup, by use of a moisture barrier or by other means, so that the a_w of the food does not increase to an unsafe level.

(15) Food such as, but not limited to, acid and acidified food, that relies principally on the control of pH for preventing the growth of undesirable microorganisms shall be monitored and maintained at a pH of 4.6 or below. Compliance with this requirement may be accomplished by any effective means, including employment of one or more of the following practices:

(i) Monitoring the pH of raw materials, food in process, and finished food.

(ii) Controlling the amount of acid or acidified food added to low-acid food.

(16) When ice is used in contact with food, it shall be made from water that is safe and of adequate sanitary quality, and shall be used only if it has been manufactured in accordance with current good manufacturing practice as outlined in this part.

(17) Food-manufacturing areas and equipment used for manufacturing human food should not be used to manufacture nonhuman food-grade animal feed or inedible products, unless there is no reasonable possibility for the contamination of the human food.

§ 110.93 Warehousing and distribution.

Storage and transportation of finished food shall be under conditions that will protect food against physical, chemical, and microbial contamination as well as against deterioration of the food and the container.

Subpart F—[Reserved]

Subpart G—Defect Action Levels

§ 110.110 Natural or unavoidable defects in food for human use that present no health hazard.

(a) Some foods, even when produced under current good manufacturing practice, contain natural or unavoidable defects that at low levels are not hazardous to health. The Food and Drug Administration establishes maximum levels for these defects in foods produced under current good manufacturing practice and uses these levels in deciding whether to recommend regulatory action.

(b) Defect action levels are established for foods whenever it is necessary and feasible to do so. These levels are subject to change upon the development of new technology or the availability of new information.

(c) Compliance with defect action levels does not excuse violation of the requirement in section 402(a)(4) of the act that food not be prepared, packed, or held under unsanitary conditions or the requirements in this part that food manufacturers, distributors, and holders shall observe current good manufacturing practice. Evidence indicating that such a violation exists causes the food to be adulterated within the meaning of the act, even though the amounts of natural or unavoidable defects are lower than the currently established defect action levels. The manufacturer, distributor, and holder of food shall at all times utilize quality control operations that reduce natural or unavoidable defects to the lowest level currently feasible.

(d) The mixing of a food containing defects above the current defect action level with another lot of food is not permitted and renders the final food adulterated within the meaning of the act, regardless of the defect level of the final food.

(e) A compilation of the current defect action levels for natural or unavoidable defects in food for human use that present no health hazard may be obtained upon request from the Industry Programs Branch (HFF-326), Center for Food Safety and Applied Nutrition, Food and Drug Administration, 200 C St. SW., Washington, DC 20204.

THERMALLY PROCESSED LOW-ACID FOODS PACKAGED IN HERMETICALLY SEALED CONTAINERS

Code of Federal Regulations
Title 21, Part 113

CONTENTS

21 CFR PART 113—THERMALLY PROCESSED LOW-ACID FOODS PACKAGED IN HERMETICALLY SEALED CONTAINERS

AUTHORITY: Secs. 402, 701, 704 of the Federal Food, Drug, and Cosmetic Act (21 U.S.C. 342, 371, 374); sec. 361 of the Public Health Service Act (42 U.S.C. 264).

SOURCE: 44 FR 16215, Mar. 16, 1979, unless otherwise noted.

Subpart A—General Provisions

§ 113.3 Definitions.

For the purposes of this part, the following definitions apply:

(a) *Aseptic processing and packaging* means the filling of a commercially sterilized cooled product into presterilized containers, followed by aseptic hermetical sealing, with a presterilized closure, in an atmosphere free of microorganisms.

(b) *Bleeders* means openings used to remove air that enters with steam from retorts and steam chambers and to promote circulation of steam in such retorts and steam chambers. Bleeders may serve as a means of removing condensate.

(c) *Come-up-time* means the time which elapses between the introduction of steam into the closed retort and the time when the retort reaches the required processing temperature.

(d) *Commercial processor* includes any person engaged in commercial, custom, or institutional (church, school, penal, or other organization) processing of food, including pet food. Persons engaged in the production of foods that are to be used in market or consumer tests are also included.

(e) *Commercial sterility*:
  (1) "Commercial sterility" of thermally processed food means the condition achieved—
    (i) By the application of heat which renders the food free of—
      (*a*) Microorganisms capable of reproducing in the food under normal nonrefrigerated conditions of storage and distribution; and
      (*b*) Viable microorganisms (including spores) of public health significance; or
    (ii) By the control of water activity and the application of heat, which renders the food free of microorganisms capable of reproducing in the food under normal nonrefrigerated conditions of storage and distribution.
  (2) "Commercial sterility" of equipment and containers used for aseptic processing and packaging of food means the condition achieved by application of heat, chemical sterilant(s), or other appropriate treatment that renders the equipment and containers free of viable microorganisms having public health significance, as well as microorganisms of nonhealth significance, capable of reproducing in the food under normal nonrefrigerated conditions of storage and distribution.

(f) *Critical factor* means any property, characteristic, condition, aspect, or other parameter, variation of which may affect the scheduled process and the attainment of commercial sterility.

(g) *Flame sterilizer* means an apparatus in which hermetically sealed containers are agitated at atmospheric pressure, by either continuous, discontinuous, or reciprocating movement, with impinging gas flames to achieve sterilization temperatures. A holding period in a heated section may follow the initial heating period.

(h) *Headspace, gross* is the vertical distance between the level of the product (generally the liquid surface) in an upright rigid container and the top edge of the container (the top of the double seam of a can or the top edge of a glass jar).

(i) *Headspace, net* of a container is the vertical distance between the level of the product (generally the liquid surface) in the upright rigid container and the inside surface of the lid.

(j) *Hermetically sealed container* means a container that is designed and intended to be secure against the entry of microorganisms and thereby to maintain the commercial sterility of its contents after processing.

(k) *Incubation* means the holding of a sample(s) at a specified temperature for a specified period of time for the purpose of permitting or stimulating the growth of microorganisms.

(l) *Initial temperature* means the average temperature of the contents of the coldest container to be processed at the time the thermal processing cycle begins, as determined after thorough stirring or shaking of the filled and sealed container.

(m) *Lot* means that amount of a product produced during a period of time indicated by a specific code.

(n) *Low-acid foods* means any foods, other than alcoholic beverages, with a finished equilibrium pH greater than 4.6 and a water activity (a_w) greater than 0.85. Tomatoes and tomato products having a finished equilibrium pH less than 4.7 are not classed as low-acid foods.

191

(o) *Minimum thermal process* means the application of heat to food, either before or after sealing in a hermetically sealed container, for a period of time and at a temperature scientifically determined to be adequate to ensure destruction of microorganisms of public health significance.

(p) *Operating process* means the process selected by the processor that equals or exceeds the minimum requirements set forth in the scheduled process.

(q) *Retort* means any closed vessel or other equipment used for the thermal processing of foods.

(r) *Scheduled process* means the process selected by the processor as adequate under the conditions of manufacture for a given product to achieve commercial sterility. This process may be in excess of that necessary to ensure destruction of microorganisms of public health significance, and shall be at least equivalent to the process established by a competent processing authority to achieve commercial sterility.

(s) *Shall* is used to state mandatory requirements.

(t) *Should* is used to state recommended or advisory procedures or to identify recommended equipment.

(u) *Vacuum-packed products* means those products that are sealed in a container under the vacuum specified in the scheduled process, the maintenance of which vacuum is critical to the adequacy of the scheduled process.

(v) *Vents* means openings through the retort shell, controlled by gate, plug cock, or other adequate valves used for the elimination of air during the venting period.

(w) *Water activity* (a_w) is a measure of the free moisture in a product and is the quotient of the water vapor pressure of the substance divided by the vapor pressure of pure water at the same temperature.

§ 113.5 Current good manufacturing practice.

The criteria in §§ 113.10, 113.40, 113.60, 113.81, 113.83, 113.87, 113.89, and 113.100 shall apply in determining whether the facilities, methods, practices, and controls used by the commercial processor in the manufacture, processing, or packing of low-acid foods in hermetically sealed containers are operated or administered in a manner adequate to protect the public health.

§ 113.10 Personnel.

The operators of processing systems, retorts, aseptic processing and packaging systems and product formulating systems (including systems wherein water activity is used in conjunction with thermal processing) and container closure inspectors shall be under the operating supervision of a person who has attended a school approved by the Commissioner for giving instruction appropriate to the preservation technology involved and who has been identified by that school as having satisfactorily completed the prescribed course of instruction. This person shall supervise only in those areas for which a school approved by the Commissioner identifies the person as having satisfactorily completed training.

Subpart B—[Reserved]

Subpart C—Equipment

§ 113.40 Equipment and procedures.

(a) *Equipment and procedures for pressure processing in steam in still retorts—*

    (1) *Indicating mercury-in-glass thermometer.* Each retort shall be equipped with at least one mercury-in-glass thermometer whose divisions are easily readable to 1°F and whose temperature range does not exceed 17°F per inch of graduated scale. Thermometers shall be tested for accuracy against a known accurate standard thermometer upon installation and at least once a year thereafter, or more frequently if necessary, to ensure their accuracy. Records of thermometer accuracy checks that specify date, standard used, method used, and person performing the test should be maintained. Each thermometer should have a tag, seal, or other means of identity that includes the date on which it was last tested for accuracy. A thermometer that has a divided mercury column or that cannot be adjusted to the standard shall be repaired or replaced before further use of the retort. Thermometers shall be installed where they can be accurately and easily read. Bulbs of indicating thermometers shall be installed either within the retort shell or in external wells attached to the retort. External wells or pipes shall be connected to the retort through at least a 3/4-inch diameter opening and equipped with a 1/16-inch or larger bleeder opening so located as to provide a full flow of steam past the length of the thermometer bulb. The bleeders for external wells shall emit steam continuously during the entire processing period. The mercury thermometer—not the recorder chart—shall be the reference instrument for indicating the processing temperature.

(2) *Temperature-recording device.* Each still retort shall have an accurate temperature-recording device. Graduations on the temperature-recording devices shall not exceed 2°F within a range of 10°F of the processing temperature. Each chart shall have a working scale of not more than 55°F per inch within a range of 20°F of the processing temperature. The temperature chart shall be adjusted to agree as nearly as possible with, but to be in no event higher than, the known accurate mercury-in-glass thermometer during the process time. A means of preventing unauthorized changes in adjustment shall be provided. A lock, or a notice from management posted at or near the recording device which provides a warning that only authorized persons are permitted to make adjustments, is a satisfactory means for preventing unauthorized changes. The recorder may be combined with the steam controller and may be a recording-controlling instrument. The temperature-recorder bulb shall be installed either within the retort shell or in a well attached to the shell. Each temperature-recorder bulb well shall have a 1/16-inch or larger bleeder which emits steam continuously during the processing period. Air-operated temperature controllers should have adequate filter systems to ensure a supply of clean, dry air.

(3) *Pressure gages.* Each retort should be equipped with a pressure gage that should be graduated in divisions of 2 pounds or less.

(4) *Steam controller.* Each retort shall be equipped with an automatic steam controller to maintain the retort temperature. This may be a recording-controlling instrument when combined with a recording thermometer. The steam controller may be air-operated and actuated by a temperature sensor positioned near the mercury-in-glass thermometer in the retort; a steam controller activated by the steam pressure of the retort is acceptable if it is carefully maintained mechanically so that it operates satisfactorily.

(5) *Steam inlet.* The steam inlet to each still retort shall be large enough to provide sufficient steam for proper operation of the retort. Steam may enter either the top portion or the bottom portion of the retort but, in any case, shall enter the portion of the retort opposite the vent; for example, steam inlet in bottom portion and vent in top portion.

(6) *Crate supports.* A bottom crate support shall be used in vertical still retorts. Baffle plates shall not be used in the bottom of still retorts.

(7) *Steam spreaders.* Steam spreaders are continuations of the steam inlet line inside the retort. Horizontal still retorts shall be equipped with steam spreaders that extend the length of the retort. For steam spreaders along the bottom of the retort, the perforations should be along the top 90° of this pipe, that is, within 45° on either side of the top center. Horizontal still retorts over 30 feet long should have two steam inlets connected to the spreader. In vertical still retorts, the steam spreaders, if used, should be perforated along the center line of the pipe facing the interior of the retort or along the sides of the pipe. The number of perforations should be such that the total cross-sectional area of the perforations is equal to 1 1/2 to 2 times the cross-sectional area of the smallest restriction in the steam inlet line.

(8) *Bleeders.* Bleeders, except those for thermometer wells, shall be one-eighth inch or larger and shall be wide open during the entire process, including the come-up-time. For horizontal still retorts, bleeders shall be located within approximately 1 foot of the outermost locations of containers at each end along the top of the retort; additional bleeders shall be located not more than 8 feet apart along the top. Bleeders may be installed at positions other than those specified above, as long as there is evidence in the form of heat distribution data that they accomplish adequate removal of air and circulation of steam within the retort. Vertical retorts shall have at least one bleeder opening located in that portion of the retort opposite the steam inlet. In retorts having top steam inlet and bottom venting, a bleeder shall be installed in the bottom of the retort to remove condensate. All bleeders shall be arranged so that the operator can observe that they are functioning properly.

(9) *Stacking equipment and position of containers.* Crates, trays, gondolas, etc., for holding containers shall be made of strap iron, adequately perforated sheet metal, or other suitable material. When perforated sheet metal is used for the bottoms, the perforations should be approximately the equivalent of 1-inch holes on 2-inch centers. If dividers are used between the layers of containers, they should be perforated as above. The positioning of containers in the retort, when specified in the scheduled process, shall be in accordance with that process.

(10) *Air valves.* Retorts using air for pressure cooling shall be equipped with a suitable valve to prevent air leakage into the retort during processing.

(11) *Water valves.* Retorts using water for cooling shall be equipped with a suitable valve to prevent leakage of water into the retort during processing.

(12) *Vents.* Vents shall be installed in such a way that air is removed from the retort before timing of the process is started. Vents shall be controlled by gate, plug cock, or other adequate type valves which shall be fully open to permit rapid discharge of air from the retort during the venting period. Vents shall not be connected directly to a closed drain system. If the overflow is used as a vent, there shall be an atmospheric break in the line before it connects to a closed drain. The vent shall be located in that portion of the retort opposite the steam inlet; for example, steam inlet in bottom portion and vent in top portion. Where a retort manifold

connects several vent pipes from a single still retort, it shall be controlled by a gate, plug cock, or other adequate type valve. The retort manifold shall be of a size that the cross-sectional area of the pipe is larger than the total cross-sectional area of all connecting vents. The discharge shall not be directly connected to a closed drain without an atmospheric break in the line. A manifold header connecting vents or manifolds from several still retorts shall lead to the atmosphere. The manifold header shall not be controlled by a valve and shall be of a size that the cross-sectional area is at least equal to the total cross-sectional area of all connecting retort manifold pipes from all retorts venting simultaneously. Timing of the process shall not begin until the retort has been properly vented and the processing temperature has been reached. Some typical installations and operating procedures reflecting the requirements of this section for venting still retorts are given in paragraph (a)(12)(i)(a) through (d) and (ii)(a) and (b) of this section.

(i) *Venting horizontal retorts.*

(a) Venting through multiple 1-inch vents discharging directly to atmosphere.

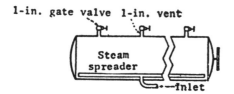

Specifications. One 1-inch vent for every 5 feet of retort length, equipped with a gate or plug cock valve and discharging to atmosphere; end vents not more than 2 1/2 feet from ends of retort.

Venting method. Vent valves should be wide open for at least 5 minutes and to at least 225°F, or at least 7 minutes and to at least 220°F.

(b) Venting through multiple 1-inch vents discharging through a manifold to atmosphere.

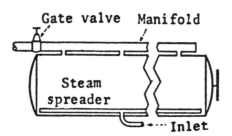

Specifications. One 1-inch vent for every 5 feet of retort length; and vents not over 2 1/2 feet from ends of retort: Size of manifold-for retorts less than 15 feet in length, 2 1/2 inches; for retorts 15 feet and over in length, 3 inches.

Venting method. Manifold vent gate or plug cock valve should be wide open for at least 6 minutes and to at least 225°F, or for at least 8 minutes and to at least 220°F.

(c) Venting through water spreaders.

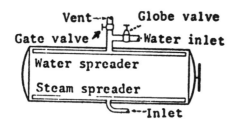

Size of vent and vent valve. For retorts less than 15 feet in length, 2 inches; for retorts 15 feet and over in length, 2 1/2 inches.

Size of water spreader. For retorts less than 15 feet in length, 1 1/2 inches; for retorts 15 feet and over in length, 2 inches. The number of holes should be such that their total cross-sectional area is approximately equal to the cross-sectional area of the vent pipe inlet.

Venting method. Water spreader vent gate or plug cock valve should be wide open for at least 5 minutes and to at least 225°F, or for at least 7 minutes and to at least 220°F.

(d) Venting through a single 2 1/2-inch top vent (for retorts not exceeding 15 feet in length).

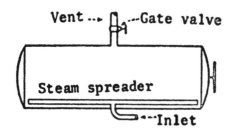

Specifications: A 2 1/2-inch vent equipped with a 2 1/2-inch gate or plug cock valve and located within 2 feet of the center of the retort.

Venting method: Vent gate or plug cock valve should be wide open for at least 4 minutes and to at least 220°F.

(ii) *Venting vertical retorts.*
(a) Venting through a 1 1/2-inch overflow.

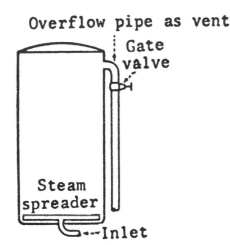

Specifications. A 1 1/2-inch overflow pipe equipped with a 1 1/2-inch gate or plug cock valve and with not more than 6 feet of 1 1/2-inch pipe beyond the valve before break to the atmosphere or to a manifold header.

Venting method. Vent gate or plug cock valve should be wide open for at least 4 minutes and to at least 218°F, or for at least 5 minutes and to at least 215°F.

(b) Venting through a single 1-inch side or top vent.

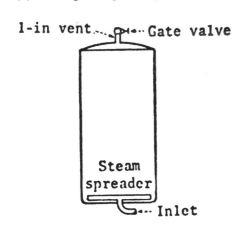

Specifications. A 1-inch vent in lid or top side, equipped with a 1-inch gate or plug cock valve and discharging directly into the atmosphere or to a manifold header.

Venting method. Vent gate or plug cock valve should be wide open for at least 5 minutes and to at least 230°F, or for at least 7 minutes and to at least 220°F.

(iii) Other installations and operating procedures that deviate from the above specifications may be used if there is evidence in the form of heat distribution data, which shall be kept on file, that they accomplish adequate venting of air.

(13) *Critical factors.* Critical factors specified in the scheduled process shall be measured and recorded on the processing record at intervals of sufficient frequency to ensure that the factors are within the limits specified in the scheduled process.

   (i) When maximum fill-in or drained weight is specified in the scheduled process, it shall be measured and recorded at intervals of sufficient frequency to ensure that the weight of the product does not exceed the maximum for the given container size specified in the scheduled process.

   (ii) Closing machine vacuum in vacuum-packed products shall be observed and recorded at intervals of sufficient frequency to ensure that the vacuum is as specified in the scheduled process.

   (iii) Such measurements and recordings should be made at intervals not to exceed 15 minutes.

   (iv) When the product style results in stratification or layering of the primary product in the containers, the positioning of containers in the retort shall be according to the scheduled process.

(b) *Equipment and procedures for pressure processing in water in still retorts—*

   (1) *Indicating mercury-in-glass thermometer.* Each retort shall be equipped with at least one mercury-in-glass thermometer whose divisions are easily readable to 1°F and whose temperature range does not exceed 17°F per inch of graduated scale. Thermometers shall be tested for accuracy against a known accurate standard thermometer upon installation and at least once a year thereafter, or more frequently if necessary, to ensure their accuracy. Records of thermometer accuracy checks which specify date, standard used, method used,

and person performing the test should be maintained. Each thermometer should have a tag, seal, or other means of identity that includes the date when it was last tested for accuracy. A thermometer that has a divided mercury column or that cannot be adjusted to the standard shall be repaired or replaced before further use of the retort. Thermometers shall be installed where they can be accurately and easily read. Bulbs of indicating thermometers shall be located in such a position that they are beneath the surface of the water throughout the process. On horizontal retorts, this entry should be made in the side at the center, and the thermometer bulbs shall be inserted directly into the retort shell. In both vertical and horizontal retorts, the thermometer bulbs shall extend directly into the water a minimum of at least 2 inches without a separable well or sleeve. The mercury thermometer—not the recorder chart—shall be the reference instrument for indicating the processing temperature.

(2) *Temperature-recording device.* Each still retort shall have an accurate temperature-recording device. Graduations on the temperature-recording devices shall not exceed 2°F within a range of 10°F of the processing temperature. Each chart shall have a working scale of not more than 55°F per inch within a range of 20°F of the processing temperature. The temperature chart shall be adjusted to agree as nearly as possible with, but to be in no event higher than, the known accurate mercury-in-glass thermometer during the process time. A means of preventing unauthorized changes in adjustment shall be provided. A lock, or a notice from management posted at or near the recording device which provides a warning that only authorized persons are permitted to make adjustments, is a satisfactory means for preventing unauthorized changes. The recorder may be combined with the steam controller and may be a recording-controlling instrument. The recording-thermometer bulb should be located adjacent to the bulb of the mercury-in-glass thermometer, except in the case of a vertical retort equipped with a combination recorder-controller. In such vertical retorts, the temperature recorder-control bulb shall be located at the bottom of the retort below the lowest crate rest in such a position that the steam does not strike it directly. In horizontal retorts, the temperature recorder-control bulb shall be located between the water surface and the horizontal plane passing through the center of the retort so that there is no opportunity for direct steam impingement on the control bulb. Air-operated temperature controllers should have adequate filter systems to ensure a supply of clean, dry air.

(3) *Pressure gages.*
   (i) Each retort should be equipped with a pressure gage, which should be graduated in divisions of 2 pounds or less.
   (ii) Each retort should have an adjustable pressure relief or control valve of a capacity sufficient to prevent an undesired increase in retort pressure when the water valve is wide open and should be installed in the overflow line.

(4) *Steam controller.* Each retort shall be equipped with an automatic steam controller to maintain the retort temperature. This may be a recording-controlling instrument when combined with a recording thermometer.

(5) *Steam introduction.* Steam shall be distributed in the bottom of the retort in a manner adequate to provide uniform heat distribution throughout the retort. In vertical retorts, uniform steam distribution can be achieved by any of several methods. In horizontal retorts, the steam distributor shall run the length of the bottom of the retort with perforations distributed uniformly along the upper part of the pipe.

(6) *Crate supports.* A bottom crate support shall be used in vertical still retorts. Baffle plates shall not be used in the bottom of the retort. Centering guides should be installed so as to ensure that there is about a 1 1/2-inch clearance between the side wall of the crate and the retort wall.

(7) *Stacking equipment and position of containers.* Crates, trays, gondolas, etc., for holding containers shall be made of strap iron, adequately perforated sheet metal, or other suitable material. When perforated sheet metal is used for the bottoms, the perforations should be approximately the equivalent of 1-inch holes on 2-inch centers. If divider plates are used between the layers of containers, they should be perforated as above. The positioning of containers in the retort, when specified in the scheduled process, shall be in accordance with that process. Dividers, racks, trays, or other means of positioning of flexible containers shall be designed and employed to ensure even circulation of heating medium around all containers in the retort.

(8) *Drain valve.* A nonclogging, water-tight valve shall be used. Screens should be installed over all drain openings.

(9) *Water level indicator.* There shall be a means of determining the water level in the retort during operation, e.g., by using a gage, water glass, or petcock(s). Water shall cover the top layer of containers during the entire come-up-time and processing periods and should cover the top layer of containers during the cooling periods. The operator shall check and record the water level at intervals sufficient to ensure its adequacy.

(10) (i) *Air supply and controls.* In both horizontal and vertical still retorts for pressure processing in water, a means shall be provided for introducing compressed air at the proper pressure and rate. The proper pressure shall be controlled by an automatic pressure control unit. A check valve shall be provided in the air supply line to prevent water from entering the system. Air or water circulation shall be maintained continuously during the come-up-time and during processing and cooling periods; the adequacy of the air or water circulation for uniform heat distribution within the retort shall be established in accordance

with procedures recognized by a competent processing authority and records shall be kept on file; if air is used to promote circulation, it shall be introduced into the steam line at a point between the retort and the steam control valve at the bottom of the retort.

    (ii) *Water circulation.* When a water circulating system is used for heat distribution, it shall be installed in such a manner that water will be drawn from the bottom of the retort through a suction manifold and discharged through a spreader which extends the length of the top of the retort. The holes in the water spreader shall be uniformly distributed and should have an aggregate area not greater than the cross-section area of the outlet line from the pump. The suction outlets should be protected with nonclogging screens to keep debris from entering the circulating system. The pump shall be equipped with a pilot light or other signaling device to warm the operator when it is not running, and with a bleeder to remove air when starting operations. Alternative methods for circulation of water in the retort may be used when established by a competent authority as adequate for even heat distribution.

(11) *Cooling water supply.* In vertical retorts the cooling water should be introduced at the top of the retort between the water and container levels; in horizontal retorts the cooling water should be introduced into the suction side of the pump. A check valve should be included in the cooling water line.

(12) *Retort headspace.* The headspace necessary to control the air pressure should be maintained between the water level and the top of the retort shell.

(13) *Vertical and horizontal still retorts.* Vertical and horizontal still retorts should follow the arrangements in the diagrams below in this paragraph. Other installation and operating procedures that deviate from these arrangements may be used, as long as there is evidence in the form of heat distribution data or other suitable information, which shall be kept on file, that demonstrates that the heat distribution is adequate.

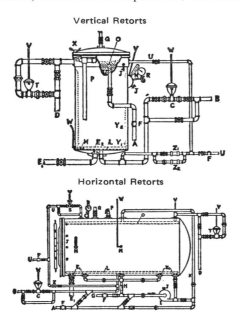

Vertical Retorts

Horizontal Retorts

LEGEND FOR VERTICAL AND HORIZONTAL STILL RETORTS

A — Water line.
B — Steam line.
C — Temperature control.
D — Overflow line.
E_1 — Drain line.
E_2 — Screens.
F — Check valves.
G — Line from hot water storage.
H — Suction line and manifold.
I — Circulating pump.
J — Petcocks.
K — Recirculating line.
L — Steam distributor.
M — Temperature controller bulb.
N — Thermometer.
O — Water spreader.
P — Safety valve.
Q — Vent valve for steam processing.
R — Pressure gage.
S — Inlet air control.
T — Pressure control.
U — Air line.
V — To pressure control instrument.
W — To temperature control instrument.
X — Wing nuts.
Y_1 — Crate support.
Y_2 — Crate guides.
Z — Constant flow orifice valve.
Z_1 — Constant flow orifice valve used during come-up.
Z_2 — Constant flow orifice valve used during cook.

(14) *Critical factors.* Critical factors specified in the scheduled process shall be measured and recorded on the processing record at intervals of sufficient frequency to ensure that the factors are within the limits specified in the scheduled process.

    (i) When maximum fill-in or drained weight is specified in the scheduled process, it shall be measured and recorded at intervals of sufficient frequency to ensure that the weight of the product does not exceed the maximum for the given container size specified in the scheduled process.

    (ii) Closing machine vacuum in vacuum-packed products shall be observed and recorded at intervals of sufficient frequency to ensure that the vacuum is as specified in the scheduled process.

    (iii) Such measurements and recordings should be made at intervals not to exceed 15 minutes.

    (iv) When the product style results in stratification or layering of the primary product in the containers, the positioning of containers in the retort shall be according to the scheduled process.

(c) *Equipment and procedures for pressure processing in steam in continuous agitating retorts—*

    (1) *Indicating mercury-in-glass thermometer.* Each retort shall be equipped with at least one mercury-in-glass thermometer whose divisions are easily readable to 1°F and whose temperature range does not exceed 17°F

per inch of graduated scale. Thermometers shall be tested for accuracy against a known accurate standard thermometer upon installation and at least once a year thereafter, or more frequently if necessary, to ensure their accuracy. Records of thermometer accuracy checks which specify date, standard used, method used, and person performing the test should be maintained. Each thermometer should have a tag, seal, or other means of identity that includes the date on which it was last tested for accuracy. A thermometer that has a divided mercury column or that cannot be adjusted to the standard shall be repaired or replaced before further use of the retort. Thermometers shall be installed where they can be accurately and easily read. Bulbs in indicating thermometers shall be installed either within the retort shell or in external wells attached to the retort. External wells or pipes shall be connected to the retort through at least a 3/4-inch diameter opening, and equipped with a 1/16-inch or larger bleeder opening so located as to provide a full flow of steam past the length of the thermometer bulb. The bleeders for external wells shall emit steam continuously during the entire processing period. The mercury thermometer—not the recorder chart—shall be the reference instrument for indicating the processing temperature.

(2) *Temperature-recording device.* Each retort shall have an accurate temperature-recording device. Graduations on the temperature-recording devices shall not exceed 2°F within a range of 10°F of the processing temperature. Each chart shall have a working scale of not more than 55°F per inch within a range of 20°F of the processing temperature. The temperature chart shall be adjusted to agree as nearly as possible with, but to be in no event higher than, the known accurate mercury-in-glass thermometer during the process time. A means of preventing unauthorized changes in adjustment shall be provided. A lock, or a notice from management posted at or near the recording device that provides a warning that only authorized persons are permitted to make adjustments, is a satisfactory means of preventing unauthorized changes. The recorder may be combined with the steam controller and may be a recording-controlling instrument. The temperature-recorder bulb shall be installed either within the retort shell or in a well attached to the shell. Each temperature-recorder bulb well shall have a 1/16-inch or larger bleeder opening emitting steam continuously during the processing period. Air-operated temperature controllers should have adequate filter systems to ensure a supply of clean, dry air.

(3) *Pressure gages.* Each retort should be equipped with a pressure gage that should be graduated in divisions of 2 pounds or less.

(4) *Steam controller.* Each retort shall be equipped with an automatic steam controller to maintain the retort temperature. This may be a recording-controlling instrument when combined with a recording thermometer. A steam controller activated by the steam pressure of the retort is acceptable if it is carefully maintained mechanically so that it operates satisfactorily.

(5) *Bleeders.* Bleeders, except those for thermometer wells, shall be one-eight inch or larger and shall be wide open during the entire process, including the come-up-time. Bleeders shall be located within approximately 1 foot of the outermost location of containers at each end along the top of the retort; additional bleeders shall be located not more than 8 feet apart along the top of the retort. All bleeders shall be arranged so that the operator can observe that they are functioning properly. The condensate bleeder shall be checked with sufficient frequency to ensure adequate removal of condensate or shall be equipped with an automatic alarm system(s) that would serve as a continuous monitor of condensate-bleeder functioning. Visual checks should be done at intervals of not more than 15 minutes. A record of such checks should be kept to show that the bleeder is functioning properly.

(6) *Venting and condensate removal.* Vents shall be located in that portion of the retort opposite the steam inlet. Air shall be removed before processing is started. Heat distribution data or documentary proof from the manufacturer or from a competent processing authority, demonstrating that adequate venting is achieved, shall be kept on file. At the time steam is turned on, the drain should be opened for a time sufficient to remove steam condensate from the retort, and provision shall be made for continuing drainage of condensate during the retort operation. The condensate bleeder in the bottom of the shell serves as an indicator of continuous condensate removal.

(7) *Retort speed timing.* The rotational speed of the retort shall be specified in the scheduled process. The speed shall be adjusted and recorded when the retort is started, at any time a speed change is made, and at intervals of sufficient frequency to ensure that the retort speed is maintained as specified in the scheduled process. These adjustments and recordings should be made every 4 hours or less. Alternatively, a recording tachometer may be used to provide a continuous record of the speed. A means of preventing unauthorized speed changes on retorts shall be provided. A lock, or a notice from management posted at or near the speed adjustment device that provides a warning that only authorized persons are permitted to make adjustments, is a satisfactory means of preventing unauthorized changes.

(8) *Emergency stops.* If a retort jams or breaks down during processing operations, necessitating cooling the retort for repairs, the retort shall be operated in such a way that ensures that the product is commercially sterile, or the retort is to be cooled promptly and all containers either reprocessed, repacked and reprocessed,

or discarded. When operated as a still retort, all containers shall be given a full still retort process before the retort is cooled. If, in such an emergency, a scheduled still process or another process established to ensure commercial sterility is to be used, it shall be made readily available to the retort operator.

(i) Any containers in the retort intake valve or in transfer valves between cooker shells of a continuous retort at the time of breakdown shall either be reprocessed, repacked and reprocessed, or discarded.

(ii) Both the time at which the reel stopped and the time the retort was used for a still retort process, if so used, shall be marked on the recording chart and entered on the other production records required in this chapter. If the alternative procedure of prompt cooling is followed, the subsequent handling methods used for the containers in the retort at the time of stopping and cooling shall be entered on the production records.

(9) *Temperature drop.* If the temperature of the continuous retort drops below the temperature specified in the scheduled process while containers are in the retort, the retort reel shall be stopped promptly. An automatic device should be used to stop the reel when the temperature drops below the specified process temperature. Before the reel is restarted, all containers in the retort shall be given a complete scheduled still retort process if the temperature drop was 10°F or more below the specified temperature, or alternatively, container entry to the retort shall be stopped and the reel restarted to empty the retort. The discharged containers shall be either reprocessed, repacked and reprocessed, or discarded. Both the time at which the reel stopped and the time the retort was used for a still retort process, if so used, shall be marked on the recording chart and entered on the other production records required in this chapter. If the alternative procedure of emptying the retort is followed, the subsequent handing methods used for the containers in the retort at the time of the temperature drop shall be entered on the production records. If the temperature drop was less than 10°F, a scheduled authorized emergency still process approved by a qualified person(s) having expert knowledge of thermal processing requirements may be used before restarting the retort reel. Alternatively, container entry to the retort shall be stopped and an authorized emergency agitating process may be used before container entry to the retort is restarted. When emergency procedures are used, no containers may enter the retort and the process and procedures used shall be noted on the production records.

(10) *Critical factors.* Critical factors specified in the scheduled process shall be measured and recorded on the processing record at intervals of sufficient frequency to ensure that the factors are within the limits specified in the scheduled process. The minimum headspace of containers, if specified in the scheduled process, shall be measured and recorded at intervals of sufficient frequency to ensure that the headspace is as specified in the scheduled process. The headspace of solder-tipped, lapseam (vent hole) cans may be measured by net weight determinations. The headspace of double seamed cans may also be measured by net weight determinations for homogenous liquids, taking into account the specific can end profile and other factors which affect the headspace, if proof of the accuracy of such measurements is maintained and the procedure and resultant headspace is in accordance with the scheduled process. When the product consistency is specified in the scheduled process, the consistency of the product shall be determined by objective measurements on the product taken from the filler before processing and recorded at intervals of sufficient frequency to ensure that the consistency is as specified in the scheduled process. Minimum closing machine vacuum in vacuum-packed products, maximum fill-in or drained weight, minimum net weight, and percent solids shall be as specified in the scheduled process for all products when deviations from such specifications may affect the scheduled process. All measurements and recordings of critical factors should be made at intervals not to exceed 15 minutes.

(d) *Equipment and procedures for pressure processing in steam in discontinuous agitating retorts—*

(1) *Indicating mercury-in-glass thermometer.* Each retort shall be equipped with at least one mercury-in-glass thermometer whose divisions are easily readable to 1°F and whose temperature range does not exceed 17°F per inch of graduated scale. Thermometers shall be tested for accuracy against a known accurate standard thermometer upon installation and at least once a year thereafter, or more frequently if necessary, to ensure their accuracy. Records of thermometer accuracy checks which specify date, standard used, method used, and person performing the test should be maintained. Each thermometer should have a tag, seal, or other means of identity that includes the date on which it was last tested for accuracy. A thermometer that has a divided mercury column or that cannot be adjusted to the standard shall be repaired or replaced before further use of the retort. Thermometers shall be installed where they can be accurately and easily read. Bulbs of indicating thermometers shall be installed either within the retort shell or in external wells attached to the retort. External wells or pipes shall be connected to the retort through at least a 3/4-inch diameter opening, and equipped with a 1/16-inch or larger bleeder opening so located as to provide a full flow of steam past the length of the thermometer bulb. The bleeder for external wells shall emit steam continuously during the entire processing period. The mercury thermometer—not the recorder chart—shall be the reference instrument for indicating the processing temperature.

(2) *Temperature-recording device.* Each retort shall have an accurate temperature-recording device. Graduations on the temperature-recording devices shall not exceed 2°F within a range of 10°F of the processing temperature. Each chart shall have a working scale of not more than 55°F per inch within a range of 20°F of the processing temperature. The temperature chart shall be adjusted to agree as nearly as possible with, but to be in no event higher than, the known accurate mercury-in-glass thermometer during the process time. A means of preventing unauthorized changes in adjustment shall be provided. A lock, or a notice from management posted at or near the recording device that provides a warning that only authorized persons are permitted to make adjustments, is a satisfactory means for preventing unauthorized changes. The recorder may be combined with the steam controller and may be a recording-controlling instrument. The temperature-recorder bulb shall be installed either within the retort shell or in a well attached to the shell. Each temperature-recorder bulb well shall have a 1/16-inch or larger bleeder opening emitting steam continuously during the processing period. Air-operated temperature controllers should have adequate filter systems to ensure a supply of clean, dry air.

(3) *Pressure gages.* Each retort should be equipped with a pressure gage, which should be graduated in divisions of 2 pounds or less.

(4) *Steam controller.* Each retort shall be equipped with an automatic steam controller to maintain the retort temperature. This may be a recording-controlling instrument when combined with a recording thermometer. A steam controller activated by the steam pressure of the retort is acceptable if it is mechanically maintained so that it operates satisfactorily.

(5) *Bleeders.* Bleeders, except those for thermometer wells, shall be one-eighth inch or larger and shall be wide open during the entire process, including the come-up-time. Bleeders shall be located within approximately 1 foot of the outermost location of containers, at each end along the top of the retort; additional bleeders shall be located not more than 8 feet apart along the top. Bleeders may be installed at positions other than those specified above, as long as there is evidence in the form of heat distribution data that they accomplish adequate removal of air and circulation of heat within the retort. In retorts having top steam inlet and bottom venting, a bleeder shall be installed in the bottom of the retort to remove condensate. All bleeders shall be arranged in a way that enables the operator to observe that they are functioning properly.

(6) *Venting and condensate removal.* The air in each retort shall be removed before processing is started. Heat distribution data or documentary proof from the manufacturer or from a competent processing authority, demonstrating that adequate venting is achieved, shall be kept on file. At the time steam is turned on, the drain should be opened for a time sufficient to remove steam condensate from the retort and provision should be made for containing drainage of condensate during the retort operation.

(7) *Retort speed timing.* The rotational speed of the retort shall be specified in the schedules process. The speed shall be adjusted, as necessary, to ensure that the speed is as specified in the scheduled process. The rotational speed as well as the process time shall be recorded for each retort load processed. Alternatively, a recording tachometer may be used to provide a continuous record of the speed. A means of preventing unauthorized speed changes on retorts shall be provided. A lock, or a notice from management posted at or near the speed-adjustment device that provides a warning that only authorized persons are permitted to make adjustments, is a satisfactory means of preventing unauthorized changes.

(8) *Critical factors.* Critical factors specified in the scheduled process shall be measured and recorded on the processing record at intervals of sufficient frequency to ensure that the factors are within the limits specified in the scheduled process. The minimum headspace of containers in each retort load to be processed, if specified in the scheduled process, shall be measured and recorded at intervals of sufficient frequency to ensure that the headspace is as specified in the scheduled process. The headspace of solder-tipped, lap seam (vent hole) cans may be measured by net weight determinations. When the product consistency is specified in the scheduled process, the consistency of the product shall be determined by objective measurements on the product taken from the filler before processing and recorded at intervals of sufficient frequency to ensure that the consistency is as specified in the scheduled process. Minimum closing machine vacuum in vacuum-packed products, maximum fill-in or drained weight, minimum net weight, and percent solids shall be as specified in the scheduled process for all products for which deviations from such specifications may affect the scheduled process. All measurements and recordings of critical factors should be made at intervals not to exceed 15 minutes.

(e) *Equipment and procedures for pressure processing in water in discontinuous agitating retorts—*

(1) *Indicating mercury-in-glass thermometer.* Each retort shall be equipped with at least one mercury-in-glass thermometer whose divisions are easily readable to 1°F and whose temperature range does not exceed 17°F per inch of graduated scale. Thermometers shall be tested for accuracy against a known accurate standard thermometer upon installation and at least once a year thereafter, or more frequently if necessary, to ensure their accuracy. Records of thermometer accuracy checks which specify date, standard use, method used, and person performing the test should be maintained. Each thermometer should have a tag, seal, or other means

of identity that includes the date on which it was last tested for accuracy. A thermometer that has a divided mercury column or that cannot be adjusted to the standard shall be repaired or replaced before further use of the retort. Thermometers shall be installed where they can be accurately and easily read. Bulbs of indicating thermometers shall be installed either within the retort shell or in external wells attached to the retort. The mercury thermometer—not the recorder chart—shall be the reference instrument for indicating the processing temperature.

(2) *Temperature-recording device.* Each retort shall have an accurate temperature-recording device. Graduations on the temperature-recording devices shall not exceed 2°F within a range of 10°F of the processing temperature. Each chart shall have a working scale of not more than 55°F per inch within a range of 20°F of the processing temperature. The temperature chart shall be adjusted to agree as nearly as possible with, but to be in no event higher than, the known accurate mercury-in-glass thermometer during the process time. A means of preventing unauthorized changes in adjustment shall be provided. A lock, or a notice from management posted at or near the recording device that provides a warning that only authorized persons are permitted to make adjustment, is a satisfactory means for preventing unauthorized changes. This recorder may be combined with the steam controller and may be a recording-controlling instrument. The temperature-recorder bulb shall be installed either within the retort shell or in a well attached to the shell. Air-operated temperature controllers should have adequate filter systems to ensure a supply of clean dry air.

(3) *Pressure gages.* Each retort should be equipped with a pressure gage which should be graduated in divisions of 2 pounds or less.

(4) *Steam controller.* Each retort shall be equipped with an automatic steam controller to maintain the retort temperature. This may be a recording-controlling instrument when combined with a recording thermometer.

(5) *Retort speed timing.* The rotational speed of the retort shall be specified in the scheduled process. The speed shall be adjusted, as necessary, to ensure that the speed is as specified in the scheduled process. The rotational speed as well as the process time shall be recorded for each retort load processed. Alternatively, a recording tachometer may be used to provide a continuous record of the speed. A means of preventing unauthorized speed changes shall be provided. A lock, or a notice from management posted at or near the speed adjustment device that provides a warning that only authorized persons are permitted to make adjustment, is a satisfactory means of preventing unauthorized changes.

(6) *Air supply and controls.* Means shall be provided for introducing compressed air at the proper pressure and rate, which shall be controlled by an automatic pressure control unit. A check valve shall be provided in the air supply line to prevent water from entering the system.

(7) *Critical factors.* Critical factors specified in the scheduled process shall be measured and recorded on the processing record at intervals of sufficient frequency to ensure that the factors are within the limits specified in the scheduled process. The minimum headspace of containers, if specified in the scheduled process, shall be measured and recorded at intervals of sufficient frequency to ensure that the headspace is as specified in the scheduled process. The headspace of solder-tipped, lap seam (vent hole) cans may be measured by net weight determinations. When the product consistency is specified in the scheduled process, the consistency of the product shall be determined by objective measurements on the product taken from the filler before processing and recorded at intervals of sufficient frequency to ensure that the consistency is as specified in the scheduled process. Minimum closing machine vacuum in vacuum-packed products, maximum fill-in or drained weight, minimum net weight, and percent solids shall be as specified in the scheduled process for all products when deviations from such specifications may affect the scheduled process. All measurements and recordings of critical factors should be made at intervals not to exceed 15 minutes.

(f) *Equipment and procedures for pressure processing in steam in hydrostatic retorts—*

(1) *Indicating mercury-in-glass thermometer.* Each retort shall be equipped with at least one mercury-in-glass thermometer whose divisions are easily readable to 1°F and whose temperature range does not exceed 17°F per inch of graduated scale. Thermometer shall be tested for accuracy against a known accurate standard thermometer upon installation and at least once a year thereafter, or more frequently if necessary, to ensure their accuracy. Records of thermometer accuracy checks which specify date, standard used, method used, and person performing the test should be maintained. Each thermometer should have a tag, seal, or other means of identity that includes the date on which it was last tested for accuracy. A thermometer that has a divided mercury column or that cannot be adjusted to the standard shall be repaired or replaced before further use of the retort. Thermometers shall be installed where they can be accurately and easily read. The thermometer shall be located in the steam dome near the steam-water interface. When the scheduled process specifies maintenance of particular temperatures in the hydrostatic water legs, a mercury-in-glass thermometer shall be located in each hydrostatic water leg in a position near the bottom automatic recorder. The mercury thermometer—not the recorder chart—shall be the reference instrument for indicating the processing temperature.

(2) *Temperature-recording device.* Each retort shall have an accurate temperature-recording device. Graduations on the temperature-recording devices shall not exceed 2°F within a range of 10°F of the processing temperature. Each chart shall have a working scale of not more than 55°F per inch within a range of 20°F of the processing temperature. The temperature chart shall be adjusted to agree as nearly as possible with, but to be in no event higher than, the known accurate mercury-in-glass thermometer during the process time. A means of preventing unauthorized changes in adjustment shall be provided. A lock, or a notice from management posted at or near the recording device that provides a warning that only authorized persons are permitted to make adjustments, is a satisfactory means for preventing unauthorized changes. The recorder may be combined with the steam controller and may be a recording-controlling instrument. The temperature-recorder bulb shall be installed either within the steam dome or in a well attached to the dome. Each temperature-recorder bulb well shall have a 1/16-inch or larger bleeder opening which emits steam continuously during the processing period. Additional temperature-recorder bulbs shall be installed in the hydrostatic water legs if the scheduled process specified maintenance of particular temperatures in the hydrostatic water legs. Air-operated temperature controllers should have adequate filter systems to ensure a supply of clean dry air.

(3) *Pressure gages.* Each retort should be equipped with a pressure gage which should be graduated in divisions of 2 pounds or less.

(4) *Recording of temperatures.* Temperatures indicated by the mercury-in-glass thermometer or thermometers shall be entered on a suitable form during processing operations. Temperatures shall be recorded by an accurate automatic recorder or recorders at the following points:

    (i)   In the steam chamber between the steam-water interface and the lowest container position.

    (ii) Near the top and the bottom of each hydrostatic water leg if the scheduled process specifies maintenance of particular temperatures in the legs.

(5) *Steam controller.* Each retort shall be equipped with an automatic steam controller to maintain the retort temperature. This may be a recording-controlling instrument when combined with a recording thermometer. A steam controller activated by the steam pressure of the retort is acceptable if it is carefully mechanically maintained so that it operates satisfactorily.

(6) *Venting.* Before the start of processing operations, the retort steam chamber or chambers shall be vented to ensure removal of air.

(7) *Bleeders.* Bleeder openings 1/4-inch or larger shall be located at the top of the steam chamber or chambers opposite the point of steam entry. Bleeders shall be wide open and shall emit steam continuously during the entire process, including the come-up-time. All bleeders shall be arranged in such a way that the operator can observe that they are functioning properly.

(8) *Retort speed.* The speed of the container-conveyor chain shall be specified in the scheduled process and shall be determined and recorded at the start of processing and at intervals of sufficient frequency to ensure that the retort speed is maintained as specified. The speed should be determined and recorded every 4 hours. An automatic device should be used to stop the chain when the temperature drops below that specified in the scheduled process. A means of preventing unauthorized speed changes shall be provided. A lock, or a notice from management posted at or near the speed-adjusting device that provides a warning that only authorized persons are permitted to make adjustments, is a satisfactory means of preventing unauthorized changes.

(9) *Critical factors.* Critical factors specified in the scheduled process shall be measured and recorded on the processing record at intervals of sufficient frequency to ensure that the factors are within the limits specified in the scheduled process.

    (i)   When maximum fill-in or drained weight is specified in the scheduled process, it shall be measured and recorded at intervals of sufficient frequency to ensure that the weight of the product does not exceed the maximum for the given container size specified in the scheduled process.

    (ii) Closing machine vacuum in vacuum-packed products shall be observed and recorded at intervals of sufficient frequency to ensure that the vacuum is as specified in the scheduled process.

    (iii) Such measurements and recordings should be made at intervals not to exceed 15 minutes.

(g) *Aseptic processing and packaging systems —*

    (1) *Product sterilizer —*

        (i)   *Equipment —*

            (a) *Temperature-indicating device.* Each product sterilizer shall be equipped with at least one mercury-in-glass thermometer or an equivalent temperature-indicating device, such as a thermocouple-recorder. Mercury-in-glass thermometers shall have divisions that are easily readable to 1°F and whose temperature range does not exceed 17°F per inch of graduated scale. Thermometers and temperature-indicating devices shall be tested for accuracy against a known accurate standard thermometer upon installation and at least once a year thereafter, or more frequently if necessary, to ensure their accuracy. Records of accuracy checks which specify date, standard used, method used, and person performing the test should be maintained. Each thermometer and temperature-indicating device should have a tag, seal, or other means of identity that includes the date on which it was last tested for accuracy. A thermometer that has a divided mercury column or that cannot be adjusted to essential agreement with the standard shall be repaired or replaced. Thermometers and temperature-indicating devices shall be installed where they can be accurately and easily read. The temperature-indicating device shall be the reference instrument for indicating the processing temperature.

(b) *Temperature-recording device.* There shall be an accurate temperature recording device on each product sterilizer. The device shall be installed in the product at the holding-tube outlet between the holding tube and the inlet to the cooler. Temperature-recording devices shall have graduations that do not exceed 2°F within a range of 10°F of the processing temperature. Each chart shall have a working scale of not more than 55°F per inch within a range of 20°F of the desired product-sterilization temperature. The temperature chart shall be adjusted to agree as nearly as possible with, but to be in no event higher than, a known accurate mercury-in-glass thermometer. A means of preventing unauthorized changes in adjustment shall be provided. A lock, or a notice from management posted at or near the recording device that provides a warning that only authorized persons are permitted to make adjustments, is a satisfactory means for preventing unauthorized changes.

(c) *Temperature recorder-controller.* An accurate temperature recorder-controller shall be located in the product sterilizer at the final heater outlet. It shall be capable of ensuring that the desired product sterilization temperature is maintained. The chart graduations shall not exceed 2°F within a range of 10°F of the desired product sterilization temperature. Air-operated temperature controllers should have adequate filter systems to ensure a supply of clean, dry air.

(d) *Product-to-product regenerators.* When a product-to-product regenerator is used to heat the cold unsterilized product entering the sterilizer by means of a heat exchange system, it shall be designed, operated, and controlled so that the pressure of the sterilized product in the regenerator is greater than the pressure of any unsterilized product in the regenerator to ensure that any leakage in the regenerator is from the sterilized product into the unsterilized product.

(e) *Differential pressure recorder-controller.* When a product-to-product regenerator is used, there shall be an accurate differential pressure recorder-controller installed on the regenerator. The scale divisions shall not exceed 2 pounds per square inch on the working scale of not more than 20 pounds per square inch per inch. The controller shall be tested for accuracy against a known accurate standard pressure indicator upon installation and at least once every 3 months of operation thereafter, or more frequently if necessary, to ensure its accuracy. One pressure sensor shall be installed at the sterilized product regenerator outlet and the other pressure sensor shall be installed at the unsterilized product regenerator inlet.

(f) *Metering pump.* A metering pump shall be located upstream from the holding tube and shall be operated to maintain the required rate of product flow. A means of preventing unauthorized speed changes shall be provided. A lock, or a notice from management posted at or near the speed-adjusting device that provides a warning that only authorized persons are permitted to make adjustments, is a satisfactory means of preventing unauthorized changes.

(g) *Product holding tube.* The product-sterilizing holding tube shall be designed to give continuous holding of every particle of food for at least the minimum holding time specified in the scheduled process. The holding tube shall be designed so that no portion of the tube between the product inlet and the product outlet can be heated, and it must be sloped upward at least 0.25 inch per foot.

(h) *Flow-diversion systems.* If a processor elects to install a flow-diversion system, it should be installed in the product piping located between the product cooler and the product filler or aseptic surge tank and should be designed to divert flow away from the filler or aseptic surge tank automatically. Controls and/or warning systems should be designed and installed with necessary sensors and actuators to operate whenever the sterilizing temperature in the holding tube or pressure differential in the product regenerator drops below specified limits. Flow-diversion systems should be designed and operated in accordance with recommendations of an aseptic processing and packaging authority.

(i) *Equipment downstream from the holding tube.* Product coolers, aseptic surge tanks, or any other equipment downstream from the holding tube, with rotating or reciprocating shafts, valve stems, instrument connections, or other such points, are subject to potential entry of microorganisms into the product. Such locations in the system should be equipped with steam seals or other effective barriers at the potential access points. Appropriate means should be provided to permit the operator to monitor the performance of the seals or barriers during operations.

(ii) *Operation —*

(a) *Startup.* Before the start of aseptic processing operations the product sterilizer and all product-contact surfaces downstream shall be brought to a condition of commercial sterility.

(b) *Temperature drop in product-sterilizing holding tube.* When product temperature in the holding tube drops below the temperature specified in the scheduled process, product flow should be diverted away from the filler or aseptic surge tank by means of a flow-diversion system. If for any reason product subjected to a temperature drop below the scheduled process is filled into containers, the product shall be segregated from product that received the scheduled process. The processing deviation shall be handled in accordance with § 113.89. The product holding tube and any further system portions affected shall be returned to a condition of commercial sterility before product flow is resumed to the filler or to the aseptic surge tank.

(c) *Loss of proper pressures in the regenerator.* When a regenerator is used, the product may lose sterility whenever the pressure of sterilized product in the regenerator is less than 1 pound per square inch greater than the pressure of unsterilized product in the regenerator. In this case, product flow should be diverted away from the filler or aseptic surge tank by means of the flow-diversion system. If for any reason the product is filled into containers, the product shall be segregated from product that received the scheduled process and shall be reprocessed or destroyed. Product flow to the filler or to the aseptic surge tank shall not be resumed until the cause of the improper pressure relationships in the regenerator has been corrected and the affected system(s) has been returned to a condition of commercial sterility.

(d) *Loss of sterile air pressure or other protection level in the aseptic surge tank.* When an aseptic surge tank is used, conditions of commercial sterility may be lost when the sterile air overpressure or other means of protection drops below the scheduled process value. Product flow to and/or from the aseptic surge tank shall not be resumed until the potentially contaminated product in the tank is removed, and the aseptic surge tank has been returned to a condition of commercial sterility.

(e) *Records.* Readings at the following points shall be observed and recorded at the start of aseptic packaging operations and at intervals of sufficient frequency to ensure that these values are as specified in the scheduled process: Temperature-indicating device in holding tube outlet; temperature recorder in holding tube outlet; temperature recorder-controller at final heater outlet; differential pressure recorder-controller, if a product-to-product regenerator is used; product flow rate as established by the metering pump or as determined by filling and closing rates and, if an aseptic surge tank is used, sterile air pressure or other protection means; and proper performance of seam seals or other similar devices. The measurements and recordings should be made at intervals not to exceed 1 hour.

(2) *Container sterilizing, filling, and closing operation —*
   (i) *Equipment —*
      (a) *Recording device.* The container and closure sterilization system and product filling and closing system shall be instrumented to demonstrate that the required sterilization is being accomplished continuously. Automatic recording devices shall be used to record, when applicable, the sterilization media flow rates, temperature, concentration, or other factors. When a batch system is used for container sterilization, the sterilization conditions shall be recorded.
      (b) *Timing method(s).* A method(s) shall be used either to give the retention time of containers, and closures if applicable, in the sterilizing environment specified in the scheduled process, or to control the sterilization cycle at the rate specified in the scheduled process. A means of preventing unauthorized speed changes must be provided. A lock, or a notice from management posted at or near the speed adjusting device that provides a warning that only authorized persons are permitted to make adjustments, is a satisfactory means of preventing unauthorized changes.
   (ii) *Operation —*
      (a) *Startup.* Before the start of packaging operations, both the container and closure sterilizing system and the product filling and closing system shall be brought to a condition of commercial sterility.
      (b) *Loss of sterility.* A system shall be provided to stop packaging operations, or alternatively to ensure segregation of any product packaged when the packaging conditions fall below scheduled processes. Compliance with this requirement may be accomplished by diverting product away from the filler, by preventing containers from entering the filler, or by other suitable means. In the event product is packaged under conditions below those specified in the scheduled process, all such product shall be segregated and handled in accordance with § 113.89. In the event of loss of sterility, the system(s) shall be returned to a condition of commercial sterility before resuming packaging operations.
      (c) *Records.* Observations and measurements of operating conditions shall be made and recorded at intervals of sufficient frequency to ensure that commercial sterility of the food product is being achieved; such measurements shall include the sterilization media flow rates, temperatures, the container and closure rates (if applicable) through the sterilizing system, and the sterilization condi-

tions if a batch system is used for container sterilization. The measurements and recordings should be made at intervals not to exceed 1 hour.

    (3) *Incubation.* Incubation tests should be conducted on a representative sample of containers of product from each code; records of the test results should be maintained.

    (4) *Critical factors.* Critical factors specified in the scheduled process shall be measured and recorded on the processing record at intervals of sufficient frequency to ensure that the factors are within the limits specified in the scheduled process. Such measurements and recordings should be done at intervals not to exceed 15 minutes.

(h) *Equipment and procedures for flame sterilizers.* The container conveyor speed shall be specified in the scheduled process. The container conveyor speed shall be measured and recorded at the start of operations and at intervals of sufficient frequency to ensure that the conveyor speed is as specified in the scheduled process. Such measurements and recordings should be done at 1-hour intervals. Alternatively, recording tachometer may be used to provide a continuous record of the speed. A means of preventing changes in flame intensity and unauthorized speed changes on the conveyor shall be provided. A lock, or a notice from management posted at or near the speed adjusting device that provides a warning that only authorized persons are permitted to make adjustments, is a satisfactory means of preventing unauthorized changes. The surface temperature of at least one container from each conveyor channel shall be measured and recorded at the entry and at the end of the holding period at intervals of sufficient frequency to ensure that the temperatures specified in the scheduled process are maintained. Such measurements and recordings should be done at intervals not to exceed 15 minutes.

    (1) *Process interruption.* In the event of process interruption wherein the temperature of the product may have dropped, an authorized, scheduled emergency plan approved by a qualified person having expert knowledge of the process requirements may be used.

    (2) *Critical factors.* Critical factors specified in the scheduled process shall be measured and recorded on the processing record at intervals of sufficient frequency to ensure that the factors are within the limits specified in the scheduled process.

(i) *Equipment and procedures for thermal processing of foods wherein critical factors such as water activity are used in conjunction with thermal processing.* The methods and controls used for the manufacture, processing, and packing of such foods shall be as established in the scheduled process and shall be operated or administered in a manner adequate to ensure that the product is safe. The time and temperature of processing and other critical factors specified in the scheduled process shall be measured with instruments having the accuracy and dependability adequate to ensure that the requirements of the scheduled process are met. All measurements shall be made and recorded at intervals of sufficient frequency to ensure that the critical factors are within the limits specified in the scheduled process.

(j) *Other systems.* All systems, whether or not specifically mentioned in this part, for the thermal processing of low-acid foods in hermetically sealed containers shall conform to the applicable requirements of this part and the methods and controls used for the manufacture, processing, and packing of these foods shall be as established in the scheduled process. These systems shall be operated or administered in a manner adequate to ensure that commercial sterility is achieved. Critical factors specified in the scheduled process shall be measured and recorded at intervals of sufficient frequency to ensure that the critical factors are within the limits specified in the scheduled process.

Subpart D—Control of Components, Food Product Containers, Closures, and In-Process Materials

§ 113.60 Containers.

(a) *Closures.* Regular observations shall be maintained during production runs for gross closure defects. Any such defects shall be recorded and corrective action taken and recorded. At intervals of sufficient frequency to ensure proper closure, the operator, closure supervisor, or other qualified container closure inspection person shall visually examine either the top seam of a can randomly selected from each seaming head or the closure of any other type of container being used and shall record the observations made. For double-seam cans, each can should be examined for cutover or sharpness, skidding or deadheading, false seam, droop at the crossover or lap, and condition of inside of countersink wall for evidence of broken chuck. Such measurements and recordings should be made at intervals not to exceed 30 minutes. Additional visual closure inspections shall be made immediately following a jam in a closing machine, after closing machine adjustment, or after startup of a machine following a prolonged shutdown. All pertinent observations shall be recorded. When irregularities are found, the corrective action shall be recorded.

(1) Teardown examinations for double-seam cans shall be performed by a qualified individual and the results therefrom shall be recorded at intervals of sufficient frequency on enough containers from each seaming station to ensure maintenance of seam integrity. Such examinations and recordings should be made at intervals not to exceed 4 hours. The results of the teardown examinations shall be recorded and the corrective action taken, if any, shall be noted.

(i) Required and optional can seam measurements:

(a) Micrometer measurement system:

Required	Optional
Cover hook Body hook Width (length, height) Tightness (observation for wrinkle) Thickness	Overlap (by calculation) Countersink

(b) Seam scope or projector:

Required	Optional
Body hook Overlap Tightness (observation for wrinkle) Thickness by micrometer	Width (length, height) Cover hook Countersink

(c) Can double seam terminology:

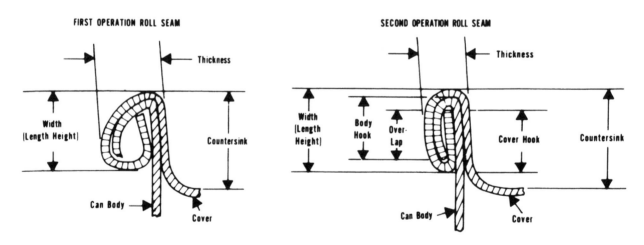

(1) "Crossover": The portion of a double seam at the lap.
(2) "Cutover": A fracture, sharp bend, or break in the metal at the top of the inside portion of the double seam.
(3) "Deadhead": A seam which is incomplete due to chuck spinning in the countersink.
(4) "Droop": Smooth projection of double seam below bottom of normal seam.
(5) "False seam": A small seam breakdown where the cover hook and the body hook are not over-lapped.
(6) "Lap": Two thicknesses of material bonded together.

(ii) Two measurements at different locations, excluding the side seam, shall be made for each double seam characteristic if a seam scope or seam projector is used. When a micrometer is used, three measurements shall be made at points approximately 120° apart, excluding the side seam.

    (iii) Overlap length can be calculated by the following formula:

The theoretical overlap length =

CH + BH + T-W, where
CH = cover hook
BH = body hook
T = cover thickness, and
W = seam width (height, length)

    (2) For glass containers with vacuum closures, capper efficiency must be checked by a measurement of the cold water vacuum. This shall be done before actual filling operations, and the results shall be recorded.

    (3) For closures other than double seams and glass containers, appropriate detailed inspections and tests shall be conducted by qualified personnel at intervals of sufficient frequency to ensure proper closing machine performance and consistently reliable hermetic seal production. Records of such tests shall be maintained.

(b) *Cooling water.* Container cooling water shall be chlorinated or otherwise sanitized as necessary for cooling canals and for recirculated water supplies. There should be a measurable residual of the sanitizer employed at the water discharge point of the container cooler.

(c) *Coding.* Each hermetically sealed container of low-acid processed food shall be marked with an identifying code that shall be permanently visible to the naked eye. When the container does not permit the code to be embossed or inked, the label may be legibly perforated or otherwise marked, if the label is securely affixed to the product container. The required identification shall identify in code the establishment where packed, the product contained therein, the year packed, the day packed, and the period during which packed. The packing period code shall be changed with sufficient frequency to enable ready identification of lots during their sale and distribution. Codes may be changed on the basis of one of the following: intervals of 4 to 5 hours; personnel shift changes; or batches, as long as the containers that constitute the batch do not extend over a period of more than one personnel shift.

(d) *Postprocess handling.* When cans are handled on belt conveyors, the conveyors should be so constructed as to minimize contact by the belt with the double seam, i.e., cans should not be rolled on the double seam. All worn and frayed belting, can retarders, cushions, etc. should be replaced with new nonporous material. All tracks and belts that come into contact with the can seams should be thoroughly scrubbed and sanitized at intervals of sufficient frequency to avoid product contamination. Automatic equipment used in handling filled containers should be so designed and operated as to preserve the can seam or other container closure integrity.

Subpart E—Production and Process Controls

§ 113.81 Product preparation.

(a) Before using raw materials and ingredients susceptible to microbiological contamination, the processor shall ensure that those materials and ingredients are suitable for use in processing low-acid food. Compliance with this requirement may be accomplished by receiving the raw materials and ingredients under a supplier's guarantee that they are suitable for use, by examining them for their microbiological condition, or by other acceptable means.

(b) Blanching by heat, when required in the preparation of food for canning, should be effected by heating the food to the required temperature, holding it at this temperature for the required time, and then either rapidly cooling the food or passing it to subsequent processing without delay. Thermophilic growth and contamination in blanchers should be minimized by the use of adequate operating temperatures and by cleaning. If the blanched food product is washed before filling, potable water should be used.

(c) The filling of containers, either mechanically or by hand, shall be controlled so as to ensure that the filling requirements specified in the scheduled process are met.

(d) The exhausting of containers for the removal of air shall be controlled so as to meet the conditions for which the process was designed. Compliance with the requirement may be accomplished by heat exhausting, mechanical exhausting, hot brining, or steam injection.

(e) When the maintenance of pH (above 4.6) of a normally low-acid food is a basis for a scheduled process, there shall be careful supervision to ensure that the equilibrium pH of the finished product meets that of the scheduled process. The methodology described in § 114.90 of this chapter should be used.

(f) When the scheduled process sets forth critical factors to prevent the growth of microorganisms not destroyed by the thermal process, the factors shall be carefully controlled to ensure that the limits established in the scheduled process are not exceeded. When normally low-acid foods require sufficient solute to permit safe processing at low temperatures, such as in boiling water, there shall be careful supervision to ensure that the equilibrium water activity (a_w) of the finished product meets that of the scheduled process. The scheduled thermal processes for foods having an a_w greater than 0.85 and less than the a_w that would allow the growth of spores of microorganisms of public health significance shall be sufficient to render the food free of microorganisms capable of reproducing in the food under normal nonrefrigerated conditions of storage and distribution.

§ 113.83 Establishing scheduled processes.

Scheduled processes for low-acid foods shall be established by qualified persons having expert knowledge of thermal processing requirements for low-acid foods in hermetically sealed containers and having adequate facilities for making such determinations. The type, range, and combination of variations encountered in commercial production shall be adequately provided for in establishing the scheduled process. Critical factors, e.g., minimum headspace, consistency, maximum fill-in or drained weight, a_w, etc., that may affect the scheduled process, shall be specified in the scheduled process. Acceptable scientific methods of establishing heat sterilization processes shall include, when necessary, but shall not be limited to, microbial thermal death time data, process calculations based on product heat penetration data, and inoculated packs. Calculation shall be performed according to procedures recognized by competent processing authorities. If incubation tests are necessary for process confirmation, they shall include containers from test trials and from actual commercial production runs during the period of instituting the process. The incubation tests for confirmation of the scheduled processes should include the containers from the test trials and a number of containers from each of four or more actual commercial production runs. The number of containers from actual commercial production runs should be determined on the basis of recognized scientific methods to be of a size sufficient to ensure the adequacy of the process. Complete records covering all aspects of the establishment of the process and associated incubation tests shall be prepared and shall be permanently retained by the person or organization making the determination.

§ 113.87 Operations in the thermal processing room.

(a) Operating processes and retort venting procedures to be used for each product and container size being packed shall either be posted in a conspicuous place near the processing equipment or be made readily available to the retort or processing system operator and any duly authorized employee of the Food and Drug Administration. Scheduled processes must be made readily available to the supervisor and any duly authorized employee of the Food and Drug Administration.

(b) A system for product traffic control in the retort room shall be established to prevent unretorted product from bypassing the retort process. Each retort basket, truck, car, or crate used to hold containers in a retort, or one or more containers therein, shall, if it contains any retorted food product, be plainly and conspicuously marked with a heat-sensitive indicator, or by other effective means that will indicate visually, to thermal processing personnel, those units that have been retorted. A visual check shall be performed to determine whether or not the appropriate change has occurred in the heat-sensitive indicator as a result of retorting for all retort baskets, trucks, cars, or crates, to ensure that each unit of product has been retorted. A written record of these checks should be made.

(c) The initial temperature of the contents of the containers to be processed shall be determined and recorded with sufficient frequency to ensure that the temperature of the product is no lower than the minimum initial temperature specified in the scheduled process. For those operations that use water during the filling of the retort or during processing, provision shall be made to ensure that the water will not, before the start of each thermal process, lower the initial temperature of the product below that specified in the scheduled process.

(d) Timing devices used in recording thermal process time information shall be accurate to the extent needed to ensure that the processing time and venting time specified in the scheduled process are achieved. Pocket or wrist watches are not considered satisfactory for timing purposes. Digital clocks may be used if the operating process and the venting schedule have a 1-minute or greater safety factor over the scheduled process.

(e) Clock times on recording-temperature charts should reasonably correspond to the time of day on the written processing records to provide correlation of these records.

(f) The steam supply to the thermal processing system shall be adequate to the extent needed to ensure that sufficient steam pressure is maintained during thermal processing, regardless of other demands of steam by the plant.

(g) If mufflers are used on bleeders or vent systems, evidence that the bleeders or vents are operated in a manner that does not significantly impede the removal of air shall be kept on file. This evidence may be in the form of heat distribution data or other satisfactory evidence such as a letter from the manufacturer, the designer, or a competent processing authority.

§ 113.89 Deviations in processing, venting, or control of critical factors.

Whenever any process is less than the scheduled process or when critical factors are out of control for any low-acid food or container system as disclosed from records by processor check or otherwise, the commercial processor of that low-acid food shall either fully reprocess that portion of the production involved, keeping full records of the reprocessing conditions or, alternatively, must set aside that portion of the product involved for further evaluation as to any potential public health significance. Such evaluation shall be made by a competent processing authority and shall be in accordance with procedures recognized by competent processing authorities as being adequate to detect any potential hazard to public health. Unless this evaluation demonstrates that the product had been given a thermal process that rendered it free of microorganisms of potential public health significance, the product set aside shall be either fully reprocessed to render it commercially sterile or destroyed. A record shall be made of the evaluation procedures used and the results. Either upon completion of full reprocessing and the attainment of commercial sterility or after the determination that no significant potential for public health hazard exists, that portion of the product involved may be shipped in normal distribution. Otherwise, the portion of the product involved shall be destroyed. All process deviations involving a failure to satisfy the minimum requirements of the scheduled process, including emergencies arising from a jam or breakdown of a continuous agitating retort necessitating cooling the retort for repairs, shall be recorded and made the subject of a separate file (or a log identifying the appropriate data) detailing those deviations and the actions taken.

Subpart F—Records and Reports

§ 113.100 Processing and production records.

(a) Processing and production information shall be entered at the time it is observed by the retort or processing system operator, or other designated person, on forms that include the product, the code number, the date, the retort or processing system number, the size of container, the approximate number of containers per coding interval, the initial temperature, the actual processing time, the mercury-in-glass and recording thermometer readings, and other appropriate processing data. Closing machine vacuum in vacuum-packed products, maximum fill-in or drained weight, or other critical factors specified in the scheduled process shall also be recorded. In addition, the following records shall be maintained:

   (1) *Still retorts.* Time steam on; time temperature up to processing temperature; time steam off; venting time and temperature to which vented.

   (2) *Agitating retorts.* Functioning of condensate bleeder; retort speed; and, when specified in the scheduled process, headspace, consistency, maximum drained weight, minimum net weight, and percent solids.

   (3) *Hydrostatic retorts.* The temperature in the steam chamber between the steam-water interface and the lowest container position; speed of the container conveyor chain; and, when the scheduled process specifies maintenance of particular temperatures in the hydrostatic water legs, the temperatures near the top and the bottom of each hydrostatic water leg.

   (4) *Aseptic processing and packaging systems.* Product temperature in the holding tube outlet as indicated by the temperature-indicating device and the temperature recorder; product temperature in the final heater outlet as indicated by the temperature recorder-controller; differential pressure as indicated by the differential pressure recorder-controller, if a product-to-product regenerator is used; product flow rate, as determined by the metering pump or by filling and closing rates; sterilization media flow rate or temperature or both; retention time of containers, and closures when applicable, in the sterilizing environment; and, when a batch system is used for container and/or closure sterilization, sterilization cycle times and temperatures.

   (5) *Flame sterilizers.* Container conveyor speed; surface temperature at the beginning and at the end of the holding period; nature of container.

   (6) *Food preservation methods wherein critical factors such as water activity are used in conjunction with thermal processing.* Product formulation and scheduled processes used, including the thermal process, its associated critical factors, as well as other critical factors, and results of a_w determinations.

   (7) *Other systems.* Critical factors specified in the formulation of the product or in the scheduled process.

(b) Recording thermometer charts shall be identified by date, retort number, and other data as necessary, so they can be correlated with the written record of lots processed. Each entry on the processing and production records shall be made by the retort or processing system operator, or other designated person, at the time the specific retort or processing system condition or operation occurs, and this retort or processing system operator or other designated person shall sign or initial each record form. Not later that 1 working day after the actual process, and before shipment or release for distribution, a representative of plant management who is qualified by suitable training or experience shall review all processing and production records for completeness and to ensure that the product received the scheduled process. The records, including the recording thermometer chart(s), shall be signed or initialed and dated by the reviewer.

(c) Written records of all container closure examinations shall specify the product code, the date and time of container closure inspections, the measurements obtained, and all corrective actions taken. Records shall be signed or initialed by the container closure inspector and reviewed by management with sufficient frequency to ensure that the containers are hermetically sealed.

(d) Records shall be maintained to identify the initial distribution of the finished product to facilitate, when necessary, the segregation of specific food lots that may have become contaminated or otherwise rendered unfit for their intended use.

(e) Copies of all records provided for in this part, except those required under § 113.83 establishing scheduled processes, shall be retained at the processing plant for a period of not less than 1 year from the date of manufacture, and at the processing plant or other reasonably accessible location for an additional 2 years. If, during the first year of the 3-year record-retention period, the processing plant is closed for a prolonged period between seasonal packs, the records may be transferred to some other reasonably accessible location at the end of the seasonal pack.

ACIDIFIED FOODS
Code of Federal Regulations
Title 21, Part 114

CONTENTS

21 CFR PART 114—ACIDIFIED FOODS

AUTHORITY: Secs. 402, 701, 704 of the Federal Food, Drug, and Cosmetic Act (21 U.S.C. 342, 371, 374); sec. 361 of the Public Health Service Act (42 U.S.C. 264).

SOURCE: 44 FR 16235, Mar. 16, 1979, unless otherwise noted.

Subpart A—General Provisions

§ 114.3 Definitions.

For the purposes of this part, the following definitions apply.

(a) *Acid foods* means foods that have a natural pH of 4.6 or below.

(b) *Acidified foods* means low-acid foods to which acid(s) or acid food(s) are added; these foods include, but are not limited to, beans, cucumbers, cabbage, artichokes, cauliflower, puddings, peppers, tropical fruits, and fish, singly or in any combination. They have a water activity (a_w) greater than 0.85 and have a finished equilibrium pH of 4.6 or below. These foods may be called, or may purport to be, "pickles" or "pickled _____ ." Carbonated beverages, jams, jellies, preserves, acid foods (including such foods as standardized and nonstandardized food dressings and condiment sauces) that contain small amounts of low-acid food(s) and have a resultant finished equilibrium pH that does not significantly differ from that of the predominant acid or acid food, and foods that are stored, distributed, and retailed under refrigeration are excluded from the coverage of this part.

(c) *Lot* means the product produced during a period indicated by a specific code.

(d) *Low-acid foods* means any foods, other than alcoholic beverages, with a finished equilibrium pH greater than 4.6 and a water activity (a_w) greater than 0.85. Tomatoes and tomato products having a finished equilibrium pH less than 4.7 are not classed as low-acid foods.

(e) *Scheduled process* means the process selected by a processor as adequate for use under the conditions of manufacture for a food in achieving and maintaining a food that will not permit the growth of microorganisms having public health significance. It includes control of pH and other critical factors equivalent to the process established by a competent processing authority.

(f) *Shall* is used to state mandatory requirements.

(g) *Should* is used to state recommended or advisory procedures or to identify recommended equipment.

(h) *Water activity* (a_w) is a measure of the free moisture in a product and is the quotient of the water vapor pressure of the substance divided by the vapor pressure of pure water at the same temperature.

§ 114.5 Current good manufacturing practice.

The criteria in §§ 114.10, 114.80, 114.83, 114.89, and 114.100, as well as the criteria in part 110 of this chapter, apply in determining whether an article of acidified food is adulterated (1) within the meaning of section 402(a)(3) of the act (21 U.S.C. 342(a)(3)) in that it has been manufactured under such conditions that it is unfit for food, or (2) within the meaning of section 402(a)(4) of the act (21 U.S.C. 342(a)(4)) in that it has been prepared, packed, or held under insanitary conditions whereby it may have become contaminated with filth, or whereby it may have been rendered injurious to health.

§ 114.10 Personnel.

All operators of processing and packaging systems shall be under the operating supervisions of a person who has attended a school approved by the Commissioner for giving instruction in food-handling techniques, food-protection principles, personal hygiene and plant sanitation practices, pH controls and critical factors in acidification, and who has been identified by that school as having satisfactorily completed the prescribed course of instruction. The commissioner will consider students who have satisfactorily completed the required portions of the courses presented under § 108.35 and part 113 of this chapter before March 16, 1979, to be in compliance with the requirement of this section.

Subparts B-D—[Reserved]

Subpart E—Production and Process Controls

§ 114.80 Processes and controls.

(a) *Processing operations.* The manufacturer shall employ appropriate quality control procedures to ensure that finished foods do not present a health hazard.

   (1) Acidified foods shall be so manufactured, processed, and packaged that a finished equilibrium pH value of 4.6 or lower is achieved within the time designated in the scheduled process and maintained in all finished foods. Manufacturing shall be in accordance with the scheduled process. Acidified foods shall be thermally processed to an extent that is sufficient to destroy the vegetative cells of microorganisms of public health significance and those of nonhealth significance capable of reproducing in the food under the conditions in which the food is stored, distributed, retailed and held by the user. Permitted preservatives may be used to inhibit reproduction of microorganisms of nonhealth significance (in lieu of thermal processing).

   (2) Sufficient control, including frequent testing and recording of results, shall be exercised so that the finished equilibrium pH values for acidified foods are not higher than 4.6. Measurement of acidity of foods in-process may be made by potentiometric methods, titratable acidity, or colorimetric methods. If the finished equilibrium pH of the food is above 4.0, the measurement of the finished equilibrium pH shall be by a potentiometric method, and the in-process measurements by titration or colorimetry shall be related to the finished equilibrium pH. If the finished equilibrium pH is 4.0 or below, then the measurement of acidity of the final product may be made by any suitable method. Special care should be taken when food ingredients have been subjected to lye, lime, or similar high pH materials.

   (3) Procedures for acidification to attain acceptable equilibrium pH levels in the final food include, but are not limited to, the following:

   (i) Blanching of the food ingredients in acidified aqueous solutions.

   (ii) Immersion of the blanched food in acid solutions. Although immersion of food in an acid solution is a satisfactory method for acidification, care must be taken to ensure that the acid concentration is properly maintained.

   (iii) Direct batch acidification, which can be achieved by adding a known amount of an acid solution to a specified amount of food during acidification.

   (iv) Direct addition of a predetermined amount of acid to individual containers during production. Liquid acids are generally more effective than solid or pelleted acids. Care must be taken to ensure that the proper amount of acid is added to each container.

   (v) Addition of acid foods to low-acid foods in controlled proportions to conform to specific formulations.

   (4) Testing and examinations of containers shall occur often enough to ensure that the container suitably protects the food from leakage or contamination.

(b) *Coding.* Each container or product shall be marked with an identifying code permanently visible to the naked eye. If the container does not permit the code to be embossed or inked, the label may be legibly perforated or otherwise marked, as long as the label is securely affixed to the product container. The required identification shall specify in code the establishment where the product was packed, the product contained therein, and the year, day, and period during which it was packed. The packing period code shall be changed often enough to enable ready identification of lots during their sale and distribution. Codes may be changed periodically on one of the following bases: intervals of 4 to 5 hours; personnel shift changes; or batches, as long as the containers constituting the batch do not represent those processed during more than one personnel shift.

§ 114.83 Establishing scheduled processes.

The scheduled process shall be established by a qualified person who has expert knowledge acquired through appropriate training and experience in the acidification and processing of acidified foods.

§ 114.89 Deviations from scheduled processes.

Whenever any process operation deviates from the scheduled process for any acidified food and/or the equilibrium pH of the finished product is higher than 4.6, the commercial processor of the acidified food shall either: (a) Fully reprocess that portion of the food by a process established by a competent processing authority as adequate to ensure a safe product; (b) thermally process it as a low-acid food under part 113 of this chapter; or (c) set aside that portion of the food involved for further evaluation as to any potential public health significance. The evaluation shall be made by a competent processing authority and shall be in accordance with procedures recognized by competent processing authorities as being adequate to detect any potential hazard to public health. Unless the evaluation demonstrates that the food has undergone a process that has rendered it safe, the food set aside shall either be fully reprocessed to render it safe, or be destroyed. A record shall be made of the procedures used in the evaluation and the results. Either upon completion of full reprocessing and the attainment of a safe food, or after the determination that no significant potential for public health hazard exists, that portion of the food involved may be shipped in normal distribution. Otherwise, the portion of the food involved shall be destroyed.

§ 114.90 Methodology.

Methods that may be used to determine pH or acidity for acidified foods include, but are not limited to, the following:
(a) *Potentiometric method for the determination of pH—*
    (1) *Principles.* The term "pH" is used to designate the intensity or degree of acidity. The value of pH, the logarithm of the reciprocal of the hydrogen ion concentration in solution, is determined by measuring the difference in potential between two electrodes immersed in a sample solution. A suitable system consists of a potentiometer, a glass electrode, and a reference electrode. A precise pH determination can be made by making an electromotive force (emf) measurement of a standard buffer solution whose pH is known, and then comparing that measurement to an emf measurement of a sample of the solution to be tested.
    (2) *Instruments.* The primary instrument for use in pH determination is the pH meter or potentiometer. For most work, an instrument with a direct-reading pH scale is necessary. Battery and line-operated instruments are available commercially. If the line voltage is unstable, line-operated instruments should be fitted with voltage regulators to eliminate drifting of meter-scale readings. Batteries should be checked frequently to ensure proper operation of battery operated instruments. An instrument using an expanded unit scale or a digital readout system is preferred since it allows more precise measurements.
    (3) *Electrodes.* The typical pH meter is equipped with a glass membrane electrode and a reference electrode or a single probe combination electrode. Various types of electrodes designed for specific uses are available. The most commonly used reference electrode is the calomel electrode, which incorporates a salt bridge filled with saturated potassium chloride solution.
        (i) *Care and use of electrodes.* Calomel electrodes should be kept filled with saturated potassium chloride solution or other solution specified by the manufacturer because they may become damaged if they are allowed to dry out. For best results, electrodes should be soaked in buffer solution, distilled or deionized water, or other liquid specified by the manufacturer for several hours before using and kept ready by storing with tips immersed in distilled water or in buffer solution used for standardization. Electrodes should be rinsed with water before immersing in the standard buffers and rinsed with water or the solution to be measured next between sample determinations. A lag in meter response may indicate aging effects or fouling of the electrodes, and cleaning and rejuvenation of the electrodes may be necessary and may be accomplished by placing the electrodes in 0.1 molar sodium hydroxide solution for 1 minute and then transferring them to 0.1 molar hydrochloric acid solution for 1 minute. The cycle should be repeated two times, ending with the electrodes in the acid solution. The electrodes should then be thoroughly rinsed with water and blotted with soft tissue before proceeding with the standardization.
        (ii) *Temperature.* To obtain accurate results, a uniform temperature should be maintained for the electrodes, the standard buffer solutions, and the samples. Tests should be made at a temperature between 20° and 30°C, the optimum being 25°C. Any temperature determinations made without meter compensation may affect pH values. An automatic temperature compensator may be used.
        (iii) *Accuracy.* The accuracy of most pH meters is stated to be approximately 0.1 pH unit, and reproducibility is usually ± 0.05 pH unit or less. Some meters permit the expansion of any pH unit range to cover the entire scale and have an accuracy of approximately ± 0.01 pH unit and a reproducibility of ± 0.005 pH units.
    (4) *General procedure for determining pH.* When operating an instrument, the operator should use the manufacturer's instructions and should observe the following techniques for pH determinations:
        (i) Switch the instrument on and allow the electronic components to warm up and stabilize before proceeding.
        (ii) Standardize the instrument and electrodes with commercially prepared standard 4.0 pH buffer or with freshly prepared 0.05 molar potassium acid phthalate buffer solution prepared as outlined in "Official Methods of Analysis of the Association of Official Analytical Chemists" (AOAC), 13th Ed. (1980), section 50.007(c), under "Buffer Solutions for Calibration of pH Equipment—Official Final Action," which is incorporated by reference. Copies may be obtained from the Association of Official Analytical Chemists, 2200 Wilson Blvd., Suite 400, Arlington, VA 22201-3301, or may be examined at the Office of the Federal Register, 800 North Capitol Street, NW., suite 700, Washington, DC. Note the temperature of the buffer solution and set the temperature compensator control at the observed temperature (room temperature is near 25°C).

214

(iii) Rinse the electrodes with water and blot, but do not wipe, with soft tissue.

(iv) Immerse the tips in the buffer solution and take the pH reading, allowing about 1 minute for the meter to stabilize. Adjust the standardization control so that the meter reading corresponds to the pH of the known buffer (for example, 4.0) for the temperature observed. Rinse the electrodes with water and blot with soft tissue. Repeat procedure with fresh portions of buffer solution until the instrument remains in balance on two successive trials. To check the operation of the pH meter, check the pH reading using another standard buffer such as one having a pH of 7.0, or check it with freshly prepared 0.025 molar phosphate solution prepared as outlined in the AOAC, 13th Ed. (1980), section 50.007(e), which is incorporated by reference. The availability of this incorporation by reference is given in paragraph (a)(4)(ii) of this section. Expanded scale pH meters may be checked with pH 3.0 or pH 5.0 standard buffers. Buffers and instruments can be further checked by comparison with values obtained with a second properly standardized instrument.

(v) Indicating electrodes may be checked for proper operation by first using an acid buffer and then a base buffer. First standardize the electrodes using a pH 4.0 buffer at or near 25°C. Standardization control should be adjusted so that the meter reads exactly 4.0. Electrodes should be rinsed with water, then blotted and immersed in a pH 9.18 borax buffer prepared as outlined in the AOAC, 13th Ed. (1980), section 50.007(f), which is incorporated by reference. The availability of this incorporation by reference is given in paragraph (a)(4)(ii) of this section. The pH reading should be within ± 0.3 units of the 9.18 value.

(vi) The pH meter can be tested for proper operation by shorting the glass and reference electrode inputs, thereby reducing the voltage to zero. In some meters this shorting is done by switching the instrument to standby, and in other instruments by use of a shorting strap. With the instrument shorted out, standardization control should be turned from one extreme to another. This operation should produce a deflection greater than ± 1.5 pH unit from center scale.

(5) *Determining pH on samples.*

(i) Adjust the temperature of the sample to room temperature (25°C), and set the temperature compensator control to the observed temperature. With some expanded scale instruments, the sample temperature must be the same as the temperature of the buffer solution used for the standardization.

(ii) Rinse and blot the electrodes. Immerse the electrodes in the sample and take the pH reading, allowing 1 minute for the meter to stabilize. Rinse and blot the electrodes and repeat on a fresh portion of sample. Oil and grease from the samples may coat the electrodes; therefore, it is advisable to clean and standardize the instrument frequently. When oily samples cause fouling problems, it may become necessary to rinse the electrodes with ethyl ether.

(iii) Determine two pH values on the well-mixed sample. These readings should agree with one another to indicate that the sample is homogeneous. Report values to the nearest 0.05 pH unit.

(6) *Preparation of samples.* Some food products may consist of a mixture of liquid and solid components that differ in acidity. Other food products may be semisolid in character. The following are examples of preparation procedures for pH testing for each of these categories:

(i) *Liquid and solid component mixtures.* Drain the contents of the container for 2 minutes on a U.S. standard No. 8 sieve (preferably stainless steel) inclined at a 17- to 20-degree angle. Record weight of the liquid and solid portions and retain each portion separately.

(a) If the liquid contains sufficient oil to cause electrode fouling, separate the layers with a separatory funnel and retain the aqueous layer. The oil layer may be discarded. Adjust the temperature of the aqueous layer to 25°C and determine its pH.

(b) Remove the drained solids from the sieve, blend to a uniform paste, adjust the temperature of the paste to 25°C and determine its pH.

(c) Mix aliquots of solid and liquid fractions in the same ratio as found in the original container and blend to a uniform consistency. Adjust the temperature of the blend to 25°C and determine the equilibriated pH. Alternatively, blend the entire contents of the container to a uniform paste, adjust the temperature of the paste to 25°C, and determine the equilibriated pH.

(ii) *Marinated oil products.* Separate the oil from the solid product. Blend the solid in a blender to a paste consistency; it may become necessary to add a small amount of distilled water to some samples to facilitate the blending. A small amount of added water will not alter the pH of most food products, but caution must be exercised concerning poorly buffered foods. No more than 20 milliliters of distilled water should be added to each 100 grams of product. Determine the pH by immersing electrodes in the prepared paste after adjusting the temperature to 25°C.

(iii) *Semisolid products.* Food products of a semisolid consistency, such as puddings, potato salad, etc., may be blended to a paste consistency, and the pH may be determined on the prepared paste. If more fluidity is required, 10 to 20 milliliters of distilled water may be added to 100 grams of product. Adjust the temperature of the prepared paste to 25°C and determine its pH.

(iv) *Special product mixtures.* For special product mixtures such as antipasto, pour off the oil, blend the remaining product to a paste, and determine the pH of the blended paste. If more fluidity is required, add 10 to 20 milliliters of distilled water to each 100 grams of product and blend. Adjust the temperature of the prepared paste to 25°C and determine its pH.

(7) *Process pH determination.* Obtain sample portions of material for pH determination.

    (i) For process liquids, adjust the temperature of the liquid to 25°C and determine the pH by immersing the electrodes in the liquid.

    (ii) Drain solid materials on a sieve and blend to a workable paste. Adjust the temperature of the prepared paste to 25°C and determine its pH.

    (iii) If enough solid materials are available to make a paste, blend representative aliquots of liquid and solid materials to a workable paste. Adjust the temperature of the prepared paste to 25°C and determine the equilibrated pH. Alternatively, blend the entire contents of the container to a uniform paste, adjust the temperature of the paste to 25°C, and determine the equilibrated pH.

(b) *Colorimetric methods for the determination of pH.* This method may be used in lieu of the potentiometric method if the pH is 4.0 or lower.

    (1) *Principle.* The colorimetric method for pH involves the use of indicator dyes in solutions that gradually change color over limited pH ranges. An indicator that has the greatest color change at approximately the pH of the sample being tested is selected. The pH is determined by the color of the indicator when exposed to the sample under test.

    (2) *Indicator solutions.* Most indicator solutions are prepared as a 0.04 percent solution of the indicator dye in alcohol. In testing, a few drops of indicator solution are added to 10-milliliter portions of the sample solution. Colors should be compared using a bright background. Approximate determinations can be made on white porcelain spot plates, the test colors being compared thereon with a set of color standards. More accurate colorimetric tests can be made using a comparator block fitted with sets of tubes of standard indicator solutions of known pH.

    (3) *Indicator paper.* A paper tape treated with indicator dye is dipped into the sample solution. Depending upon the pH of the solution, the tape will change color and an approximate pH can be determined by comparison with a standard color chart.

(c) *Titratable acidity.* Acceptable methods for determining titratable acidity are described in the AOAC, 13th Ed. (1980), section 22.060, under "Titratable Acidity—Official Final Action," for "Indicator Method," and section 22.061 for "Glass Electrode Method-Official Final Action," which is incorporated by reference. The availability of this incorporation by reference is given in paragraph (a)(4)(ii) of this section. The procedure for preparing and standardizing the sodium hydroxide solution is described in the AOAC, 13th Ed. (1980), sections 50.032-50.035, under "Sodium Hydroxide—Official Final Action" by the "Standard Potassium Hydroxide Phthalate Method," which is also incorporated by reference and available as set forth in paragraph (a)(4)(ii) of this section.

[44 FR 16235, Mar. 16, 1979, as amended at 47 FR 11822, Mar. 19, 1982; 49 FR 5609, Feb. 14, 1984; 54 FR 24892, June 12, 1989]

Subpart F—Records and Reports

§ 114.100 Records.

(a) Records shall be maintained of examinations of raw materials, packaging materials, and finished products, and of suppliers' guarantees or certifications that verify compliance with Food and Drug Administration regulations and guidelines or action levels.

(b) Processing and production records showing adherence to scheduled processes, including records of pH measurements and other critical factors intended to ensure a safe product, shall be maintained and shall contain sufficient additional information such as product code, date, container size, and product, to permit a public health hazard evaluation of the processes applied to each lot, batch, or other portion of production.

(c) All departures from scheduled processes having a possible bearing on public health or the safety of the food shall be noted and the affected portion of the product identified; these departures shall be recorded and made the subject of a separate file (or log identifying the appropriate data) delineating them, the action taken to rectify them, and the disposition of the portion of the product involved.

(d) Records shall be maintained identifying initial distribution of the finished product to facilitate, when necessary, the segregation of specific food lots that may have become contaminated or otherwise unfit for their intended use.

(e) Copies of all records provided for in paragraphs (b), (c), and (d) of this section shall be retained at the processing plant or other reasonably accessible location for a period of 3 years from the date of manufacture.

USDA CANNING REGULATIONS
CANNING AND CANNED PRODUCTS

Code of Federal Regulations
Title 9, Part 318 (381)[1]

CONTENTS

Subpart G—Canning and Canned Products

Section

---

[1]Because the following regulations are essentially identical, only 9 CFR 318 Subpart G has been reprinted in this text.

9CFR318 Subpart G (.300–.311)—Canning and Canned Products (Meat)
9CFR381 Subpart X (.300–.311)—Canning and Canned Products (Poultry)

9 CFR PART 318—USDA Canning Regulations

SOURCE: 51 FR 45619, Dec. 19, 1986, unless otherwise noted.

Subpart G—Canning and Canned Products

§ 318.300 Definitions.

(a) *Abnormal container.* A container with any sign of swelling or product leakage or any evidence that the contents of the unopened container may be spoiled.

(b) *Acidified low acid product.* A canned product which has been formulated or treated so that every component of the finished product has a pH of 4.6 or lower within 24 hours after the completion of the thermal process unless data are available from the establishment's processing authority demonstrating that a longer time period is safe.

(c) *Bleeders.* Small orifices on a retort through which steam, other gasses, and condensate are emitted from the retort throughout the entire thermal process.

(d) *Canned product.* A meat food product with a water activity above 0.85 which receives a thermal process either before or after being packed in a hermetically sealed container. Unless otherwise specified, the term ''product'' as used in this subpart G shall mean ''canned product.''

(e) *Closure technician.* The individual(s) identified by the establishment as being trained to perform specific container integrity examinations as required by this subpart and designated by the establishment to perform such examinations.

(f) *Code lot.* All production of a particular product in a specific size container marked with a specific container code.

(g) *Come-up time.* The elapsed time, including venting time (if applicable), between the introduction of the heating medium into a closed retort and the start of process timing.

(h) *Critical factor.* Any characteristic, condition or aspect of a product, container, or procedure that affects the adequacy of the process schedule. Critical factors are established by processing authorities.

(i) *Headspace.* That portion of a container not occupied by the product.
  (1) *Gross headspace.* The vertical distance between the level of the product (generally the liquid surface) in an upright rigid container and the top edge of the container (i.e., the flange of an unsealed can, the top of the double seam on a sealed can, or the top edge of an unsealed jar).
  (2) *Net headspace.* The vertical distance between the level of the product (generally the liquid surface) in an upright rigid container and the inside surface of the lid.

(j) *Hermetically sealed containers.* Air-tight containers which are designed and intended to protect the contents against the entry of microorganisms during and after thermal processing.
  (1) *Rigid container.* A container, the shape or contour of which, when filled and sealed, is neither affected by the enclosed product nor deformed by external mechanical pressure of up to 10 pounds per square inch gauge (0.7 kg/cm^2)(i.e., normal firm finger pressure).
  (2) *Semirigid container.* A container, the shape or contour of which, when filled and sealed, is not significantly affected by the enclosed product under normal atmospheric temperature and pressure, but can be deformed by external mechanical pressure of less than 10 pounds per square inch gauge (0.7 kg/cm^2)(i.e., normal firm finger pressure).
  (3) *Flexible container.* A container, the shape or contour of which, when filled and sealed, is significantly affected by the enclosed product.

(k) *Incubation tests.* Tests in which the thermally processed product is kept at a specific temperature for a specified period of time in order to determine if outgrowth of microorganisms occurs.

(l) *Initial temperature.* The temperature, determined at the initiation of a thermal process cycle, of the contents of the coldest container to be processed.

(m) *Low acid product.* A canned product in which any component has a pH value above 4.6.

(n) *Process schedule.* The thermal process and any specified critical factors for a given canned product required to achieve shelf stability.

(o) *Process temperature.* The minimum temperature(s) of the heating medium to be maintained as specified in the process schedule.

(p) *Process time.* The intended time(s) a container is to be exposed to the heating medium while the heating medium is at or above the process temperature(s).

(q) *Processing authority.* The person(s) or organization(s) having expert knowledge of thermal processing requirements for foods in hermetically sealed containers, having access to facilities for making such determinations, and designated by the establishment to perform certain functions as indicated in this subpart.

(r) *Program employee.* Any inspector or other individual employed by the Department or any cooperating agency who is authorized by the Secretary to do any work or perform any duty in connection with the Program (see § 301.2(f)).

(s) *Retort.* A pressure vessel designed for thermal processing of product packed in hermetically sealed containers.

(t) *Seals.* Those parts of a semirigid container and lid or of a flexible container that are fused together in order to hermetically close the container.

(u) *Shelf stability.* The condition achieved by application of heat, sufficient, alone or in combination with other ingredients and/or treatments, to render the product free of microorganisms capable of growing in the product at nonrefrigerated conditions (over 50°F or 10°C) at which the product is intended to be held during distribution and storage. Shelf stability and shelf stable are synonymous with commercial sterility and commercially sterile, respectively.

(v) *Thermal process.* The heat treatment necessary to achieve shelf stability as determined by the establishment's processing authority. It is quantified in terms of:

    (1) Time(s) and temperature(s); or

    (2) Minimum product temperature.

(w) *Venting.* The removal of air from a retort before the start of process timing.

(x) *Water activity.* The ratio of the water vapor pressure of the product to the vapor pressure of pure water at the same temperature.

§ 318.301 Containers and closures.

(a) *Examination and cleaning of empty containers.*

    (1) Empty containers, closures, and flexible pouch roll stock shall be evaluated by the establishment to ensure that they are clean and free of structural defects and damage that may affect product or container integrity. Such an examination should be based upon a statistical sampling plan.

    (2) All empty containers, closures, and flexible pouch roll stock shall be stored, handled, and conveyed in such a manner that will prevent soiling and damage that could affect the hermetic condition of the sealed container.

    (3) Just before filling, rigid containers shall be cleaned to prevent incorporation of foreign matter into the finished product. Closures, semirigid containers, preformed flexible pouches, and flexible pouch roll stock contained in original wrappings do not need to be cleaned before use.

(b) *Closure examinations for rigid containers (cans) —*

    (1) *Visual examinations.* A closure technician shall visually examine the double seams formed by each closing machine head. When seam defects (e.g., cutovers, sharpness, knocked down flanges, false seams, droops) are observed, necessary corrective actions, such as adjusting or repairing the closing machine, shall be taken. In addition to the double seams, the entire container shall be examined for product leakage or obvious defects. A visual examination shall be performed on at least one container from each closing machine head, and the observations, along with any corrective actions, shall be recorded. Visual examinations shall be conducted with sufficient frequency to ensure proper closure and should be conducted at least every 30 minutes of continuous closing machine operation. Additional visual examinations shall be made by the closure technician at the beginning of production, immediately following every jam in the closing machine and after closing machine adjustment (including adjustment for changes in container size).

    (2) *Teardown examinations.* Teardown examinations of double seams formed by each closing machine head shall be performed by a closure technician at a frequency sufficient to ensure proper closure. These examinations should be made at intervals of not more than 4 hours of continuous closing machine operation. At least one container from each closing head shall be examined on the packer's end during each regular examination period. Examination results along with any necessary corrective actions, such as adjusting or repairing the closing machine, shall be promptly recorded by the closure technician. The establishment shall have container specification guidelines for double seam integrity on file and available for review by Program employees. A teardown examination of the can maker's end shall be performed on at least one container selected from each closing machine during each examination period except when teardown examinations are made on incoming empty containers or when, in the case of self-manufactured containers, the containers are made in the vicinity of the establishment and the container plant records are made available to Program employees. Additional teardown examinations on the packer's end should be made at the beginning of production, immediately following every jam in a closing machine and after closing machine adjustment (including adjustment for a change in container size). The following procedures shall be used in teardown examinations of double seams:

        (i) One of the following two methods shall be employed for dimensional measurements of the double seam.

            (a) *Micrometer measurement.* For cylindrical containers, measure the following dimensions (Figure 1) at three points approximately 120 degrees apart on the double seam excluding and at least one-half inch from the side seam juncture:

                (1) Double seam length-W;

                (2) Double seam thickness-S;

(*3*) Body hook length-BH; and

(*4*) Cover hook length-CH.

Maximum and minimum values for each dimensional measurement shall be recorded by the closure technician.

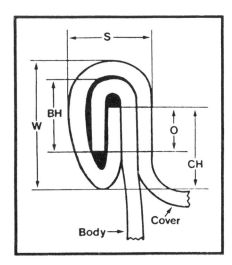

(*b*) *Seamscope or seam projector.* Required measurements of the seam include thickness, body hook, and overlap. Seam thickness shall be obtained by micrometer. For cylindrical containers, at least two locations, excluding the side seam juncture, shall be used to obtain the required measurements.

(ii) *Seam tightness.* Regardless of the dimensional measurement method used to measure seam dimensions, at a minimum, the seam(s) examined shall be stripped to assess the degree of wrinkling.

(iii) *Side seam juncture rating.* Regardless of the dimensional measurement method used to measure seam dimensions, the cover hook shall be stripped to examine the cover hook droop at the juncture for containers having side seams.

(iv) *Examination of noncylindrical containers.* Examination of noncylindrical containers (e.g., square, rectangular, ''D''-shaped, and irregularly-shaped) shall be conducted as described in paragraphs (b)(2)(i), (ii), and (iii) of this section except that the required dimension measurements shall be made on the double seam at the points listed in the establishment's container specification guidelines.

(c) *Closure examinations for glass containers —*

(1) *Visual examinations.* A closure technician shall visually assess the adequacy of the closures formed by each closing machine. When closure defects, such as loose or cocked caps, fractured or cracked containers and low vacuum jars, are observed, necessary corrective actions, such as adjusting or repairing the closing machine shall be taken and recorded. In addition to the closures, the entire container shall be examined for defects. Visual examinations shall be made with sufficient frequency to ensure proper closure and should be conducted at least every 30 minutes of continuous closing machine operation. Additional visual examinations shall be made by the closure technician and the observations recorded at the beginning of production, immediately following every jam in the closing machine, and after closing machine adjustment (including adjustment for a change in container size).

(2) *Closure examinations and tests.* Depending upon the container and closure, tests shall be performed by a closure technician at a frequency sufficient to ensure proper closure. These examinations should be made either before or after thermal processing and at intervals of not more than 4 hours of continuous closing machine operation. At least one container from each closing machine shall be examined during each regular examination period. Examination results along with any necessary corrective actions, such as adjusting or repairing the closing machine, shall be promptly recorded by the closure technician. The establishment shall have specification guidelines for closure integrity on file and available for review by Program employees. Additional closure examinations should be made at the beginning of production, immediately following every jam in the closing machine, and after closing machine adjustment (including adjustment for a change in container size).

(d) *Closure examinations for semirigid and flexible containers —*

(1) *Heat seals*

(i) *Visual examinations.* A closure technician shall visually examine the seals formed by each sealing machine. When sealing defects are observed, necessary corrective actions, such as adjusting or repairing the sealing machine, shall be taken and recorded. In addition to examining the heat seals, the entire container shall be examined for product leakage or obvious defects. Visual examinations shall be performed before and after the thermal processing operation and with sufficient frequency to ensure proper closure. These examinations should be conducted at least in accordance with a statistical sampling plan. All defects noted and corrective actions taken shall be promptly recorded.

    (ii) *Physical tests.* Tests determined by the establishment as necessary to assess container integrity shall be conducted by the closure technician at a frequency sufficient to ensure proper closure. These tests shall be performed after the thermal processing operation and should be made at least every 2 hours of continuous production. The establishment's acceptance guidelines for each test procedure shall be on file and available for review by Program employees. Test results along with any necessary corrective actions, such as adjusting or repairing the sealing machine, shall be recorded.

  (2) Double seams on semirigid or flexible containers shall be examined and the results recorded as provided in paragraph (b) of this section. Any additional measurements specified by the container manufacturer shall also be made and recorded.

(e) *Container coding.* Each container shall be marked with a permanent, legible, identifying code mark. The mark shall, at a minimum, identify in code the product (unless the product name lithographed or printed elsewhere on the container) and the day and year the product was packed.

(f) *Handling of containers after closure.*

  (1) Containers and closures shall be protected from damage which may cause defects that are likely to affect the hermetic condition of the containers. The accumulation of stationary containers on moving conveyors should be minimized to avoid damage to the containers.

  (2) The maximum time lapse between closing and initiation of thermal processing shall be 2 hours. However, the Administrator may specify a shorter period of time when considered necessary to ensure product safety and stability. A longer period of time between closing and the initiation of thermal processing may be permitted by the Administrator.

(Approved by the Office of Management and Budget under control number 0583-0015)

§ 318.302 Thermal processing.

(a) *Process schedules.* Prior to the processing of canned product for distribution in commerce, an establishment shall have a process schedule (as defined in § 318.300(n) of this subpart) for each canned meat product to be packed by the establishment.

(b) *Source of process schedules.*

  (1) Process schedules used by an establishment shall be developed or determined by a processing authority.

  (2) Any change in product formulation, ingredients, or treatments that are not already incorporated in a process schedule and that may adversely affect either the product heat penetration profile or sterilization value requirements shall be evaluated by the establishment's processing authority. If it is determined that any such change adversely affects the adequacy of the process schedule, the processing authority shall amend the process schedule accordingly.

  (3) Complete records concerning all aspects of the development or determination of a process schedule, including any associated incubation tests, shall be made available by the establishment to the Program employee upon request.

(c) *Submittal of process information.*

  (1) Prior to the processing of canned product for distribution in commerce, the establishment shall provide the inspector at the establishment with a list of the process schedules (including alternate schedules) along with any additional applicable information, such as the retort come-up operating procedures and critical factors.

  (2) Letters or other written communications from a processing authority recommending all process schedules shall be maintained on file by the establishment. Upon request by Program employees, the establishment shall make available such letters or written communications (or copies thereof). If critical factors are identified in the process schedule, the establishment shall provide the inspector with a copy of the procedures for measuring, controlling, and recording these factors, along with the frequency of such measurements, to ensure that the critical factors remain within the limits used to establish the process schedule. Once submitted, the process schedules and associated critical factors and the procedures for measuring (including the frequency), controlling, and recording of critical factors shall not be changed without the prior written submittal of the revised procedures (including supporting documentation) to the inspector at the establishment.

(Approved by the Office of Management and Budget under control number 0583-0015)

§ 318.303 Critical factors and the application of the process schedule.

Critical factors specified in the process schedule shall be measured, controlled and recorded by the establishment to ensure that these factors remain within the limits used to establish the process schedule. Examples of factors that are often critical to process schedule adequacy may include:

(a) *General.*
    (1) Maximum fill-in weight or drained weight;
    (2) Arrangement of pieces in the container;
    (3) Container orientation during thermal processing;
    (4) Product formulation;
    (5) Particle size;
    (6) Maximum thickness for flexible, and to some extent semirigid containers during thermal processing;
    (7) Maximum pH;
    (8) Percent salt;
    (9) Ingoing (or formulated) nitrite level (ppm);
    (10) Maximum water activity; and
    (11) Product consistency or viscosity.
(b) *Continuous rotary and batch agitating retorts.*
    (1) Minimum headspace; and
    (2) Retort reel speed.
(c) *Hydrostatic retorts.*
    (1) Chain or conveyor speed.
(d) *Steam/air retorts.*
    (1) Steam/air ratio; and
    (2) Heating medium flow rate.

§ 318.304 Operations in the thermal processing area.

(a) *Posting of processes.* Process schedules (or operating process schedules) for daily production, including minimum initial temperatures and operating procedures for thermal processing equipment, shall be posted in a conspicuous place near the thermal processing equipment. Alternatively, such information shall be available to the thermal processing system operator and the inspector.

(b) *Process indicators and retort traffic control.* A system for product traffic control shall be established to prevent product from bypassing the thermal processing operation. Each basket, crate or similar vehicle containing unprocessed product, or at least one visible container in each vehicle, shall be plainly and conspicuously marked with a heat sensitive indicator that will visually indicate whether such unit has been thermally processed. Exposed heat sensitive indicators attached to container vehicles shall be removed before such vehicles are refilled with unprocessed product. Container loading systems for crateless retorts shall be designed to prevent unprocessed product from bypassing the thermal processing operation.

(c) *Initial temperature.* The initial temperature of the contents of the coldest container to be processed shall be determined and recorded by the establishment at the time the processing cycle begins to assure that the temperature of the contents of every container to be processed is not lower than the minimum initial temperature specified in the process schedule. Thermal processing systems which subject the filled and sealed containers to water at any time before process timing begins shall be operated to assure that such water will not lower the temperature of the product below the minimum initial temperature specified in the process schedule.

(d) *Timing devices.* Devices used to time applicable thermal processing operation functions or events, such as process schedule time, come-up time and retort venting, shall be accurate to assure that all such functions or events are achieved. Pocket watches and wrist watches are not considered acceptable timing devices. Analog and digital clocks are considered acceptable. If such clocks do not display seconds, all required timed functions or events shall have at least a 1-minute safety factor over the specified thermal processing operation times. Temperature/time recording devices shall correspond within 15 minutes to the time of the day recorded on written records required by § 318.306.

(e) *Measurement of pH.* Unless other methods are approved by the Administrator, potentiometric methods using electronic instruments (pH meters) shall be used for making pH determinations when a maximum pH value is specified as a critical factor in a process schedule.

(Approved by Office of Management and Budget under control number 0583-0015)

§ 318.305 Equipment and procedures for heat processing systems.

(a) *Instruments and controls common to different thermal processing systems—*

    (1) *Indicating temperature devices.* Each retort shall be equipped with at least one indicating temperature device that measures the actual temperature within the retort. The indicating temperature device, not the temperature/time recording device, shall be used as the reference instrument for indicating the process temperature.

        (i) *Mercury-in-glass thermometers.* A mercury-in-glass thermometer shall have divisions that are readable to $1F°$ (or $0.5C°$) and whose scale contains not more than $17F°/inch$ (or $4.0C°/cm$) of graduated scale. Each mercury-in-glass thermometer shall be tested for accuracy against a known accurate standard upon installation and at least once a year to ensure its accuracy. Records that specify the date, standard used, test method, and the person or testing authority performing the test shall be maintained on file by the establishment and made available to Program employees. A mercury-in-glass thermometer that has a divided mercury column or that cannot be adjusted to the standard shall be repaired and tested for accuracy before further use, or replaced.

        (ii) *Other devices.* In lieu of mercury-in-glass thermometers, the Administrator, upon request, will consider other indicating temperature devices, such as resistance temperature detectors. Any such device that is approved shall, upon installation and at least once a year thereafter, be tested for accuracy against a known accurate standard. Records that specify the date, standard used, test method, and the person or testing authority performing the test shall be maintained on file by the establishment and made available to Program employees. Any such device which cannot be adjusted to the standard shall be replaced, or repaired and tested for accuracy before further use.

    (2) *Temperature/time recording devices.* Each thermal processing system shall be equipped with at least one temperature/time recording device to provide a permanent record of temperatures within the thermal processing system. This recording device may be combined with the steam controller and may be a recording/controlling instrument. When compared to the known accurate indicating temperature device, the recording accuracy shall be equal to or better than $1F°$ (or $0.5C°$) at the process temperature. The temperature recording chart should be adjusted to agree with, but shall never be higher than, the known accurate indicating temperature device. A means of preventing unauthorized changes in the adjustment shall be provided. For example, a lock or a notice from management posted at or near the recording device warning that only authorized persons are permitted to make adjustments, are satisfactory means for preventing unauthorized changes. Air-operated temperature controllers shall have adequate filter systems to ensure a supply of clean, dry air. The recorder timing mechanism shall be accurate.

        (i) *Chart-type devices.* Devices using charts shall be used only with the correct chart. Each chart shall have a working scale of not more than $55F°/inch$ (or $12C°/cm$) within a range of $20F°$ (or $11C°$) of the process temperature. Chart graduations shall not exceed 2F degrees (or 1C degree) within a range of 10F degrees (or 5C degrees) of the process temperature. Multipoint plotting chart-type devices shall print temperature readings at intervals that will assure that the parameters of the process time and process temperature have been met. The frequency of recording should not exceed 1-minute intervals.

        (ii) *Other devices.* In lieu of chart-type devices, the Administrator will consider for approval other recording devices upon request.

    (3) *Steam controllers.* Each retort shall be equipped with an automatic steam controller to maintain the retort temperature. This may be a recording/controlling instrument when combined with a temperature/time recording device.

    (4) *Air valves.* All air lines connected to retorts designed for pressure processing in steam shall be equipped with a globe valve or other equivalent-type valve or piping arrangement that will prevent leakage of air into the retort during the process cycle.

    (5) *Water valves.* All retort water lines that are intended to be closed during a process cycle shall be equipped with a globe valve or other equivalent-type valve or piping arrangement that will prevent leakage of water into the retort during the process cycle.

(b) *Pressure processing in steam—*

    (1) *Batch still retorts.*

        (i) The basic requirements and recommendations for indicating temperature devices and temperature/time recording devices are described in paragraphs (a)(1) and (2) of this section. Additionally, bulb sheaths or probes of indicating temperature devices and probes of temperature/time recording devices shall be installed either within the retort shell or in external wells attached to the retort. External wells shall be connected to the retort through at least a 3/4 inch (1.9 cm) diameter opening and equipped with a 1/16 inch (1.6 mm) or larger bleeder opening so located as to provide a constant flow of steam past the length of the bulb or probe. The bleeder for external wells shall emit steam continuously during the entire thermal processing period.

(ii) Steam controllers are required as described under paragraph (a)(3) of this section.

(iii) *Steam inlet.* The steam inlet to each retort shall be large enough to provide steam for proper operation of the retort, and shall enter at a point to facilitate air removal during venting.

(iv) *Crate supports.* Vertical still retorts with bottom steam entry shall employ bottom retort crate supports. Baffle plates shall not be used in the bottom of retorts.

(v) *Steam spreader.* Perforated steam spreaders, if used, shall be maintained to ensure they are not blocked or otherwise inoperative. Horizontal still retorts shall be equipped with perforated steam spreaders that extend the full length of the retort unless the adequacy of another arrangement is documented by heat distribution data or other documentation from a processing authority. Such information shall be maintained on file by the establishment and made available to Program employees for review.

(vi) *Bleeders and condensate removal.* Bleeders, except those for external wells of temperature devices, shall have 1/8 inch (or 3 mm) or larger openings and shall be wide open during the entire process, including the come-up time. For horizontal still retorts, bleeders shall be located within approximately 1 foot (or 30 cm) of the outermost locations of containers at each end along the top of the retort. Additional bleeders shall be located not more than 8 feet (2.4 m) apart along the top. Bleeders may be installed at positions other than those specified above, as long as the establishment has heat distribution data or other documentation from the manufacturer or from a processing authority demonstrating that the bleeders accomplish removal of air and circulate the steam within the retort. This information shall be maintained on file by the establishment and made available to Program employees for review. All bleeders shall be arranged in a way that enables the retort operator to observe that they are functioning properly. Vertical retorts shall have at least one bleeder opening located in the portion of the retort opposite the steam inlet. All bleeders shall be arranged so that the retort operator can observe that they are functioning properly. In retorts having a steam inlet above the level of the lowest container, a bleeder shall be installed in the bottom of the retort to remove condensate. The condensate bleeder shall be so arranged that the retort operator can observe that it is functioning properly. The condensate bleeder shall be checked with sufficient frequency to ensure adequate removal of condensate. Visual checks should be performed at intervals of not more than 15 minutes and the results recorded. Intermittent condensate removal systems shall be equipped with an automatic alarm system that will serve as a continuous monitor of condensate bleeder functioning. The automatic alarm system shall be tested at the beginning of each shift for proper functioning and the results recorded. If the alarm system is not functioning properly, it must be repaired before the retort is used.

(vii) *Stacking equipment—*

    (*a*) *Equipment for holding or stacking containers in retorts.* Crates, trays, gondolas, carts, and other vehicles for holding or stacking product containers in the retort shall be so constructed to ensure steam circulation during the venting, come-up, and process times. The bottom of each vehicle shall have perforations at least 1 inch (2.5 cm) in diameter on 2 inch (or 5 cm) centers or the equivalent unless the adequacy of another arrangement is documented by heat distribution data or other documentation from a processing authority and such information is maintained on file by the establishment and made available to Program employees for review.

    (*b*) *Divider plates.* Whenever one or more divider plates are used between any two layers of containers or placed on the bottom of a retort vehicle, the establishment shall have on file documentation that the venting procedure allows the air to be removed from the retort before timing of the thermal process is started. Such documentation shall be in the form of heat distribution data or documentation from a processing authority. This information shall be made available to Program employees for review.

(viii) *Bleeder and vent mufflers.* If mufflers are used on bleeders or vent systems, the establishment shall have on file documentation that the mufflers do not impede the removal of air from the retort. Such documentation shall consist of either heat distribution data or documentation from the muffler manufacturer or from a processing authority. This information shall be made available to Program employees for review.

(ix) *Vents*

    (*a*) Vents shall be located in that portion of the retort opposite the steam inlet and shall be designed, installed, and operated in such a way that air is removed from the retort before timing of the thermal process is started. Vents shall be controlled by a gate, plug cock, or other full-flow valve which shall be fully opened to permit rapid removal of air from retorts during the venting period.

    (*b*) Vents shall not be connected to a closed drain system without an atmospheric break in the line. Where a retort manifold connects several pipes from a single retort, the manifold shall be controlled by a gate, plug cock, or other full-flow valve and the manifold shall be of a size such that the cross-sectional area of the manifold is larger than the total cross-sectional area of all connecting vents. The discharge shall not be connected to a closed drain without an atmospheric break in the line. A manifold header connecting vents or manifolds from several still retorts shall lead to the atmosphere. The manifold header shall not be controlled by a valve and shall be of a size such that the cross-sectional area is at least equal to the total cross-sectional area of all connecting retort manifold pipes from the maximum number of retorts to be vented simultaneously.

(c) Some typical installations and operating procedures are described below. Other retort installations, vent piping arrangements, operating procedures or auxiliary equipment such as divider plates may be used provided there is documentation that the air is removed from the retort before the process is started. Such documentation shall be in the form of heat distribution data or other documentation from the equipment manufacturer or processing authority. This information shall be maintained on file by the establishment and made available to Program employees for review.

(d) For crateless retort installations, the establishment shall have heat distribution data or other documentation from the equipment manufacturer or from a processing authority that demonstrates that the venting procedure used accomplishes the removal of air and condensate. This information shall be maintained on file by the establishment and made available to Program employees for review.

(e) Examples of typical installations and operating procedures that comply with the requirements of this section are as follows:

(1) Venting horizontal retorts.

(i) Venting through multiple 1 inch (2.5 cm) vents discharging directly to the atmosphere.

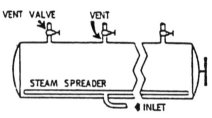

Figure 1.

Specifications (Figure 1): One, 1-inch(2.5 cm) vent for every 5 feet (1.5 m) of retort length, equipped with a gate, plug cock, or other full-flow valve and discharging to atmosphere. The end vents shall not be more than 2 1/2 feet (or 75 cm) from ends of retort.

Venting method (Figure 1): Vent valves shall be wide open for at least 5 minutes and to at least 225°F (or 107°C), or at least 7 minutes and to at least 220°F (or 104.5°C).

(ii) Venting through multiple 1 inch (2.5 cm) vents discharging through a manifold to the atmosphere.

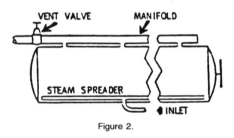

Figure 2.

Specifications (Figure 2): One, 1-inch (2.5 cm) vent for every 5 feet (1.5 m) of retort length; vents not over 2 1/2 feet (or 75 cm) from ends of retort; size of manifold for retorts less than 15 feet (4.6 m) in length, 2 1/2 inches (6.4 cm), and for retorts 15 feet (4.6 m) and over in length, 3 inches (7.6 cm).

Venting method (Figure 2): The manifold vent gate, plug cock, or other full-flow valve shall be wide open for at least 6 minutes and to at least 225°F (or 107°C) or for at least 8 minutes and to at least 220°F (or 104.5°C).

(iii) Venting through water spreaders.

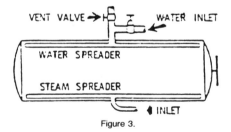

Figure 3.

Specifications (Figure 3): Size of vent and vent valve. For retorts less than 15 feet (4.6 m) in length, 2 inches (or 5 cm); for retorts 15 feet (4.6 m) and over in length, 2 1/2 inches (6.4 cm).

Size of water spreader (Figure 3): For retorts less than 15 feet (4.6 m) in length, 1 1/2 inches (3.8 cm); for retorts 15 feet (4.6 m) and over in length, 2 inches (or 5 cm). The number of holes shall be such that their total cross-sectional area is equal to the cross-sectional area of the vent pipe inlet.

Venting method (Figure 3): The gate, plug cock, or other full-flow valve on the water spreader vent shall be wide open for at least 5 minutes and to at least 225°F (or 107°C), or for at least 7 minutes and to at least 220°F (or 4.5°C).

226

(*iv*) Venting through a single 2 1/2 inch (6.4 cm) top vent for retorts not exceeding 15 feet (4.6 m) in length.

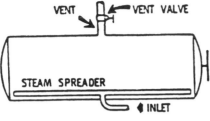

Figure 4.

Specifications (Figure 4): A 2 1/2 inch (6.4 cm) vent equipped with a 2 1/2 inch (6.4 cm) gate, plug cock, or other full-flow valve and located within 2 feet (61 cm) of the center of the retort.
Venting method (Figure 4): The vent valve shall be wide open for at least 4 minutes and to at least 220°F (or 104.5°C).

(*2*) Venting vertical retorts.
　(*i*)　Venting through a 1 1/2 inch (3.8 cm) overflow.

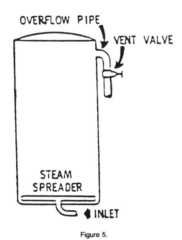

Figure 5.

Specifications (Figure 5): A 1 1/2 inch (3.8 cm) overflow pipe equipped with a 1 1/2 inch (3.8 cm) gate, plug cock, or other full-flow valve and with not more than 6 feet (1.8 m) of 1 1/2 inch (3.8 cm) pipe beyond the valve before a break to the atmosphere or to a manifold header.
Venting method (Figure 5): The vent valve shall be wide open for at least 4 minutes and to at least 218°F (or 103.5°C), or for at least 5 minutes and to at least 215°F (or 101.5°C).

(*ii*)　Venting through a single 1 inch (2.5 cm) side or top vent.

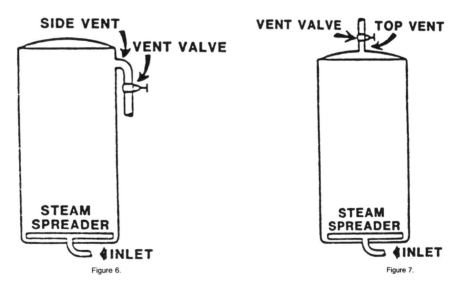

Figure 6.　　　　　　　　Figure 7.

Specifications (Figure 6 or 7): A 1 inch (2.5 cm) vent in lid or top side, equipped with a gate, plug cock, or other full-flow valve and discharging directly into the atmosphere or to a manifold header.
Venting method (Figure 6 or 7): The vent valve shall be wide open for at least 5 minutes and to at least 230°F (110°C), or for at least 7 minutes and to at least 220°F (or 104.5°C).

227

(2) *Batch agitating retorts.*

(i) The basic requirements for indicating temperature devices and temperature/time recording devices are described in paragraphs (a)(1) and (2) of this section. Additionally, bulb sheaths or probes of indicating temperature devices and probes of temperature/time recording devices shall be installed either within the retort shell or in external wells attached to the retort. External wells shall be connected to the retort through at least a 3/4 inch (1.9 cm) diameter opening and equipped with a 1/16 (1.6 mm) or larger bleeder opening so located as to provide a constant flow of steam past the length of the bulbs or probes. The bleeder for external wells shall emit steam continuously during the entire thermal processing period.

(ii) Steam controllers are required as described in paragraph (a)(3) of this section.

(iii) *Steam inlet.* The steam inlet to each retort shall be large enough to provide steam for proper operation of the retort and shall enter at a point(s) to facilitate air removal during venting.

(iv) *Bleeders.* Bleeders, except those for external wells of temperature devices, shall be 1/8 inch (or 3 mm) or larger and shall be wide open during the entire process including the come-up time. Bleeders shall be located within approximately 1 foot (or 30 cm) of the outermost location of containers, at each end along the top of the retort. Additional bleeders shall be located not more than 8 feet (2.4 m) apart along the top. Bleeders may be installed at positions other than those specified above, as long as the establishment has heat distribution data or other documentation from the manufacturer or from a processing authority that the bleeders accomplish removal of air and circulate the steam within the retort. This information shall be maintained on file by the establishment and made available to Program employees for review. All bleeders shall be arranged in a way that enables the retort operator to observe that they are functioning properly.

(v) *Venting and condensate removal.* The air in the retort shall be removed before processing is started. Heat distribution data or other documentation from the manufacturer or from the processing authority who developed the venting procedure shall be kept on file by the establishment and made available to Program employees for review. At the time the steam is turned on, the drain shall be opened to remove steam condensate from the retort. A bleeder shall be installed in the bottom of the retort to remove condensate during retort operation. The condensate bleeder shall be so arranged that the retort operator can observe that it is functioning properly. The condensate bleeder shall be checked with sufficient frequency to ensure adequate removal of condensate. Visual checks should be performed at intervals of not more than 15 minutes and the results recorded. Intermittent condensate removal systems shall be equipped with an automatic alarm system that will serve as a continuous monitor of condensate bleeder functioning. The automatic alarm system shall be tested at the beginning of each shift for proper functioning and the results recorded. If the alarm system is not functioning properly, it must be repaired before the retort is used.

(vi) *Retort or reel speed timing.* The retort or reel speed shall be checked before process timing begins and, if needed, adjusted as specified in the process schedule. In addition, the rotational speed shall be determined and recorded at least once during process timing of each retort load processed. Alternatively, a recording tachometer can be used to provide a continuous record of the speed. The accuracy of the recording tachometer shall be determined and recorded at least once per shift by checking the retort or reel speed using an accurate stopwatch. A means of preventing unauthorized speed changes on retorts shall be provided. For example, a lock or a notice from management posted at or near the speed adjustment device warning that only authorized persons are permitted to make adjustments are satisfactory means of preventing unauthorized changes.

(vii) *Bleeder and vent mufflers.* If mufflers are used on bleeders or vent systems, the establishment shall have documentation that the mufflers do not impede the removal of air from the retort. Such documentation shall consist of either heat distribution data or documentation from the muffler manufacturer or from a processing authority. This information shall be maintained on file by the establishment and made available to Program employees for review.

(3) *Continuous rotary retorts.*

(i) The basic requirements for indicating temperature devices and temperature/time recording devices are described in paragraphs (a)(1) and (2) of this section. Additionally, bulb sheaths or probes of indicating temperature devices and probes of temperature/time recording devices shall be installed either within the retort shell or in external wells attached to the retort. External wells shall be connected to the retort through at least a 3/4 inch (1.9 cm) diameter opening and equipped with a 1/16 inch (1.6 mm) or larger bleeder opening so located as to provide a constant flow of steam past the length of the bulbs or probes. The bleeder for external wells shall emit steam continuously during the entire thermal processing period.

(ii) Steam controllers are required as described in paragraph (a)(3) of this section.

(iii) *Steam inlet.* The steam inlet to each retort shall be large enough to provide steam for proper operation of the retort, and shall enter at a point(s) to facilitate air removal during venting.

(iv) *Bleeders.* Bleeders, except those for external wells of temperature devices, shall be 1/8 inch (3.2 mm) or larger and shall be wide open during the entire process, including the come-up time. Bleeders shall be located within approximately 1 foot (or 30 cm) of the outermost location of containers at each end along the top of the retort. Additional bleeders shall be located not more than 8 feet (2.4 m) apart along the top of the retort. Bleeders may be installed at positions other than those specified above, as long as the establishment has heat distribution data or other documentation from the manufacturer or a processing authority that the bleeders accomplish removal of air and circulate the steam within the retort. This information shall be maintained on file by the establishment and made available to Program employees for review. All bleeders shall be arranged so that the retort operator can observe that they are functioning properly.

(v) *Venting and condensate removal.* The air in the retort shall be removed before processing is started. Heat distribution data or other documentation from the manufacturer or from the processing authority who developed the venting procedure shall be kept on file by the establishment and made available to Program employees for review. At the time the steam is turned on, the drain shall be opened to remove steam condensate from the retort. A bleeder shall be installed in the bottom of the shell to remove condensate during the retort operation. The condensate bleeder shall be so arranged that the retort operator can observe that it is functioning properly. The condensate bleeder shall be checked with sufficient frequency to ensure adequate removal of condensate. Visual checks should be performed at intervals of not more than 15 minutes and the results recorded. Intermittent condensate removal systems shall be equipped with an automatic alarm system that will serve as a continuous monitor of condensate bleeder functioning. The automatic alarm system shall be tested at the beginning of each shift for proper functioning and the results recorded. If the alarm system is not functioning properly, it must be repaired before the retort is used.

(vi) *Retort speed timing.* The rotational speed of the retort shall be specified in the process schedule. The speed shall be adjusted as specified, and recorded by the establishment when the retort is started, and checked and recorded at intervals not to exceed 4 hours to ensure that the correct retort speed is maintained. Alternatively, a recording tachometer may be used to provide a continuous record of the speed. If a recording tachometer is used, the speed shall be manually checked against an accurate stopwatch at least once per shift and the results recorded. A means of preventing unauthorized speed changes on retorts shall be provided. For example, a lock or a notice from management posted at or near the speed adjustment device warning that only authorized persons are permitted to make adjustments are satisfactory means of preventing unauthorized changes.

(vii) *Bleeders and vent mufflers.* If mufflers are used on bleeders or vent systems, the establishment shall have documentation that the mufflers do not impede the removal of air from the retort. Such documentation shall consist of either heat distribution data or other documentation from the muffler manufacturer or from a processing authority. This information shall be maintained on file by the establishment and made available to Program employees for review.

(4) *Hydrostatic retorts.*

(i) The basic requirements for indicating temperature devices and temperature/time recording devices are described in paragraphs (a)(1) and (2) of this section. Additionally, indicating temperature devices shall be located in the steam dome near the steam/water interface. Where the process schedule specifies maintenance of particular water temperatures in the hydrostatic water legs, at least one indicating temperature device shall be located in each hydrostatic water leg so that it can accurately measure water temperature and be easily read. The temperature/time recorder probe shall be installed either within the steam dome or in a well attached to the dome. Each probe shall have a 1/16 inch (1.6 mm) or larger bleeder opening which emits steam continuously during the processing period. Additional temperature/time recorder probes shall be installed in the hydrostatic water legs if the process schedule specifies maintenance of particular temperatures in these water legs.

(ii) Steam controllers are required as described in paragraph (a)(3) of this section.

(iii) *Steam inlet.* The steam inlets shall be large enough to provide steam for proper operation of the retort.

(iv) *Bleeders.* Bleeder openings 1/4 inch (or 6 mm) or larger shall be located in the steam chamber(s) opposite the point of steam entry. Bleeders shall be wide open and shall emit steam continuously during the entire process, including the come-up time. All bleeders shall be arranged in such a way that the operator can observe that they are functioning properly.

(v) *Venting.* Before the start of processing operations, the retort steam chamber(s) shall be vented to ensure removal of air. Heat distribution data or other documentation from the manufacturer or from a processing authority demonstrating that the air is removed from the retort prior to processing shall be kept on file at the establishment and made available to Program employees for review.

(vi) *Conveyor speed.* The conveyor speed shall be calculated to obtain the required process time and recorded by the establishment when the retort is started. The speed shall be checked and recorded at intervals not to exceed 4 hours to ensure that the correct conveyor speed is maintained. A recording device may be used to provide a continuous record of the conveyor speed. When a recording device is used, the speed shall be manually checked against an accurate stopwatch at least once per shift by the establishment. A means of preventing unauthorized speed changes of the conveyor shall be provided. For example, a lock or a notice from management posted at or near the speed adjustment device warning that only authorized persons are permitted to make adjustments are satisfactory means of preventing unauthorized changes.

(vii) *Bleeders and vent mufflers.* If mufflers are used on bleeders or vent systems, the establishment shall have documentation that the muffler do not impede the removal of air from the retort. Such documentation shall consist of either heat distribution data or other documentation from the muffler manufacturer or from a processing authority. This information shall be maintained on file by the establishment and made available to Program employees for review.

(c) *Pressure processing in water—*

(1) *Batch still retorts.*

(i) The basic requirements for indicating temperature devices and temperature/time recording devices are described in paragraphs (a)(1) and (2) of this section. Additionally, bulbs or probes of indicating temperature devices shall be located in such a position that they are beneath the surface of the water throughout the process. On horizontal retorts, the indicating temperature device bulb or probe shall be inserted directly into the retort shell. In both vertical and horizontal retorts, the indicating temperature device bulb or probe shall extend directly into the water a minimum of 2 inches (or 5 cm) without a separable well or sleeve. In vertical retorts equipped with a recorder/controller, the controller probe shall be located at the bottom of the retort below the lowest crate rest in such a position that the steam does not strike it directly. In horizontal retorts so equipped, the controller probe shall be located between the water surface and the horizontal plane passing through the center of the retort so that there is no opportunity for direct steam impingement on the controller probe. Air-operated temperature controllers shall have filter systems to ensure a supply of clean, dry air.

(ii) *Pressure recording device.* Each retort shall be equipped with a pressure recording device which may be combined with a pressure controller.

(iii) Steam controllers are required as described in paragraph (a)(3) of this section.

(iv) *Heat distribution.* Heat distribution data or other documentation from the equipment manufacturer or a processing authority demonstrating uniform heat distribution within the retort shall be kept on file at the establishment and made available to Program employees for review.

(v) *Crate supports.* A bottom crate support shall be used in vertical retorts. Baffle plates shall not be used in the bottom of the retort.

(vi) *Stacking equipment.* For filled flexible containers and where applicable, semirigid containers, stacking equipment shall be designed to ensure that the thickness of the filled containers does not exceed that specified in the process schedule and that the containers do not become displaced and overlap or rest on one another during the thermal process.

(vii) *Drain valve.* A nonclogging, water-tight drain valve shall be used. Screens shall be installed over all drain openings.

(viii) *Water level.* There shall be a means of determining the water level in the retort during operation (i.e., by using a gauge, electronic sensor, or sight glass indicator). For retorts requiring complete immersion of containers, water shall cover the top layer of containers during the entire come-up time and thermal processing periods and should cover the top layer of containers during cooling. For retorts using cascading water or water sprays, the water level shall be maintained within the range specified by the retort manufacturer or processing authority during the entire come-up, thermal processing, and cooling periods. A means to ensure that water circulation continues as specified throughout the come-up, thermal processing, and cooling periods shall be provided. The retort operator shall check and record the water level at intervals to ensure it meets the specified processing parameters.

(ix) *Air supply and controls.* In both horizontal and vertical still retorts, a means shall be provided for introducing compressed air or steam at the pressure required to maintain container integrity. Compressed air and steam entry shall be controlled by an automatic pressure control unit. A nonreturn valve shall be provided in the air supply line to prevent water from entering the system. Overriding air or steam pressure shall be maintained continuously during the come-up, thermal processing, and cooling periods. If air is used to promote circulation, it shall be introduced into the steam line at a point between the retort and the steam control valve at the bottom of the retort. The adequacy of the air circulation for maintaining uniform heat distribution within the retort shall be documented by heat distribution data or other documentation from a processing authority, and such data shall be maintained on file by the establishment and made available to Program employees for review.

    (x) *Water recirculation.* When a water recirculation system is used for heat distribution, the water shall be drawn from the bottom of the retort through a suction manifold and discharged through a spreader that extends the length or circumference of the top of the retort. The holes in the water spreader shall be uniformly distributed. The suction outlets shall be protected with screens to keep debris from entering the recirculation system. The pump shall be equipped with a pilot light or a similar device to warn the operator when it is not running, and with a bleeder to remove air when starting operations. Alternatively, a flow-meter alarm system can be used to ensure proper water circulation. The adequacy of water circulation for maintaining uniform heat distribution within the retort shall be documented by heat distribution or other documentation from a processing authority and such data shall be maintained on file by the establishment and made available to Program employees for review. Alternative methods for recirculation of water in the retort may be used, provided there is documentation in the form of heat distribution data or other documentation from a processing authority maintained on file by the establishment and made available to Program employees for review.

    (xi) *Cooling water entry.* In retorts for processing product packed in glass jars, the incoming cooling water should not directly strike the jars, in order to minimize glass breakage by thermal shock.

  (2) *Batch agitating retorts.*

    (i) The basic requirements and recommendations for indicating temperature devices and temperature/time recording devices are described in paragraphs (a)(1) and (2) of this section. Additionally, the indicating temperature device bulb or probe shall extend directly into the water without a separable well or sleeve. The recorder/controller probe shall be located between the water surface and the horizontal plane passing through the center of the retort so that there is no opportunity for steam to directly strike the controller bulb or probe.

    (ii) *Pressure recording device.* Each retort shall be equipped with a pressure recording device which may be combined with a pressure controller.

    (iii) Steam controllers are required as described in paragraph (a)(3) of this section.

    (iv) *Heat distribution.* Heat distribution data or other documentation from the equipment manufacturer or a processing authority shall be kept on file by the establishment and made available to Program employees for review.

    (v) *Stacking equipment.* All devices used for holding product containers (e.g., crates, trays, divider plates) shall be so constructed to allow the water to circulate around the containers during the come-up and thermal process periods.

    (vi) *Drain valve.* A nonclogging, water-tight drain valve shall be used. Screens shall be installed over all drain openings.

    (vii) *Water level.* There shall be a means of determining the water level in the retort during operation (i.e., by using a gauge, electronic sensor, or sight glass indicator). Water shall completely cover all containers during the entire come-up, thermal processing, and cooling periods. A means to ensure that water circulation continues as specified throughout the come-up, thermal processing, and cooling periods shall be provided. The retort operator shall check and record the adequacy of the water level with sufficient frequency to ensure it meets the specified processing parameters.

    (viii) *Air supply and controls.* Retorts shall be provided with a means for introducing compressed air or steam at the pressure required to maintain container integrity. Compressed air and steam entry shall be controlled by an automatic pressure control unit. A nonreturn valve shall be provided in the air supply line to prevent water from entering the system. Overriding air or steam pressure shall be maintained continuously during the come-up, thermal processing, and cooling periods. If air is used to promote circulation, it shall be introduced into the steam line at a point between the retort and the steam control valve at the bottom of the retort. The adequacy of the air circulation for maintaining uniform heat distribution within the retort shall be documented by heat distribution data or other documentation from a processing authority, and such data shall be maintained on file by the establishment and made available to Program employees for review.

    (ix) *Retort or reel speed timing.* The retort or reel speed timing shall be checked before process timing begins and, if needed, adjusted as specified in the process schedule. In addition, the rotational speed shall be determined and recorded at least once during process timing of each retort load processed. Alternatively, a recording tachometer can be used to provide a continuous record of the speed. The accuracy of the recording tachometer shall be determined and recorded at least once per shift by the establishment by checking the retort or reel speed using an accurate stopwatch. A means of preventing unauthorized speed changes on retorts shall be provided. For example, a lock or a notice from management posted at or near the speed adjustment device warning that only authorized persons are permitted to make adjustments are satisfactory means of preventing unauthorized changes.

    (x) *Water recirculation.* If a water recirculation system is used for heat distribution, it shall be installed in such a manner that water will be drawn from the bottom of the retort through a suction manifold and discharged through a spreader which extends the length of the top of the retort. The holes in the water spreader shall be uniformly distributed. The suction outlets shall be protected with screens to keep debris from entering the recirculation system. The pump shall be equipped with a pilot light or a similar device to warn the operator when it is not running and with a bleeder to remove air when starting operations. Alternatively, a flow-meter alarm system can be used to ensure proper water circulation. The adequacy of water circulation for maintaining uniform heat distribution within the retort shall be documented by heat distribution data or other documentation from a processing authority, and such data shall be maintained on file by the establishment and made available to Program employees for review. Alternative methods for recirculation of water in the retort may be used provided there is documentation in the form of heat distribution data or other documentation from a processing authority maintained on file by the establishment and made available to Program employees for review.

    (xi) *Cooling water entry.* In retorts for processing product packed in glass jars, the incoming cooling water should not directly strike the jars, in order to minimize glass breakage by thermal shock.

(d) *Pressure processing with steam/air mixtures in batch retorts*

    (1) The basic requirements for indicating temperature devices and temperature/time recording devices are described in paragraphs (a)(1) and (2) of this section. Additionally, bulb sheaths or probes for indicating temperature devices and temperature/time recording devices or controller probes shall be inserted directly into the retort shell in such a position that steam does not strike them directly.

    (2) Steam controllers are required as described in paragraph (a)(3) of this section.

    (3) *Recording pressure controller.* A recording pressure controller shall be used to control the air inlet and the steam/air mixture outlet.

    (4) *Circulation of steam/air mixtures.* A means shall be provided for the circulation of the steam/air mixture to prevent formation of low-temperature pockets. The efficiency of the circulation system shall be documented by heat distribution data or other documentation from a processing authority, and such data shall be maintained on file by the establishment and made available to Program employees for review. The circulation system shall be checked to ensure its proper functioning and shall be equipped with a pilot light or a similar device to warn the operator when it is not functioning. Because of the variety of existing designs, reference shall be made to the equipment manufacturer for details of installation, operation, and control.

    (5) The Administrator shall be notified immediately by the official establishment of any such system in use or placed into use on or after the effective date of this rule.

(e) *Atmospheric cookers—*

    (1) *Temperature/time recording device.* Each atmospheric cooker (e.g., hot water bath) shall be equipped with at least one temperature/time recording device in accordance with the basic requirements described in paragraph (a)(2) of this section.

    (2) *Heat distribution.* Each atmospheric cooker shall be equipped and operated to ensure uniform heat distribution throughout the processing system during the thermal process. Heat distribution data or other documentation from the manufacturer or a processing authority demonstrating uniform heat distribution within the cooker shall be kept on file by the establishment and made available to Program employees for review.

(f) *Other systems.* All other systems not specifically delineated in this section and used for the thermal processing of canned product will be evaluated on a case-by-case basis by the Administrator. Systems will be approved if they are found to conform to the applicable requirements of this section and to produce shelf stable products consistently and uniformly.

(g) *Equipment maintenance*

    (1) Upon installation, all instrumentation and controls shall be checked by the establishment for proper functioning and accuracy and, thereafter, at any time their functioning or accuracy is suspect.

    (2) At least once a year each thermal processing system shall be examined by an individual not directly involved in daily operations to ensure the proper functioning of the system as well as all auxiliary equipment and instrumentation. In addition, each thermal processing system should be examined before the resumption of operation following an extended shutdown.

    (3) Air and water valves that are intended to be closed during thermal processing shall be checked by the establishment for leaks. Defective valves shall be repaired or replaced as needed.

    (4) Vent and bleeder mufflers shall be checked and maintained or replaced by the establishment to prevent any reduction in vent or bleeder efficiency.

(5) When water spreaders are used for venting, a maintenance schedule shall be developed and implemented to assure that the holes are maintained at their original size.

(6) Records shall be kept on all maintenance items that could affect the adequacy of the thermal process. Records shall include the date and type of maintenance performed and the person conducting the maintenance.

(h) *Container cooling and cooling water.*

(1) Potable water shall be used for cooling except as provided for in paragraphs (h)(2) and (3) of this section.

(2) Cooling canal water shall be chlorinated or treated with a chemical approved by the Administrator as having a bactericidal effect equivalent to chlorination. There shall be a measurable residual of the sanitizer in the water at the discharge point of the canal. Cooling canals shall be cleaned and replenished with potable water to prevent the buildup of organic matter and other materials.

(3) Container cooling waters that are recycled or reused shall be handled in systems that are so designed, operated, and maintained so there is no buildup of microorganisms, organic matter, and other materials in the systems and in the waters. System equipment, such as pipelines, holding tanks and cooling towers, shall be constructed and installed so that they can be cleaned and inspected. In addition, the establishment shall maintain, and make available to Program employees for review, information on at least the following:

(i) System design and construction;

(ii) System operation including the rates of renewal with fresh, potable water and the means for treating the water so that there is a measurable residual of an acceptable sanitizer, per paragraph (h)(2) of this section, in the water at the point where the water exits the container cooling vessel;

(iii) System maintenance including procedures for the periodic cleaning and sanitizing of the entire system; and

(iv) Water quality standards, such as microbiological, chemical and physical, monitoring procedures including the frequency and site(s) of sampling, and the corrective actions taken when water quality standards are not met.

(i) *Post-process handling of containers.* Containers shall be handled in a manner that will prevent damage to the hermetic seal area. All worn and frayed belting, can retarders, cushions, and the like shall be replaced with nonporous materials. To minimize container abrasions, particularly in the seal area, containers should not remain stationary on moving conveyors. All post-process container handling equipment should be kept clean so there is no buildup of microorganisms on surfaces in contact with the containers.

(Approved by the Office of Management and Budget under control number 0583-0015)

§ 318.306 Processing and production records.

At least the following processing and production information shall be recorded by the establishment: date of production; product name and style; container code; container size and type; and the process schedule, including the minimum initial temperature. Measurements made to satisfy the requirements of § 318.303 regarding the control of critical factors shall be recorded. In addition, where applicable, the following information and data shall also be recorded:

(a) *Processing in steam*—

(1) *Batch still retorts.* For each retort batch, record the retort number or other designation, the approximate number of containers or the number of retort crates per retort load, product initial temperature, time steam on, the time and temperature vent closed, the start of process timing, time steam off, and the actual processing time. The indicating temperature device and the temperature recorder shall be read at the same time at least once during process timing and the observed temperatures recorded.

(2) *Batch agitating retorts.* In addition to recording the information required for batch, still steam retorts in paragraph (a)(1) of this section, record the functioning of the condensate bleeder(s) and the retort or reel speed.

(3) *Continuous rotary retorts.* Record the retort system number, the approximate total number of containers retorted, product initial temperature, time steam on, the time and temperature vent closed, time process temperature reached, the time the first can enters and the time the last can exits the retort. The retort or reel speed shall be determined and recorded at intervals not to exceed 4 hours. Readings of the indicating temperature device(s) and temperature recorder(s) shall be made and recorded at the time the first container enters the retort and thereafter with sufficient frequency to ensure compliance with the process schedule. These observations should be made and recorded at intervals not exceeding 30 minutes of continuous retort operation. Functioning of the condensate bleeder(s) shall be observed and recorded at the time the first container enters the retort and thereafter as specified in § 318.305(b)(3)(v).

(4) *Hydrostatic retorts.* Record the retort system number, the approximate total number of containers retorted, product initial temperature, time steam on, the time and temperature vent(s) closed, time process temperature reached, time first containers enter the retort, time last containers exit the retort, and, if specified in the

process schedule, measurements of temperatures in the hydrostatic water legs. Readings of the temperature indicating device, which is located in the steam/water interface, and the temperature recording device shall be observed and the temperatures recorded at the time the first containers enter the steam dome. Thereafter, these instruments shall be read and the temperatures recorded with sufficient frequency to ensure compliance with the temperature specified in the process schedule and should be made at least every hour of continuous retort operation. Container conveyor speed, and for agitating hydrostatic retorts, the rotative chain speed, shall be determined and recorded at intervals of sufficient frequency to ensure compliance with the process schedule and should be performed at least every 4 hours.

(b) *Processing in water—*

    (1) *Batch still retorts.* For each retort batch, record the retort number or other designation, the approximate number of containers or number of retort crates per retort load, product initial temperature, time steam on, the start of process timing, water level, water recirculation rate (if critical), overriding pressure maintained, time steam off, and actual processing time. The indicating temperature device and the temperature recorder shall be read at the same time at least once during process timing and the observed temperatures recorded.

    (2) *Batch agitating retorts.* In addition to recording the information required in paragraph (b)(1) of this section, record the retort or reel speed.

(c) *Processing in steam/air mixtures.* For each retort batch, record the retort number or other designation, the approximate number of containers or number of retort crates per retort load, product initial temperature, time steam on, venting procedure, if applicable, the start of process timing, maintenance of circulation of the steam/air mixture, air flow rate or forced recirculation flow rate (if critical), overriding pressure maintained, time steam off, and actual processing time. The indicating temperature device and the temperature recorder shall be read at the same time at least once during process timing and the observed temperatures recorded.

(d) *Atmospheric cookers—*

    (1) *Batch-type systems.* For each cooker batch, record the cooker number or other designation and the approximate number of containers. In addition, record all critical factors of the process schedule such as cooker temperature, initial temperature, the time the thermal process cycle begins and ends, hold time, and the final internal product temperature.

    (2) *Continuous-type systems.* Record the cooker number or other designation, the time the first containers enter and the last containers exit a cooker, and the approximate total number of containers processed. In addition, record all critical factors of the process schedule such as the initial temperature, cooker speed, and final internal product temperature.

(Approved by the Office of Management and Budget under control number 0583-0015)

§ 318.307 Record review and maintenance.

(a) *Process records.* Charts from temperature/time recording devices shall be identified by production date, container code, processing vessel number or other designation, and other data as necessary to enable correlation with the records required in § 318.306. Each entry on a record shall be made at the time the specific event occurs, and the recording individual shall sign or initial each record form. No later than 1 working day after the actual process, the establishment shall review all processing and production records to ensure completeness and to determine if all product received the process schedule. All records, including the temperature/time recorder charts and critical factor control records, shall be signed or initialed and dated by the person conducting the review. All processing and production records required in this subpart shall be made available to Program employees for review.

(b) *Automated process monitoring and recordkeeping.* When requested by an establishment, the Administrator will consider the approval of automated process monitoring and recordkeeping systems. An approved system, alone or in combination with written records, shall be designed and operated in a manner which will ensure compliance with the applicable requirements of § 318.306.

(c) *Container closure records.* Written records of all container closure examinations shall specify the container code, the date and time of container closure examination, the measurement(s) obtained, and any corrective actions taken. Records shall be signed or initialed by the container closure technician and shall be reviewed and signed by the establishment within 1 working day after the actual production to ensure that the records are complete and that the closing operations have been properly controlled. All container closure examination records required in this subpart shall be made available to Program employees for review.

(d) *Distribution of product.* Records shall be maintained by the establishment identifying initial distribution of the finished product to facilitate, if necessary, the segregation of specific production lots that may have been contaminated or are otherwise unsound for their intended use.

(e) *Retention of records.* Copies of all processing and production records required in § 318.306 shall be retained for no less than 1 year at the establishment, and for an additional 2 years at the establishment or other location from which the records can be made available to Program employees within 3 working days.

(Approved by the Office of Management and Budget under control number 0583-0015)

§ 318.308 Deviations in processing.

(a) Whenever the actual process is less than the process schedule or when any critical factor does not comply with the requirements for that factor as specified in the process schedule, it shall be considered a deviation in processing.

(b) Deviations in processing (or process deviations) shall be handled under an approved quality control program as provided in paragraph (c) of this section or shall be handled in accordance with paragraph (d) of this section.

(c) Any partial quality control program or any portion of a total quality control system for handling process deviations shall be prepared and submitted to the Administrator for approval in accordance with § 318.4.

(d) Handling process deviations without an approved quality control program.

    (1) *Deviations identified in-process.* If a deviation is noted at any time before the completion of the intended process schedule, the establishment shall:

        (i) Immediately reprocess the product using the full process schedule; or

        (ii) Use an appropriate alternate process schedule provided such a process schedule has been established in accordance with § 318.302 (a) and (b) and is filed with the inspector in accordance with § 318.302(c); or

        (iii) Hold the product involved and have the deviation evaluated by a processing authority to assess the safety and stability of the product. Upon completion of the evaluation, the establishment shall provide the inspector the following:

            (*a*) A complete description of the deviation along with all necessary supporting documentation;

            (*b*) A copy of the evaluation report; and

            (*c*) A description of any product disposition actions, either taken or proposed.

        (iv) Product handled in accordance with paragraph (d)(1)(iii) of this section shall not be shipped from the establishment until the Program has reviewed all of the information submitted and approved the product disposition actions.

        (v) If an alternate process schedule is used that is not on file with the inspector or if an alternate process schedule is immediately calculated and used, the product shall be set aside for further evaluation in accordance with paragraphs (d)(1)(iii) and (iv) of this section.

        (vi) When a deviation occurs in a continuous rotary retort, the product shall be handled in accordance with paragraphs (d)(1)(iii) and (iv) of this section or in accordance with the following procedures:

        (*a*) Emergency stops.

            (*1*) When retort jams or breakdowns occur during the processing operations, all containers shall be given an emergency still process (developed per § 318.302(b)) before the retort is cooled or the retort shall be cooled promptly and all containers removed and either reprocessed, repacked and reprocessed, or destroyed. Regardless of the procedure used, containers in the retort intake valve and in transfer valves between retort shells at the time of a jam or breakdown shall be removed and either reprocessed, repacked and reprocessed and or destroyed. Product to be destroyed shall be handled as "U.S. Inspected and Condemned", as defined in § 301.2(ttt) of this subchapter, and disposed of in accordance with part 314 of this subchapter.

            (*2*) The time the retort reel stopped and the time the retort is used for an emergency still retort process shall be noted on the temperature/time recording device and entered on the other production records required in § 318.306.

        (*b*) Temperature drops. When the retort temperature drops below the temperature specified in the process schedule, the reel shall be stopped and the following actions shall be taken:

            (*1*) For temperature drops of less than 10°F (or 5.5°C) either,

                (*i*) all containers in the retort shall be given an emergency still process (developed per § 318.302(b)) before the reel is restarted;

                (*ii*) container entry to the retort shall be prevented and an emergency agitating process (developed per § 318.302(b)) shall be used before container entry to the retort is restarted; or

                (*iii*) container entry to the retort shall be prevented and the reel restarted to empty the retort. The discharged containers shall be reprocessed, repacked and reprocessed, or destroyed. Product to be destroyed shall be handled as "U.S. Inspected and Condemned", as defined in § 301.2(ttt) of this subchapter, and disposed of in accordance with part 314 of this subchapter.

(2) For temperature drops of 10°F (or 5.5°C) or more, all containers in the retort shall be given an emergency still process (developed per § 318.302(b)). The time the reel was stopped and the time the retort was used for a still retort process shall be marked on the temperature/time recording device by the establishment and entered on the other production records required in § 318.306. Alternatively, container entry to the retort shall be prevented and the reel restarted to empty the retort. The discharged containers shall be either reprocessed, repacked and reprocessed, or destroyed. Product to be destroyed shall be handled as "U.S. Inspected and Condemned", as defined in § 301.2(ttt) of this subchapter, and disposed of in accordance with part 314 of this subchapter.

(2) *Deviations identified through record review.* Whenever a deviation is noted during review of the processing and production records required by § 318.307 (a) and (b), the establishment shall hold the product involved and the deviation shall be handled in accordance with paragraphs (d)(1)(iii) and (iv) of this section.

(e) Process deviation file. The establishment shall maintain full records regarding the handling of each deviation. Such records shall include, at a minimum, the appropriate processing and production records, a full description of the corrective actions taken, the evaluation procedures and results, and the disposition of the affected product. Such records shall be maintained in a separate file or in a log that contains the appropriate information. The file or log shall be retained in accordance with § 318.307(e) and shall be made available to Program employees upon request.

(Approved by the Office of Management and Budget under control number 0583-0015) [51 FR 45619, Dec. 19, 1986, as amended at 53 FR 49848, Dec. 12, 1988]

§ 318.309 Finished product inspection.

(a) Finished product inspections shall be handled under an approved quality control program as provided in paragraph (b) or paragraph (c) of this section or shall be handled in accordance with paragraph (d) of this section.

(b) Any partial quality control program for finished product inspection shall be prepared and submitted to the Administrator for approval in accordance with § 318.4 of this part.

(c) That portion of a total quality control system for finished product inspection shall be prepared and submitted to the Administrator for approval in accordance with § 318.4 of this part.

(d) Handling finished product inspections without an approved quality control program.

  (1) *Incubation of shelf stable canned product—*

  (i) *Incubator.* The establishment shall provide incubation facilities which include an accurate temperature/time recording device, an indicating temperature device, a means for the circulation of the air inside the incubator to prevent temperature variations, and a means to prevent unauthorized entry into the facility. The Program is responsible for the security of the incubator.

  (ii) *Incubation temperature.* The incubation temperature shall be maintained at 95 ± 5°F (35 ± 2.8°C). If the incubation temperature falls below 90°F (or 32°C) or exceeds 100°F (or 38°C) but does not reach 103°F (or 39.5°C), the incubation temperature shall be adjusted within the required range and the incubation time extended for the time the sample containers were held at the deviant temperature. If the incubation temperature is at or above 103°F (or 39.5°C) for more than 2 hours, the incubation test(s) shall be terminated, the temperature lowered to within the required range, and new sample containers incubated for the required time.

  (iii) *Product requiring incubation.* Shelf stable product requiring incubation includes:
  (*a*) Low acid products as defined in § 318.300(m); and
  (*b*) Acidified low acid products as defined in § 318.300(b).

  (iv) *Incubation samples.*
  (*a*) From each load of product processed in a batch-type thermal processing system (still or agitation), the establishment shall select at least one container for incubation.
  (*b*) For continuous rotary retorts, hydrostatic retorts, or other continuous-type thermal processing systems, the establishment shall select at least one container per 1,000 for incubation.
  (*c*) Only normal-appearing containers shall be selected for incubation.

  (v) *Incubation time.* Canned product requiring incubation shall be incubated for not less than 10 days (240 hours) under the conditions specified in paragraph (d)(1)(ii) of this section.

  (vi) *Incubation checks and record maintenance.* Designated establishment employees shall visually check all containers under incubation each working day and the inspector shall be notified when abnormal containers are detected. All abnormal containers should be allowed to cool before a final decision on their condition is made. For each incubation test the establishment shall record at least the product name, container size, container code, number of containers incubated, in and out dates, and incubation results. The establishment shall retain such records, along with copies of the temperature/time recording charts, in accordance with § 318.307(e).

(vii) *Abnormal containers.* The finding of abnormal containers (as defined in § 318.300(a)) among incubation samples is cause to officially retain at least the code lot involved.

(viii) *Shipping.* No product shall be shipped from the establishment before the end of the required incubation period except as provided in this paragraph or paragraph (b) or (c) of this section. An establishment wishing to ship product prior to the completion of the required incubation period shall submit a written proposal to the area supervisor. Such a proposal shall include provisions that will assure that shipped product will not reach the retail level of distribution before sample incubation is completed and that product can be returned promptly to the establishment should such action be deemed necessary by the incubation test results. Upon receipt of written approval from the area supervisor, product may be routinely shipped provided the establishment continues to comply with all requirements of this subpart.

(2) *Container condition*—

(i) *Normal containers.* Only normal-appearing containers shall be shipped from an establishment as determined by an appropriate sampling plan or other means acceptable to Program employees.

(ii) *Abnormal containers.* When abnormal containers are detected by any means other than incubation, the establishment shall inform the inspector, and the affected code lot(s) shall not be shipped until the Program has determined that the product is safe and stable. Such a determination will take into account the cause and level of abnormals in the affected lot(s) as well as any product disposition actions either taken or proposed by the establishment.

(Approved by the Office of Management and Budget under control number 0583-0015) [51 FR 45619, Dec. 19, 1986, as amended at 57 FR 37872, Aug. 21, 1992; 57 FR 55443, Nov. 25, 1992]

§ 318.310 Personnel and training.

All operators of thermal processing systems specified in § 318.305 and container closure technicians shall be under the direct supervision of a person who has successfully completed a school of instruction that is generally recognized as adequate for properly training supervisors of canning operations.

[51 FR 45619, Dec. 19, 1986]

§ 318.311 Recall procedure.

Establishments shall prepare and maintain a current procedure for the recall of all canned product covered by this subpart. Upon request, the recall procedure shall be made available to Program employees for review.

(Approved by the Office of Management and Budget under control number 0583-0015)

Public reporting burden for this collection of information is estimated to average .17 hours per response, including the time for reviewing instructions, searching existing data sources, gathering and maintaining the data needed, and completing reviewing the collection of information. Send comments regarding this burden estimate or any other aspect of this collection of information, including suggestions for reducing this burden to:

Reports Clearance Officer, PHS
Hubert H. Humphrey Building, Room 721-B
200 Independence Avenue, S.W., Washington, DC 20201   Attn: PRA

and to

Office of Management and Budget
Paperwork Reduction Project (0910-0037)
Washington, DC 20503

FORM APPROVED: OMB No. 0910-0037
EXPIRATION DATE: November 30, 1995

Please DO NOT RETURN this report to either of the two addresses to the left.

DEPARTMENT OF HEALTH AND HUMAN SERVICES
Public Health Service
Food and Drug Administration

FOOD CANNING ESTABLISHMENT REGISTRATION

FOR FDA USE ONLY

	Date Received by FDA
FCE No.	
OOB Code	Date	District
Reference	

TYPE OF SUBMISSION

☐ Initial Registration
☐ Relocation *(new registration required)*
☐ Change of Registration Information

Specify Type of Change _____

Enter Current FCE: *(If applicable)* _____

FOOD PROCESSING PLANT LOCATION

Establishment Name _____

Number and Street _____
City and State or Province _____
(or other Subdivision) _____

Zip (or other Postal Code) _____
Country (if other than U.S.) _____

Telephone No. ( ) _____   Telefax No. ( ) _____

PREFERRED MAILING ADDRESS   ☐ Same as Plant Location

Establishment Name _____

Number and Street _____
City and State or Province _____
(or other Subdivision) _____

Zip (or other Postal Code) _____
Country (if other than U.S.) _____

Telephone No. ( ) _____   Telefax No. ( ) _____

LOW ACID AND/OR ACIDIFIED FOODS PROCESSED AT THIS LOCATION

Food Product Name, Form or Style, and Packing Medium
(Do not list meat and poultry foods under the jurisdiction of the Food Safety and Inspection Service of the U.S. Department of Agriculture.)

	(Check One)	
	Low-Acid	Acidified

PLEASE SEND THE FOLLOWING:

Number of Copies

___ Process filing forms used for low-acid aseptic processes

___ Process filing forms used for all processing methods except low-acid aseptic.
NOTE: A separate form is required for each product-process combination.

___ Registration and Process Filing Instructions

___ LACF & Acidified Regulations (21 CFR 108, 113, 114)

See "Instructions for Establishment Registration and Process Filing for Acidified and Low-Acid Canned Foods" for guidance in completing this form. Forward *all* copies of completed form to:

**LACF Registration Coordinator (HFS-618)
Center for Food Safety & Applied Nutrition (FDA)
200 C Street, SW
Washington, DC 20204**

AUTHORIZED COMPANY REPRESENTATIVE

Name, Address and Title of Authorized Representative: _____

at ☐ Plant Location   ☐ Mailing Address   Signature: _____

Phone Number: ( ) _____   Date: _____

NOTE: No commercial processor shall engage in the processing of low-acid or acidified foods unless completed Forms FDA 2541 and FDA 2541a or FDA 2541c have been filed with the Food and Drug Administration, 21 CFR 108.25(c)(1) and (2) and 108.35(c)(1) and (2).

FORM FDA 2541 (8/93)   PREVIOUS EDITION IS OBSOLETE.

84

DEPARTMENT OF HEALTH AND HUMAN SERVICES ■ PUBLIC HEALTH SERVICE ■ FOOD AND DRUG ADMINISTRATION

FOOD PROCESS FILING FOR ALL METHODS EXCEPT LOW-ACID ASEPTIC

(Use FDA booklet titled: "Instructions for Establishment Registration and Process Filing for Acidified and Low-Acid Canned Foods" for completing Form FDA 2541a.)

FORM APPROVED: OMB No. 0910-0037
EXPIRATION DATE: November 30, 1995

FCE _____ SID _____
Y Y M M D D S S

A. PRODUCT

Name, Form or Style, and Packing Medium: _____

Raw pH: ☐☐.☐

Governing Regulation:
— low-acid (21 CFR 108.35/113)
— acidified (21 CFR 108.25/114)

Type of Submission
— new
— replaces ___ ___ / ___ ___ / ___ ___
— cancels ___ ___ / ___ ___ / ___ ___

Process Use
— scheduled
— alternate for ___ ___ / ___ ___ / ___ ___
— emergency for ___ ___ / ___ ___ / ___ ___

B. PROCESSING METHOD

NAME OF STERILIZER (MFR. & TYPE) _____

HEATING MEDIUM (e.g., Steam, water immersion or spray, steam-air)

1. ___ Still
   a. ___ Horizontal   b. ___ Vertical
   Divider Plates (complete for a. or b.)
   — None
   — Solid   — Perforated
   c. ___ Crateless
   Bottom Surface (complete for c.)
   — Solid   — Perforated

2. ___ Agitating
   a. ___ End over End
   — Axial
   b. ___ Continuous
   — Batch

3. ___ Hydrostatic
   — Inner Chain only
   — Outer Chain only
   — Both Inner and Outer Chain
   — Single Chain
   — Multiple Chains

4. ___ Flame

5. ___ Other (explain) _____

6. ___ Acidified
   Maximum Equilibrium pH: ☐☐.☐
   Method of Acidification: _____
   Concentration: ☐☐.☐
   Acidifying Agent: _____
   Pasteurization Method: _____
   Preservative Used: _____
   Concentration: ☐☐.☐

CONTAINER TYPE:

1. ___ Tinplate/Steel Can
2. ___ Aluminum Can
   — 2-piece
   — 3-piece
   — Welded
   — Soldered
   — Cemented

3. ___ Glass or Ceramic
4. ___ Flexible Pouch (specify material): _____
5. ___ Semirigid (specify material): ___ Lid ___ Body _____
   — Seal Method
6. ___ Other (specify): _____

PROCESS ESTABLISHMENT SOURCE (Limit entry to 30 characters) _____

DATE LAST ESTABLISHED
19 ___ ___
Y Y M M

PROCESS RECOMMENDATIONS ATTACHED?
— YES ___ — NO ___

C. CRITICAL FACTORS: AS DELINEATED BY PROCESS AUTHORITY TO ASSURE COMMERCIAL STERILITY (Check or Describe)

None of the Following _____
Maximum Water Activity (a_w) ... NO ___
Consistency / Viscosity ... MW ___ (___ — ___)
   Value ... CV ___ (___ — ___)
   Units ... (___ — ___)
   Method Name ...
   Temperature ... (___ — ___)
Container Position in Retort ... CP ___
Nesting of Containers ... NC ___
Fill Method (check applicable method) ... FM ___
   Hand ...
   Machine ...
   Other (specify) ...
% Solids ... SO ___ (___ — ___)
Solid to Liquid Ratio (wt. to wt.) ... SL ___ (___ — ___)
Drained wt./Net wt. Ratio ... DW ___ (___ — ___)

Arrangements of Pieces in Container ... AP ___
Formulation Changes ... FC ___
Preparation Method ... PM ___
Product Quality ... PQ ___
Matting Tendency ... MT ___
Layer Pack ... LP ___
Max. Flexible Pouch/Semirigid Container Thickness in Retort ... MP ___ (___ — ___)
Max. Residual Air (Flexible Pouch/Semirigid Container) ... MR ___ (___ — ___) c.c.
Particle Size ... PS ___ (___ — ___)
Syrup Strength ... SS ___ (___ — ___)
Starch Added ... SA ___ (___ — ___)
   Max. %
   Type
Other Binder ... OB ___
Min. % Moisture of Dry Ingredients ... MM ___ (___ — ___)
Other (specify) ... OT ___

D. SCHEDULED PROCESS   (Do *not* write in shaded areas—Enter numerical values in boxes.)

FCE: _ _ _ _ _ _   SID: _ _ _ _ _ _ _ / _ _ _ / _ _ _ _

OTHER CRITICAL FACTORS TO ASSURE COMMERCIAL STERILITY PER SOURCE AUTHORITY

CONTAINER DIMENSIONS

Diameter or Length	Height or Width	Height or Maximum Pouch or Semirigid Container Thickness
Inches & Sixteenths	Inches & Sixteenths	Inches & Sixteenths

CAPACITY UNITS
- Oz.
- Gal.
- ML
- Other

SCHEDULED PROCESS (Check Only One in Each Column)

Cont. No.	Step No.	Temp. (°F)	Process Time (Minutes)	Sterilization Temp (°F)	Least Sterilizing Value of the Scheduled Process

LACF
- Min. IT — Process Time
- — Process Temp.

Acidified or a_w Controlled
- Min. IT — Process Time
- Fill — Process Temp
- Center — Hold Time
- N/A — Other
- — N/A

- F_0
- Other F Value
- Death Rate (z)
- Ref. Temp. (T)
- IS Value
- Other

°F   Minutes   °F

Thruput — N/A — Containers per Minute

Headspace — Net — Gross — N/A — Inches

Speed
- Reel Speed
- Reel Diameter
- Steps Per Turn of Reel
- Chain / Conveyer Speed
  - Feet
  - Carriers
  - Flights (per minute)
- — N/A
- RPM   Inches   Number   Number

Maximum Weight — Drained — Fill — N/A — Ounces

Minimum Net Weight — N/A — Ounces

Minimum Free Liq. at Closing — N/A — Ounces

Minimum Container Closing Machine Gauge Vacuum — Temp. (± 3° F) — N/A — In. Hg.

OTHER (Specify)

COMMENTS:

FOR FDA USE ONLY

AUTHORIZED INDIVIDUAL

FULL NAME (*Please Print*)

SIGNATURE

TELEPHONE NUMBER   ( )

DATE

PLANT NAME / ADDRESS

PREFERRED MAILING ADDRESS

FORM FDA 2541a (8/93)   PREVIOUS EDITION IS OBSOLETE.

NOTE: No commercial processor shall engage in the processing of low-acid or acidified foods unless completed Forms FDA-2541 and FDA-2541a have been filed with the Food and Drug Administration. 21 CFR 108.25(c)(1) and (2) and 108.35(c)(1) and (2).

DEPARTMENT OF HEALTH AND HUMAN SERVICES ■ Public Health Service ■ Food and Drug Administration

FOOD PROCESS FILING FOR LOW-ACID ASEPTIC SYSTEMS
(USE FDA BOOKLET TITLED "ASEPTIC PACKAGING SYSTEM SUPPLEMENT")

(TYPE OR PRINT ALL INFORMATION REQUESTED. IF AN ITEM DOES NOT APPLY ENTER "NA". FILE ACIDIFIED ASEPTIC (pH 4.6 or BELOW) ON FORM 2541d)

FORM APPROVED: OMB No. 0191O-0037   EXPIRATION DATE: 11/30/95

NOTE: No commercial processor shall engage in the processing of low-acid foods unless completed Forms FDA 2541 and FDA 2541c have been filed with the Food and Drug Administration, 21 CFR 108.35 (c)(1) and (2).

FDA USE ONLY
DATE RECEIVED BY FDA

1. FCE: _ _ _ _ _

FDA USE ONLY

3. SID: _ _ _ / _ _ / _ _ _   4. __ NEW __ REPLACES __ CANCELS

5. ___ SCHEDULED ___ ALTERNATE FOR _ _ _ / _ _ / _ _ _

6. SUP SID: _ _ _ / _ _ / _ _ _

2. ESTABLISHMENT NAME

ADDRESS (No. and Street)

CITY | STATE | ZIP CODE | COUNTRY

7. PRODUCT NAME, FORM OR STYLE, AND PACKING MEDIUM

8. NAMES OF STERILIZING SYSTEMS
1. Product:[1]
2. Packaging:

9. PROCESS ORIGIN
SOURCE
1.
2.

YEAR AND MONTH
1.
2.

10. CONTAINER TYPE (Check one)
1. ☐ TINPLATE OR STEEL CAN   3. ☐ GLASS
2. ☐ ALUMINUM CAN   4. ☐ OTHER (specify in 22)

11. MAXIMUM WATER ACTIVITY[2]
Normal | Maximum[3]

12. pH
Normal | Maximum[3]

13. MAXIMUM CONSISTENCY OR VISCOSITY IN CENTIPOISES OR APPROPRIATE UNITS[4]

Value at 77 ± 2°F	Value at Other Temp	Other Temp (°F)	Method Name	Units	Viscosity Characteristic (N P D)

14. SPECIFIC GRAVITY AT 77 ± 2°F

15. INSIDE DIAMETER OF HOLDING TUBE (inches)

16. HOLDING TUBE LENGTH (inches)

17. OTHER CRITICAL CONTROL FACTORS (Check all that apply)
61 ☐ PERCENT SOLIDS
62 ☐ RATIO OF SOLIDS TO LIQUIDS
63 ☐ SYRUP STRENGTH
68 ☐ METHOD OF PREPARATION
70 ☐ FORMULATION
71 ☐ REHYDRATION (specify method in 22)
72 ☐ PARTICULATES (specify maximum size in 22)
73 ☐ OTHER (specify in 22)

18. CONTAINER DIMENSIONS (inches and Sixteenths)
19. SCHEDULED PROCESS
20. MAXIMUM FOOD FLOW RATE (gal / min)
21. THRUPUT (Containers / min)

	DIAMETER OR LENGTH	HEIGHT OR WIDTH	HEIGHT	MINIMUM INITIAL[4] TEMP (°F)	TIME (sec)	TEMP (°F)	LEAST STERILIZING VALUE (F₀) OF THE SCHEDULED PROCESS[5]	FLOW CORRECTION FACTOR
01					.	.	.	
02					.	.	.	
03					.	.	.	
04					.	.	.	
05					.	.	.	
06					.	.	.	

22. COMMENTS:

AUTHORIZED COMPANY REPRESENTATIVE

NAME (Type or Print) | TITLE | SIGNATURE

PHONE NUMBER ( ) | DATE

[1] For steam injection, enter volume increase and thermal expansion factors in 22.
[2] If reduced water activity is used as an adjunct to the process, specify the maximum water activity.
[3] Where acidification is followed for normally low-acid fruits, vegetables or vegetable products for the purpose of thermal processing, specify the maximum finished product equilibrium pH.
[4] If a critical factor in the process.
[5] Or equivalent scientific basis of process adequacy.

FORM FDA 2541c (8/93)   PREVIOUS EDITION IS OBSOLETE.

GLOSSARY

ABRASION—Damage to semirigid or flexible packages caused by mechanically rubbing, scuffing or scratching.

ACID—A substance in which the hydrogen ion concentration is greater than that of the hydroxyl ion.

ACIDIFIED FOODS—Low-acid food to which an acid or an acid food is added to produce a food with a final equilibrium pH of 4.6 or less and a water activity greater than 0.85.

ADHESIVE FAILURE OF SEALS—Occurs when the closure peels away from the container flange, usually leaving behind a trace of the sealant. When the lid is peeled, the polypropylene sealing layer of the lid breaks away from the foil component of the lid and remains permanently fused to the container flange.

AEROBES—Organisms that require oxygen or air for growth.

AGITATING COOKERS—Retorts or cookers that provide product agitation during processing.

ANAEROBES—Organisms that grow in the absence of oxygen or air.

ANNULAR—The space between two concentric rings.

ASEPTIC—See COMMERCIAL STERILITY.

ASEPTIC PACKAGING SYSTEM—A continuous system where packages are sterilized, then enter a pre-sterilized environment to be filled with sterile product and sealed.

ASEPTIC PROCESSING—The filling of a commercially sterile, cooled product into pre-sterilized containers, followed by aseptic hermetic sealing with a pre-sterilized closure in an atmosphere free of microorganisms.

ASEPTIC PROCESSING SYSTEM—A system for continuously sterilizing a product.

ASEPTIC SYSTEM — The entire system necessary to produce a commercially sterile product with a commercially sterile package; includes the aseptic processing system and aseptic packaging system.

AVAILABLE CHLORINE—The amount of active chlorine that a chlorine-bearing compound can release in a water solution. Chlorine in the form of a gas is totally available as chlorine.

AVERAGE—The sum of a number of measurements divided by the number.

a_w—A measure of the available water in a food.

BACTERIA—Single-celled microscopic organisms that usually reproduce by splitting in two (called fission).

BACK PRESSURE DEVICE—A valve or orifice which creates pressure when product is pumped against it.

BASE PLATE PRESSURE—The force of the base plate that holds the can body and end against the chuck during the double seaming operation.

BEADED CAN—A can that is strengthened by reinforcing ribs or concentric depressions around the body.

BEARING SURFACE—The portion of the container on which it rests.

BLANCHING—Operation in which raw food material is immersed in hot water or exposed to live steam or hot gases.

BLEEDERS—Openings in the retort which, when open during the process, remove air entering with the steam and circulate the steam.

243

BLOW MOLDING — The process of forming a semi-rigid container by forcing or air-blowing molten plastic into a mold of the desired shape.

BODY—The principal part of a container, usually the largest part in one piece comprising the sides. May be round, cylindrical or other shapes.

BODY HOOK—The flange of the can body that is turned down in the formation of the double seam.

BOTTOM—The bottom of the container made in the bottom-plate part of the glass container mold.

BOTTOM PLATE PARTING LINE—A horizontal mark on the glass surface resulting from the matching of the body mold parts and the bottom plate.

BOTTOM SEAM—The double seam of the can end put on by the can manufacturer. Also known as factory end or can manufacturer's end.

BOURDON TUBE—A closed, coiled, flexible, metal tube that is the heart of a temperature recording device. The coil expands or contracts as the temperature rises or falls and controls the position of the inking pen.

BUCKLING—Defect in the can resulting in a permanent distortion of the end; caused by excess pressure inside the can.

BUDDING—A method of reproduction in yeasts.

BUFFER CAPACITY—The ability of a food to resist change in its pH level.

BURNT SEAL—A discolored area of the seal due to overheating.

CAN MANUFACTURER'S END—See BOTTOM SEAM.

CANNER'S END—See COVER.

CAN, SANITARY — Full open-top can with double seamed bottom. The cover or top end is double seamed after filling.

CAP TILT—A defect in the application of the PT cap. The cap should be essentially level with the transfer bead or shoulder, not cocked or tilted.

CAPPER VACUUM EFFICIENCY—Ability of capper to produce vacuum in a sealed container.

CARRIERS—The part of the container-conveyor chain that holds a stick of containers in a fixed place during movement through the hydrostatic retort system.

CHANNEL LEAKER—A patch of non-bonded area across the width of the seal creating a leak.

CHLORAMINE—Any of various compounds containing nitrogen and chlorine.

CHLORINATION—To combine or treat with chlorine.

CHLORINE DIOXIDE—A combination of chlorine and oxygen gases, prepared on-site and used like chlorine as a sanitary agent.

CHLORINE DOSAGE—Total amount of chlorine added to water.

CHUCK—Part of a closing machine that fits inside the end countersink and acts as an anvil to support the can cover and body against the pressure of the seaming rolls.

CLOSING MACHINE—Machine that assembles the end to the can body by double seaming. Also known as seamer or double seamer.

Clostridium botulinum—An anaerobic spore-forming organism capable of producing a deadly toxin when it grows.

CLOSURE—Another name for cover, seal, lid, end or cap.

CLOSURE LUG—Found only on lug twist caps. Fits under glass thread for security.

COCKED BASE PLATE — A base plate that is not parallel with the seaming chuck resulting in a body hook uneven in length.

COCKED CAP—A cap which is not level due to the cap lug or thread failing to seat under glass thread.

COCKED CAP DETECTOR—Special equipment designed to detect and reject faulty containers.

COHESIVE FAILURE OF LID STOCK—Occurs when the sealant layer of the heat sealed lid splits. When the lid is peeled, the polypropylene sealing layer of the lid breaks within itself and splits—half of the sealing layer is removed with the lid, and about half remains on the flange surface.

COLD-WATER VACUUM TEST—Method of checking capper vacuum efficiency.

COLORIMETRIC METHOD—Means of determining pH values with dyes.

COMBINED RESIDUAL CHLORINE—Amount of chlorine loosely combined with nitrogenous matter in the water. It is the total residual minus the free residual chlorine.

COME-UP-TIME—The time lapse between the introduction of steam into the closed retort and the time when the retort reaches the required processing temperature.

COMMERCIAL STERILITY—Condition when equipment and containers are free of viable microorganisms of public health significance as well as those of non-health significance which are capable of reproducing under normal conditions of storage and distribution.

COMPOUND—A sealing material consisting of a water solvent dispersion of rubber placed in the curl of the can end. The compound aids in forming a hermetic seal by filling spaces or voids in the double seam.

COMPRESSED CHLORINE GAS—Liquid chlorine gas under pressure in a portable cylindrical tank (100-150 pounds) with a valve to control its release.

CONSISTENCY—Thickness or viscosity of a product.

CONTAINER-CONVEYOR CHAIN—Conveyor that moves the containers through the hydrostatic retort system.

CONTAINER INTEGRITY—A reference to the visual condition of any container and its hermetic seal.

CONTINUOUS THREAD—Continuous spiral of a glass ridge around the finish for at least one full turn. The same term applies to metal ridge in the cap which matches with the glass thread.

COOKER—Another name for a retort.

CORNER LEAKER—A leak occurring in one of the corners of a paperboard package.

COUNTERSINK DEPTH—The measurement from the top edge of the double seam to the end panel adjacent to the chuck wall.

COVER—The end applied to the can by the packer. Also known as top, lid, packer's end or canner's end.

COVER HOOK — That part of the double seam formed from the curl of the can end.

CRITICAL DEFECT—A defect that provides evidence that the container has lost its hermetic condition or evidence that there is, or has been, microbial growth in the container's contents.

CRITICAL FACTOR—Any property, characteristic, condition, aspect or other parameter that when varied may affect the scheduled process and the attainment of commercial sterility.

CROSSOVER—The portion of a double seam at the juncture with the lap or side seam of the body.

CRUSHED LUG—Lug on cap forced over glass thread causing cap lug not to seat under glass thread.

CURL—The extreme edge of the end or cap that is turned inward after the end is formed.

CUT CODE—A fracture in the metal of a can end due to improper embossing.

CUT-OVER—A break in the metal at the top of the inside portion of the double seam.

CUT-THRU—Gasket damage caused by excessive vertical pressure.

DEADHEAD—An incomplete seam resulting from the chuck spinning in the end countersink during the double seaming operation. Also known as a spinner, skidder or slip.

DEHYDRATION—The removal of water from food.

DELAMINATION—A separation of the laminate materials which affects appearance but not the hermetic integrity.

DEVIATION—A condition which occurs when one or more of the critical factors indicated in the scheduled process are not met.

DISCHARGE LEG—Part of a hydrostatic retort through which the containers pass after leaving the pressure section.

DOUBLE SEAM—The closure formed by interlocking and compressing the curl of the end and the flange of the can body.

DROOP—A smooth projection of the double seam below the bottom of the normal seam. Usually occurs at the side seam lap.

DUD—Container with no or low vacuum.

DUD DETECTOR—Mechanism designed to identify low-vacuum containers and reject them.

ELECTRODES—The probes of a pH meter that are inserted into the food to measure the electrical potential indicating pH.

ELECTROMETRIC METHOD—The use of a pH meter to determine pH value.

EQUILIBRIUM RELATIVE HUMIDITY (ERH)—The amount of water vapor existing in the headspace of a container of a food at a given temperature.

FACE—Outside of cap.

FACTORY END—Bottom or can manufacturer's end.

FACULTATIVE ANAEROBES—Organisms that can grow with or without air.

FALSE SEAM—A double seam where a portion of the cover hook and body hook are interlocked.

FDA—U.S. Food and Drug Administration

FEATHER—See SHARP SEAM.

FEED LEG—Part of a hydrostatic retort through which the containers pass before entering the pressure section.

FILLING TEMPERATURE—Temperature of product at the time a container is filled.

FINISH—That part of the glass container that holds the cap or closure.

FINISHED EQUILIBRIUM pH—pH of the finished food.

FINISH RING—The mold which forms the finish or neck of the glass container.

FIRST OPERATION (DOUBLE SEAMING)—The operation in which the curl of the end is tucked under the flange of the can body to form the cover hook and body hook, respectively.

FIXED REEL PHASE—The can rotation phase where the cans are held in a fixed position by the reel of the cooker.

FLANGE—The outward flared edge of the can body that becomes the body hook in the double seaming operation.

FLAT—A can with both ends concave; it remains in this condition even when the can is brought down sharply on its end on a solid, flat surface.

FLEX CRACKS—Small breaks in one or more layers of the package, due to flexing, but not a leaker. Also referred to as seal cracking.

FLEXIBLE CONTAINER—A container, the shape or contour of which, when filled and sealed, is significantly affected by the enclosed product.

FLIPPER—A can that normally appears flat; when brought down sharply on its end on a flat surface, one end flips out. When pressure is applied to this end, it flips in again and the can appears flat.

FLOW DIVERSION VALVE—A valve or valve cluster used to divert potentially non-sterile product away from the filler.

FRACTURED EMBOSSED CODE —See CUT CODE.

FREE ROTATION—The can rotation phase where the cans roll freely along the retort shell and product agitation occurs.

FSIS—Food Safety and Inspection Service of the U.S. Department of Agriculture.

GASKET—Pliable material on the cap that contacts the glass sealing surface to form a hermetic seal.

GATE VALVE — A full flow type valve which has little or no restrictions which may impede movement through the valve.

Geotrichum—The name of a mold that can grow on food machinery.

GERMICIDES—Any chemical agent that kills microorganisms.

GLASS THREAD OR LUG—A horizontal, protruding ridge of glass around the periphery of the finish designed to engage the cap lug.

GLOBE VALVE — A better sealing valve than the gate valve; however, it restricts media flow through the valve.

HARD SWELL—A can bulged at both end, and so tightly that no indentation can be made with thumb pressure.

HEADSPACE—Non-filled volume of container that allows for product expansion.

HEATING MEDIUM—The means of transferring heat to the containers in the retort. Heating medium is typically steam, water or steam/air mixture.

HEAVY LAP—A lap containing excess solder. Also thick lap.

HEEL—Curved portion of glass container between the body side wall and the bottom.

HERMETIC SEAL — The condition which excludes the ingress of microorganisms, filth or other environmental contaminants that could render the product unfit for consumption or which could reduce the quality of the product to a level less than intended.

HOLD TUBE—Section of an aseptic processing line in which commercial sterility of product is achieved based on time in the tube, temperature and flow rate of product.

HOOK, BODY — See BODY HOOK.

HOOK, COVER—See COVER HOOK.

HOT BAR—A sealing method that uses sealing bars which are maintained at a constant high temperature.

HYDROSTATIC RETORT—A still retort in which pressure is maintained by water legs; it operates at a constant steam temperature while containers are continuously conveyed through it for the required process time.

HYGROMETER—An instrument for measuring relative humidity or available water.

HYPOCHLORITE—Combination of chlorine with either sodium or calcium hydroxide to give a desired level of available chlorine.

INCUBATION — Maintenance of a food sample at a specific temperature for a specific time to encourage the growth of microorganisms that may be present in the sample.

IMPULSE — A sealing method utilizing rounded sealing bars that are not hot enough to form a seal until after the two sealing surfaces have been pressed together.

INDUCTION—A sealing method that employs the generation of a current in an electromagnetic field. The electrical resistance creates heat that fuses the lid to the container flange.

INITIAL TEMPERATURE—The average temperature of the contents of the coldest container to be processed at the time the sterilization cycle begins.

INOCULATED TEST PACK — Scientific procedure using a product to which bacterial spores are added to confirm a theoretical process under actual plant conditions.

IODOPHOR — A combination of iodine with a wetting agent that slowly releases free iodine in water.

ION—Charged particle.

JUMPED SEAM — A double seam that is not rolled tight enough adjacent to the crossover.

KNOCKED DOWN FLANGE—A common term for a false seam where a portion of the body flange is bent back against the body without being engaged with the cover hook.

LAP—The section at the end of the soldered side seam consisting of two layers of metal bonded together. The lap eliminates some of the excess metal in the double seam at the side seam juncture.

LEAKAGE—Loss of the hermetic seal.

LEAKERS — Containers which have leaked.

LID—See COVER.

LIP—A projection where the cover hook metal protrudes below the double seam in one or more "V" shapes. Also known as a vee.

LOT—Amount of a product produced during a period of time indicated by a specific code.

LOW-ACID FOODS—Any foods, other than alcoholic beverages, with a finished equilibrium pH greater than 4.6 and a water activity (a_w) greater than 0.85.

LUG CAP—Convenience closure for glass containers that requires no tool for removal.

MAJOR DEFECT—A defect that results in a container that does not show visible signs of having lost its hermetic condition, but the defect is of such magnitude that it may have lost its hermetic condition.

MECHANICAL VACUUM CAPPER—Glass container closing machine that uses a vacuum pump to produce container vacuum.

MERCURY-IN-GLASS THERMOMETER (MIG) — Reference instrument which indicates retort temperature.

MESOPHILIC BACTERIA—Mid-range temperature-loving bacteria; the bacteria in this group grow readily at usual warehouse temperatures.

METERING PUMP—A pump that delivers a precise flow rate of product through an aseptic processing system.

MICRO-COOL VALVE—A valve through which containers exit from the pressure shell in a continuous agitating retort. Water sprays are installed in this valve to cool the cans as they pass by.

MICROMETER—A small precision instrument designed to measure double seams.

MICROORGANISMS — Living cells seen only with the aid of a powerful microscope. A general term usually referring to bacteria, yeast or molds.

MINOR DEFECT—A defect that has no adverse effect on the hermetic condition.

MOLDS—Multi-celled, microscopic organisms that usually reproduce by special cells called spores.

MOLD SEAM — A vertical mark on the body area of a glass container resulting from the matching of the two body mold parts.

MUFFLER—A device used on bleeders or vents to reduce noise.

MULTIPLICATION—An increase in the number of cells; usually refers to growth.

MYCELIUM—A microscopic thread-like mold part similar to a root of a plant.

NECK RING—See FINISH RING.

NECK RING PARTING LINE—A horizonal mark on the glass container surface at the bottom of the neck resulting from the matching of neck ring parts and body mold parts.

NOTCH—The small cut-out in the soldered side seam designed to eliminate excess body hook metal at the crossover.

OPEN LAP—A lap that is not properly soldered or has failed due to various strains in the solder.

OPEN TOP CAN—See CAN, SANITARY.

OPERATING PROCESS—The process selected by the processor that equals or exceeds the minimum requirements set forth in the scheduled process.

OVERLAP—The distance the cover hook laps over the body hook.

OVERPRESSURE—Pressure supplied to a retort in excess of that exerted by steam or water at a given process temperature.

PACKER'S END—See COVER.

PANEL—The flat center area in the top of the cap. May also apply to the area on the body of the container where the label is applied.

PANELING—Condition when the sides of the can are drawn in permanently.

pH—A measure of acidity or alkalinity. Chemically, pH is defined as the negative log of the hydrogen ion concentration.

pH METER—A device which measures electric potential developed between electrodes immersed in a solution and converts this to a reading known as pH.

PINHOLING—Tiny holes in the metal food container usually caused by external rusting or internal attack of the product on the container.

PLASTISOLS—Suspensions of finely divided resin in a plasticizer which are found in metal closures for glass containers and are an important component of vacuum sealing glass containers.

PLASTISOL-LINED CONTINUOUS THREAD (PLCT) CAP—A closure style with flowed-in plastisol gasket and a continuous metal spiral which engages with a corresponding glass spiral ridge around finish of a glass container.

POST-PROCESS HANDLING—Conditions to which containers are subjected after being sterilized.

PRESSURE RIDGE—The impression around the inside of the can body directly opposite the double seam.

PROCESS—Application of heat to foods either before or after sealing in containers for a period of time and at a temperature scientifically determined to be adequate to achieve commercial sterility.

PROCESS CALCULATION—Scientific procedure to determine the adequate process time and temperatures for canned products.

PROCESS DEVIATION—A change in any critical factor of the scheduled process that reduces the sterilizing value of the process, or which raises a question regarding the public health safety and/or commercial sterility of the product lot.

PROCESSING MEDIUM—See HEATING MEDIUM.

PRODUCT REGENERATOR—A type of heat exchanger that utilizes the heat of uncooled sterile product to heat non-sterile product.

PRODUCT SEALING TEMPERATURE—Recommended temperature for the product at time of sealing.

PSYCHROTROPHIC BACTERIA—Organisms capable of growing at refrigeration temperature but having higher optimum temperatures.

PT (PRESS-ON TWIST-OFF) CAP—Deep skirt cap with molded plastisol gasket. Removal requires no special tool.

PULL-UP—Term applied to distance measured from the leading edge of closure lug to vertical neck ring seam.

PURE STEAM—Saturated steam that is free of air.

PUTREFACTIVE — Bacteria capable of breaking down protein, which causes putrid odors.

QUATERNARY AMMONIUM COMPOUNDS (quats)—A wetting agent with germicidal powers.

RANGE—Difference between the highest and lowest measurement.

RECALL—A procedure for removing product from distribution and/or the marketplace.

RECORDING TACHOMETER—Instrument that measures and records the revolutions per minute in an agitating cooker.

REMOVAL TORQUE—Force required to remove glass closure.

RETORT—Any closed vessel or other equipment used for thermal processing. May also refer to the act of applying a thermal process to a canned food in a closed pressurized vessel.

RETORTABLE/MICROWAVEABLE BOWL—A semirigid container made of specific plastic blends and adhesive material.

RETORTABLE POUCH—Flexible, heat sealable, relatively flat container capable of withstanding the high temperatures required for pressure processing low-acid foods.

REVERSE—Inside of glass closure.

RIGID CONTAINER—A container that is neither affected by the enclosed contents or deformed by external pressure up to 10 psig.

ROLLSTOCK—A long roll of packaging material from which some flexible and semirigid packages are machine-formed and sealed to contain food products.

ROTARY CAPPER—A closing machine in which containers travel in a circular pattern through the capping functions.

SAFETY BUTTON (FLIP PANEL)—Circular portion of cap panel that changes from convex to concave when container has vacuum.

SANITATION—Practice of protective measures for cleanliness and health.

SATURATED STEAM—Pure steam, i.e., free of air.

SCHEDULED PROCESS—The process selected by the processor as adequate under the conditions of manufacture for a given product to achieve commercial sterility.

SEALING SURFACE—The part of the finish that contacts the gasket. See TOP SEAL or SIDE SEAL.

SEAM THICKNESS—The maximum dimension of the double seam measured across or perpendicular to the layers of the seam.

SEAMER—See CLOSING MACHINE.

SEAM WIDTH (LENGTH OR HEIGHT) — The maximum dimension of the double seam measured parallel to the folds of the seam.

SECOND OPERATION—The finishing operation in double seaming. The hooks formed in the first operation are rolled tightly against each other in the second operation.

SECURITY—Residual clamping force or tension on lugs remaining in closure application when gasket is properly seated after processing and cooling.

SEMIRIGID CONTAINER—A container, the shape or contour of which, when filled and sealed, is not significantly affected by the enclosed product under normal atmospheric temperature and pressure, but which can be deformed by external mechanical pressure of less than 10 pounds per square inch gauge.

SHALL — Means that the requirement is mandatory.

SHARP SEAM—A sharp edge at the top of the inside portion of the double seam due to the end metal being forced over the seaming chuck.

SHOULD — Is used to state recommended or advisory procedures or to identify recommended equipment.

SHOULDER—Portion of glass container where maximum cross-section area decreases to join neck. Also portion of cap between panel and skirt.

SIDE SEAL—Sealing surface on vertical portion of finish.

SIDE SEAM—The seam joining the two edges of the body blank to form a can body.

SIDE WALL—Portion of glass container between shoulder and heel.

SIGHT GLASS—A clear glass tube with both top and bottom connected to openings in the retort shell; used to visually determine water level in the retort.

SKIDDER—A can having an incomplete double seam due to the can's slipping on the base plate. In this defect, part of the seam will be incompletely rolled out. Term has same meaning as deadhead when referring to seamers that revolve the can. Also known as spinner.

SKIRT—Vertical portion of closure.

SLIDING ROTATION—The can rotation phase when the cans slide in a continuous agitating retort, and there is slight product agitation.

SOFT CRAB—Colloquial term used to describe a damaged can flange resulting in a hole between the end and the body.

SOFT SWELL—A can bulged at both end, but not so tightly that the ends cannot be pushed in somewhat with thumb pressure.

SPINNER—See DEADHEAD and SKIDDER.

SPORES—The resting stage in the growth cycle of certain bacteria that are resistant to heat and chemicals. In the case of yeasts and molds, spores are considered reproductive bodies since many spores are produced by one organism.

SPRINGER—A can with one end permanently bulged. When sufficient pressure is applied to this end, it will flip in, but the other end will flip out.

STACKING FEATURE—Special design in container bottom to aid in display stacking.

STATISTICAL QUALITY CONTROL (SQC)—Systematic methods of arranging and describing data to assure quality.

STEAM DOME—That section of a hydrostatic retort in which sterilization takes place.

STEAM FLOW CAPPER—A straight or rotary style capper that produces vacuum in containers by sweeping air from headspace with steam.

STEAM HEADER—The pipe that delivers steam to a number of retorts.

STEAM INLET — The opening through which steam is admitted to the retort.

STEAM SPREADER—Continuation of the steam line inside the retort with perforations through which steam is discharged into the load of containers.

STEAM-WATER INTERFACE—That point in the steam dome where the steam used for processing and the water used for hydrostatic pressure contact one another.

STERILIZATION—As used in this text, the act of achieving commercial sterility. See COMMERCIAL STERILITY.

STICK—In hydrostatic retorts, the row of containers on their sides which is equal to the length of a carrier on the chain conveyor.

STILL RETORT—A discontinuous (batch-type), non-agitating, vertical or horizonal, enclosed vessel used in the processing of canned foods.

STRAIGHT LINE CAPPER—A closing machine in which containers travel in a straight line through the capping functions.

STRIP CHART—Continuous recording equipment that automatically monitors temperatures in thermal processing systems.

STRIPPED CAP—Lug closure applied with too much torque which causes cap lugs to pass over glass threads. May have vacuum but has no security value.

SUPERHEATED STEAM—Steam at 212°F (100°C) or greater, but at atmospheric pressure.

SURFACE TREATMENT—Lubrication applied to outside surface of glass containers to facilitate handling.

248

SURGE TANK—A sterilizable storage device, linked to the processing line, that holds sterile product.

SWEATING—The condensation of moisture from the air on cold cans.

TACHOMETER—See RECORDING TACHOMETER.

TDT (THERMAL DEATH TIME)—Time required to destroy a specific microorganism at a given temperature.

TDT CAN—Specifically designed metal container used in determining thermal death times.

TDT TUBE—Specifically designed tubes used for determining thermal death times.

TEMPERATURE INDICATING DEVICE—A thermometer or other temperature-sensing device that serves as an indicator of the official process temperature.

TEMPERATURE/TIME RECORDING DEVICE—An automatic instrument that records time and temperature during the thermal process.

THERMAL DEATH TIME—See TDT.

THERMAL RESISTANCE—The amount of heat required to kill a bacteria.

THERMOCOUPLE—A device that measures temperature electrically.

THERMOFORMED—Semirigid containers manufactured by pressing the rollstock into a die mold to form the container.

THERMOPHILIC BACTERIA—Heat-loving bacteria that produce highly resistant spores.

THREE-NECK FLASK—A flask used in determining thermal death times.

TIGHTNESS—The degree to which the double seam is compressed by the second operation rolls.

TOP SEAL—Horizontal sealing surface that is the top of the glass finish.

TOTAL RESIDUAL CHLORINE—Represents the free residual plus the combined residual chlorine.

TRANSFER BEAD—A continuous horizontal ridge of glass near the bottom of the finish that is used to transfer the container from one part of the manufacturing operation to another.

TRANSFER VALVE—A valve through which containers pass when moving from one pressure shell to another in a continuous agitating retort.

TWIST CAP—See LUG CAP.

ULTRASONIC SEALING—A sealing method that employs the generation of ultrasonic wave vibrations.

UNEVEN HOOK—A body or cover hook that is not uniform in length.

UNSEATED—Breaking of the hermetic seal in a glass container.

USDA—U.S. Department of Agriculture.

VACUUM—A state of pressure reduction below atmospheric.

VACUUM CLOSURE—Closures designed to maintain vacuum suitable for processing.

VACUUM-PACKED FOODS—Foods that are sealed in a container under the vacuum specified in the scheduled process; the maintenance of this vacuum is critical to the adequacy of the scheduled process.

VEE—See LIP.

VENT—Opening through the retort shell controlled by gate, plug cock or other adequate valve used for the elimination of air during the venting period.

VERTICAL NECK RING SEAM—Vertical mark on glass neck surface caused by the joining of the two parts of the neck ring during formation of the jar.

WAFFLING—Embossing caused by racks during thermal processing that appears on the surface of the pouch.

WATER ACTIVITY (a_w)—A measure of the free moisture in a product. It is determined by dividing the water vapor pressure of the substance by the vapor pressure of pure water at the same temperature.

WATER LEVEL CONTROL—An automatic device that controls water level in retorts.

WRINKLE — A fold of material in the seal area.

WRINKLE (COVER HOOK)—A waviness occurring in the cover hook from which the degree of double seam tightness is determined.

YEASTS—Single-celled microscopic organisms that usually reproduce by budding. They ferment sugars to produce alcohol and carbon dioxide gas.

INDEX